Plant Physiology

A TREATISE

EDITED BY
F. C. STEWARD
Department of Botany
Cornell University, Ithaca, New York

Volume I B: Photosynthesis and Chemosynthesis

1960

ACADEMIC PRESS, *New York and London*

United Kingdom edition published by
ACADEMIC PRESS INC. (London) Ltd.
17 Old Queen Street, London, S. W. 1

Library of Congress Catalog Card Number: 59-7689

PRINTED IN THE UNITED STATES OF AMERICA

CONTRIBUTORS TO VOLUME I B

HANS GAFFRON, *Research Institutes, The University of Chicago, Chicago, Illinois**

MARTIN GIBBS, *Departments of Biochemistry and Nutrition, Cornell University, Ithaca, New York*

JEROME A. SCHIFF, *Department of Biochemistry, Brandeis University, Waltham, Massachusetts*

* Present address: Biology Department, Fels Fund, Florida State University, Tallahassee, Florida.

Preface to Volume I

Since Volume II of this treatise actually preceded Volume I, it is desirable to recapitulate certain general aims and objectives of the whole work.

The aim of this treatise is to *say* what Plant Physiology is about and to do this in sufficient detail and with sufficient analysis of, and even extracts from, the ever expanding literature, so that each volume will be in large measure self-contained.

Plant physiologists will find that the treatment is sufficiently detailed to benefit their research in their own specialized fields and that the scope is broad enough to make reading of all portions of the work both stimulating and profitable. This treatise is, therefore, designed for the use of advanced and postgraduate students, teachers, research workers, and investigators in other fields of knowledge who need information about the present status of plant physiology. While such a synthesis of current knowledge is well justified by the great advances that have been made, especially in the last quarter of a century, its accomplishment requires the knowledge and mature experience of many authors who are aware of the trends in their often rapidly advancing fields of interest. Upon these authors, therefore, rests the quality and value of the work and to each the editor acknowledges his debt.

Although the treatise is now arranged in six volumes, each has been planned as a distinct unit and consists of a group of related chapters which, together, cover a major segment of the subject. Each chapter has been written by an authority in the field and analyzes the present status of its subject matter, giving pertinent references to the literature. The chief emphasis is on a synthesis of current knowledge, but consideration is also given to significant accomplishments of the past and, where possible, an insight into the problems of the future. Thus the reader may acquire an informed outlook on each topic.

While full advantage is taken of recent advances which accrue from the application of physical and biochemical techniques and the study of subcellular systems, the need to see the subject of plant physiology in terms of the morphology and organization of living plants is recognized throughout.

The treatise is intended not solely for use as a work of reference but is to be read by those who wish to obtain a reasoned analysis of the status and development of each subject which is discussed. Admittedly, and rightly, each chapter is affected by the author's own opinions, but, so far as possible in a work of this kind, an attempt has been made to achieve a measure of integration between the different chapters. Indexes make it possible for information to be traced by reference to an author's name, to the plants used, or to the subject matter in question. For this volume the Index of Plant Names was prepared by Dr. W. J. Dress, and the Subject Index was compiled by Dr. H. Y. Mohan Ram. For this help the editor is grateful.

Volume I consists of two parts, A and B, each of which is complete with its own table of contents, separate pagination, indexes, etc. The consecutive numbering of Chapters 1 through 5, however, links these together as a single volume within the over-all plan of the treatise.

Even though Volume II has in fact preceded Volume I, it is still appropriate that the subject matter of Volume I should be considered first, for it concerns problems raised by the cellular and subcellular levels of organization within which physiological events occur, and it also deals with mechanisms by which cells store energy only to release it later for useful purposes.

While any of the subjects dealt with in Volume I could have been expanded beyond the limits of the present treatment, there were special reasons for the more extensive treatment of photosynthesis in Chapter 4 of Volume I B. The subject of photosynthesis, distinctive as it is of plants, has advanced so rapidly in recent years that an adequate treatment of all facets of the problem required a longer chapter. This plan was adopted even though it necessitated the division of Volume I A and I B into separate books. These parts now represent separate but closely related works on cells and cellular respiration in one unit (I A) and photosynthesis and chemosynthesis in the other (I B), and the hope is that the two parts will be the more useful because of their separate publication.

In both the treatment of cellular respiration, i.e. of energy release and utilization, and of photosynthesis, or energy storage, the attention is focused upon these physiological functions as they occur in cells. Other problems are to be raised at the level of organs or organisms, and these will be dealt with in Volume IV, along with other aspects of organic nutrition and of intermediary metabolism: this may account for some seeming gaps in the present treatment.

The separate acknowledgment to all those who have helped the authors and the Editor by permitting the inclusion of their published or unpublished material would be too great a task in a work of this kind. It should be understood, however, that both acknowledgment and thanks are conveyed by the form of citation in the text. The Editor wishes especially to acknowledge the helpful cooperation of the personnel of Academic Press.

F. C. STEWARD

Cornell University
November, 1959

PLANT PHYSIOLOGY

The Plan of the Treatise

The treatise is planned in three main sections, as follows:

Section on *Cell Physiology and Problems Relating to Water and Solutes*

The purpose of this section is to present the properties of cells, their energy relations (Volume I) and behavior toward water and solutes with the closely related problems of the movement of solutes within the plant body and the economy of water in plants (Volume II).

The underlying theme of Volumes I and II is the basis of plant physiology in cell physiology.

Section on *Nutrition and Metabolism*

In this section the detailed facts and knowledge of nutrition and metabolism are presented, first with reference to the need for, and utilization of, inorganic nutrients (Volume III), and second with respect to the processes of organic nutrition (Volume IV). The treatment of organic nutrition leads to a reconsideration of photosynthesis and respiration at the level of organs and organisms. Volume IV describes the intermediary metabolism of carbon and nitrogenous compounds and presents a brief comparison of plants in health and in disease.

The main theme of Volumes III and IV is the nutrition, organic and inorganic, of plants and the biochemical steps by which these processes are achieved.

Section on *Growth and Development*

The purpose of the last section is to present the problems of plant physiology as seen through the analysis of growth and development, mainly with reference to flowering plants. This entails (Volume V) a reappraisal of the main events of growth and development from the standpoint of morphology and leads to a consideration of growth of cells and of organs. Tropisms and the role of hormones and the effects of synthetic growth regulators are discussed. In Volume VI the attention is focused upon the quantitative analysis of growth and development, the physiology of reproduction, the development of fruits and seeds, the problems of dormancy and perennation. The role of environmental factors in the control of growth and development merits separate treatment. Finally the problems of growth and development are examined from the standpoint of genetic control and from the interpretation of abnormal growth as seen in the formation of tumors. Throughout this treatment the controlling mechanisms of growth are evaluated.

Thus the last section of the work provides a synthesis of knowledge about plants since all their physiological processes converge upon growth and development.

The fulfillment of these objectives is possible only through the co-operation of many authors. The scope and treatment of individual chapters reflects the special interests of the contributors. While each volume is a complete unit, with its own table of contents and indexes, it is also an integral part of the whole plan.

Outline of the Plan

Section on *Cell Physiology and Problems Relating to Water and Solutes*

Volume I A. Cellular Organization and Respiration
Volume I B. Photosynthesis and Chemosynthesis
Volume II. Plants in Relation to Water and Solutes

Section on *Nutrition and Metabolism*

Volume III. Inorganic Nutrition of Plants
Volume IV. Organic Nutrition and Metabolism

Section on *Growth and Development*

Volume V. Analysis of Growth
Volume VI. The Physiology of Development

NOTE ON THE USE OF PLANT NAMES

The policy has been to identify by its scientific name, whenever possible, any plant mentioned by a vernacular name by the contributors to this work. In general, this has been done on the first occasion in each chapter when a vernacular name has been used. Particular care was taken to ensure the correct designation of plants mentioned in tables and figures which record actual observations. Sometimes, when reference has been made by an author to work done by others, it has not been possible to ascertain the exact identity of the plant material originally used, because the original workers did not identify their material except by generic or common name.

It should be unnecessary to state that the precise identification of plant material used in experimental work is as important for the enduring value of the work as the precise definition of any other variables in the work. "Warm" or "cold" would not usually be considered an acceptable substitute for a precisely stated temperature, nor could a general designation of "sugar" take the place of the precise molecular configuration of the substance used; "sunflower" and "*Helianthus*" are no more acceptable as plant names, considering how many diverse species are covered by either designation. Plant physiologists are becoming increasingly aware that different species of one genus (even different varieties or cultivars of one species) may differ in their physiological responses as well as in their external morphology, and that experimental plants should therefore be identified as precisely as possible if the observations made are to be verified by others.

On the assumption that such common names as lettuce and bean are well understood, it may appear pedantic to append the scientific names to them—but such an assumption cannot safely be made. Workers in the United States who use the unmodified word "bean" almost invariably are referring to some form of *Phaseolus vulgaris;* whereas in Britain *Vicia faba,* a plant of another genus entirely, might be implied. "Artichoke" is another such name that comes to mind, sometimes used for *Helianthus tuberosus* (properly, the Jerusalem artichoke), though the true artichoke is *Cynara scolymus.*

By the frequent interpolation of scientific names, consideration has also been given to the difficulties that any vernacular English name alone may present to a reader whose native tongue is not English. Even some American and most British botanists would be led into a misinterpretation of the identity of "yellow poplar," for instance, if this vernacular American name were not supplemented by its scientific equivalent *Liriodendron tulipifera*, for this is not a species of *Populus* as might be expected, but a member of the quite unrelated magnolia family.

When reference has been made to the work of another investigator who, in his published papers, has used a plant name not now accepted by the nomenclatural authorities followed in the present work, that name ordinarily has been included in parentheses, as a synonym, immediately after the accepted name. In a few instances, when it seemed expedient to employ a plant name as it was used by an original author, even though that name is not now recognized as the valid one, the valid name, preceded by the sign =, has been supplied in parentheses: e.g., *Betula verrucosa* (= *B. pendula*). Synonyms have occasionally been added elsewhere also, as in the case of a plant known and frequently reported upon in the literature under more than one name: e.g., *Pseudotsuga menziesii* (*P. taxifolia*); species of *Elodea* (*Anacharis*).

Having adopted these conventions, their implementation rested first with each contributor to this work; but all outstanding problems of nomenclature have been referred to Dr. W. J. Dress of the Bailey Hortorium, Cornell University. The authorities for the nomenclature employed in this work have been Bailey's *Hortus Second* and Bailey's *Manual of Cultivated Plants* for cultivated plants. For bacteria Bergey's *Manual of Determinative Bacteriology*, for fungi Ainsworth and Bisbee's *Dictionary of the Fungi* have been used as reference sources; other names have been checked where necessary against Engler's *Syllabus der Pflanzenfamilien.* Recent taxonomic monographs and floras have been consulted where necessary. Dr. Dress' work in ensuring consistency and accuracy in the use of plant names is deeply appreciated.

THE EDITOR

CONTENTS

CONTENTS OF VOLUMES I A AND II-VI

Volume I A. CELLULAR ORGANIZATION AND RESPIRATION

Volume II. PLANTS IN RELATION TO WATER AND SOLUTES

Volume III. INORGANIC NUTRITION OF PLANTS
(*Tentative Contents*)

Volume IV. ORGANIC NUTRITION AND METABOLISM

(Tentative Contents)

Volume V. ANALYSIS OF GROWTH

(Tentative Contents)

Volume VI. THE PHYSIOLOGY OF DEVELOPMENT

(Tentative Contents)

PREAMBLE TO CHAPTERS 4 AND 5

Chapters 4 and 5 should be considered together, for they deal with the questions which surround the acquisition of energy by plants and its storage in ultimately usable chemical forms. In these chapters the emphasis is placed upon the means by which the energy transfers are negotiated, since the cellular organization of the system in which they are mediated has already been described (Chapter 1, Volume IA). The great importance of photosynthesis in the over-all economy of nature justifies the particular attention here paid to this process as the main portion of Volume IA of the treatise. It is now dramatically evident that the hydrogen transfer from water, which occurs in green cells by photolysis, plays a key role in the ultimate reduction of carbon dioxide; whereas the recombination of hydrogen with oxygen to form water is an equally important event in the means by which the energy is released from the reduced and therefore energy-rich compounds. Whereas light is the source of the energy which is built into the compounds produced in photosynthesis, the necessary energy is donated by chemical means in chemosynthetic processes. Understanding of the energy storage in chemically usable forms in cells therefore requires a consideration of both photosynthesis (Chapter 4) and chemosynthetic (Chapter 5) processes.

CHAPTER FOUR

Energy Storage: Photosynthesis

HANS GAFFRON

I. Introduction

A. Photosynthesis—Definition and General Survey

Photosynthesis—or the assimilation of carbon by plants with the aid of sunlight—is, strictly speaking, only a special chapter in the field of plant physiology. Yet, more than any other metabolic process in either plants or animals, it has aroused the interest and challenged the investigative skill of students in many branches of the natural sciences. This is easily understood if we consider that photosynthesis is the one reaction which maintains life in all its abundance on this planet.

With few minor exceptions, the carbon in natural organic matter originates from the carbon dioxide present in the air or dissolved in the oceans. It diffuses into the cells of land and water plants and, where these cells contain the green pigment, chlorophyll, carbon dioxide is transformed into carbohydrates, such as sucrose or starch which are primary nutrient materials for all things living. This transformation or synthesis occurs only in the light, and in the presence and with the participation of water. While carbon dioxide is being absorbed, the plants release an equivalent amount of oxygen gas. The light absorbed by chlorophyll is within that part of electromagnetic radiation which enables humans to see. Visible light furnishes the energy which is found stored as chemical energy in the products of photosynthesis and eventually drives the cellular machinery. The photosynthetic products are transformed by other metabolic processes into the myriad substances found in the living world. The bulk of the organisms on this earth perform these further transformations with the aid of respiratory systems and chemosynthetic mechanisms by which the energy of respiration is applied to synthesis (see Chapter 5 in this volume). In these processes the energy contained in carbohydrates is released by reactions which consume oxygen and eventually produce carbon dioxide again. Thus, in its over-all effect, respiration is the reverse of photosynthesis. Respiration goes on continuously, day and night, in plants as well as animals, and in the illuminated plants simultaneously with photosynthesis.

In the course of about a billion years, plants have exchanged nearly all available carbon dioxide for oxygen through the process of photosynthesis, so that now there is only 0.03% of carbon dioxide in the air, which is not enough to maintain photosynthesis at its maximum rate in bright daylight. This means that for a very long time photosynthesis has not increased the bulk of organic and living matter on the earth. As the deposits of coal, oil, and of limestone of recent origin reveal, there may have been periods when the earth was richer in terms of total living matter. This now more or less stationary carbon cycle involves, nevertheless, enormous quantities of carbon dioxide, water, and oxygen. According to Rabinowitch [see Vol. I in (436)] the present annual turnover is estimated at 10^{11} tons of carbon.

By contrast, plants have raised the oxygen content of the atmosphere to 21% by volume, i.e., a partial pressure over a hundred times higher than that necessary to maintain the full rate of respiration in most unicellular algae and microorganisms. For this reason the evolution of higher animals, with their elaborate internal liquid transport systems for oxygen that require a high external concentration of that gas, may be an adjustment to the consequences of relentless photosynthesis—other consequences are such accidents as forest fires which here and there destroy the accumulated products of centuries of plant growth. Yet the precarious coexistence of free oxygen and combustible material happens to be the only way by which so much life can be maintained on this earth. Oxygen is the unavoidable waste product which must be released into the atmosphere if carbon dioxide and water are to be transformed into organic matter.

In 1918, when Willstätter and Stoll published their book on the assimilation of carbon (604), systematic investigations on the life and growth of plants had been going on for a hundred and fifty years. Joseph Priestley had observed in 1771 that a certain quantity of air in which a candle had burned out would not extinguish the flame of a candle after a plant had been kept in the same glass container for some time. Later, in 1779, Ingen-Housz discovered that light is necessary for this kind of "purification" of "vitiated" air by a living plant. He was the first to see how leaves submerged in water release bubbles of gas (oxygen) when illuminated, and he correctly attributed the power to purify air to the green parts of the plant. Senebier, three years later, described experiments proving that the exhausted air contained something (fixed air = carbon dioxide) which was necessary in order that the air could be repurified by the action of illuminated plants. The first experiments showing some connection between the light metabolism of plants and water go back to de Saussure, who published his investigations in 1804. He found that his plants gained more weight than could be accounted for by the difference between carbon dioxide and oxygen and concluded that water was the third substance involved in photosynthesis. Thus at the beginning of the nineteenth century, mainly as the result of the work of these four men, the over-all aspects of the photosynthetic process had been recognized [cf. Vol. I in (436)].

Forty years later the question of energy conversion arose. Robert Meyer realized that light had energy and that this was converted into chemical energy which served to maintain not only the life of the plant, but that of animals and man as well.

We need not review in detail the experiments and hypotheses published during the century which preceded the publication of Willstätter and Stoll. Few of the experiments were exact enough to continue to serve as a source of reliable data, and the ideas concerning them have all been superseded by the modern view which originated with van Niel's work around 1930 (538) and became firmly established some ten years later (166). The earlier period has, moreover, been covered in detail by the monographs on photosynthesis of W. Stiles (479) and of H. A. Spoehr (479). A critical review of the entire field is contained in E. Rabinowitch's monumental treatise (436) which covers every aspect of the problem up to 1955. Many other smaller monographs and survey articles have been published (see Bibliographical Notes and 32, 158, 261).

At the time of Willstätter and Stoll the chemical equation:

$$CO_2 + H_2O \xrightarrow{\text{light}} (CH_2O) + O_2 \tag{a}$$

had been firmly established as representing the gas exchange of plants in the light. The carbon dioxide absorbed was found to be directly equivalent to the oxygen released, and it corresponded roughly to the increase in organic substances which could be classified as carbohydrates.

Many years later, more refined measurements of the ratio of carbon dioxide absorbed to carbon stored in the form of carbohydrates—done, as usual, with detached fresh leaves—confirmed the classical results (473), (Fig. 1). The ratio O_2 evolved/CO_2 absorbed is called the assimilatory quotient, Q_p. Q_p has been determined numerous times for

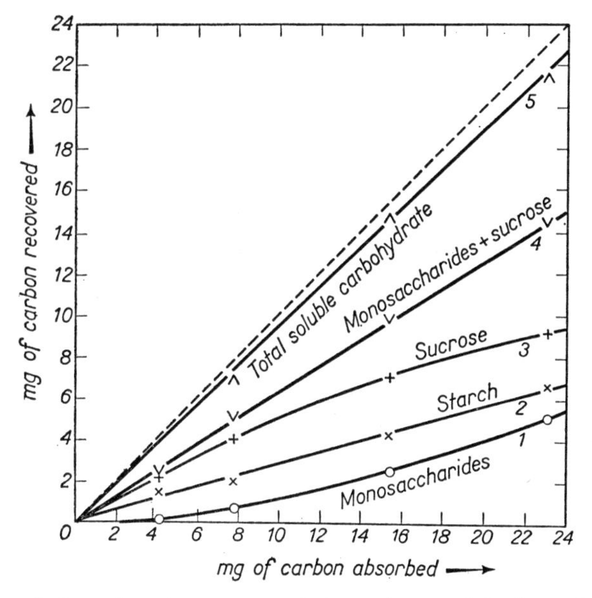

FIG. 1. Correlation of carbon recovered in various carbohydrate fractions with amount of carbon absorbed by sunflower leaves. Temperature: 20°C. From Smith (473, 474).

leaves of higher plants, green algae, blue-green algae and diatoms, and found to be unity. (Actually, a little more O_2 is released than CO_2 absorbed. See Table 10 in reference 158.)

A value of 1 for Q_p implies, according to equation (a) that photosynthesis produces only carbohydrates. This is not strictly true if the cells under observation are growing vigorously. During growth other synthetic processes rapidly transform the intermediate and final products of photosynthesis into amino acids, proteins, and fats.

Deviations of Q_p from the value of unity are indicative of other concurrent metabolic processes, and their magnitude depends on the ratio of the rates of nonphotosynthetic reactions (like respiration and nitrogen assimilation) to the rate of photosynthesis and upon the nature of the substances formed. This is easily seen by comparing, for instance, the quotients which are measured in the presence, or absence, of ammonia or nitrate (see Table I) (380). At high light intensities and with

TABLE I
CO_2/O_2 QUOTIENT FOR CELLS GROWN AT 40 FC AND STUDIED AT 40 FC[a]

Nitrogen source	CO_2/O_2 by manometric measurement	CO_2/O_2 calculated from cell analysis
NO_3^-	−0.68	−0.69
NH_4^+	−0.94	−0.91
$NO_3^- + NH_4^+$	−0.94	—

[a] From data by J. Myers (380).

full-grown leaves that are mainly factories for sucrose and little else, the influence of the slower secondary processes recedes and the ratios approximate those required by equation (a) (see Fig. 1).

On a sunny day, a sunflower (*Helianthus annuus*) leaf may gain 9% of its original dry weight per hour (604). To accomplish this, the rate of photosynthesis must be appreciably greater than that of respiration in the leaf. Photosynthesis in strong light is generally ten to thirty times faster than respiration; in certain 1-day-old *Chlorella* cultures the ratio of photosynthesis to respiration can go as high as 60:1. Unless furnished exogenous carbohydrate, a plant stays alive only so long as the synthesis remains ahead of the depletion of photosynthetic products. The least a plant must be able to do is to compensate its own dark metabolism. Thus growth may depend on the total amount of light a plant receives—among other things. In the shade of the forest small trees survive for years without showing any appreciable growth. Thus we may say that photosynthesis accomplishes two things: First, it compensates and balances the effects of respiration; second it achieves a net synthesis and a continuous accumulation of new organic matter. This division into "compensation" and "net photosynthesis" becomes meaningful if we investigate specific metabolic patterns which indicate an interaction between respiration and photosynthesis or if we analyze carefully the question of energy requirements.

As long as sugars of the general formula $(CH_2O)_n$ are the substrate of respiration, the respiratory quotient $Q_r = +CO_2/-O_2$, will also have the value 1 (158, 604). For each volume of oxygen absorbed, one volume of carbon dioxide appears:

$$(CH_2O) + O_2 \rightarrow CO_2 + H_2O$$

The simplest, most commonly used over-all chemical equation for photosynthesis is therefore the exact reversal of this equation for respiration.

The value of the respiratory quotient is, however, much less stable than that of the assimilatory quotient. The former fluctuates between 0.7 and 1.3, depending upon the nature of the compound burned in respiration. If more fats are respired, the value of the quotient tends to be below unity; if more organic acids, the value is greater than unity. This explains why thick-leaved, succulent plants which have only a thin layer of photosynthetic tissue above a mass of colorless, non-photosynthetic cells, show the greatest deviation from the normal gas exchange of a detached thin leaf or a suspension of young algae (158 and the chapter of Metabolism of Organic Acids by Beevers and Stiller in Volume IV of this treatise).

While green plants can be grown heterotrophically in the dark, they will not grow (though they continue to fix carbon) under anaerobic conditions in the light. Thus here photosynthesis is not involved directly in the growth process of green plants. In some anaerobic photosynthetic bacteria, light metabolism and growth are, however, practically synonymous.

The observations shown in the figure and table above have stood the test of time. What has changed radically is the interpretation of equation (a). Willstätter and Stoll, and most of their successors, were led astray by assuming that the over-all equation (a) implied a photochemical decomposition of carbon dioxide, or of a carbon dioxide chlorophyll complex, and they believed that the oxygen which was released came from the carbon dioxide molecule. They were well aware that some enzymatic reactions played a role in photosynthesis. The unique role of light was seen in its power to bring carbon dioxide—the final, dead waste product of all metabolizing cells—back into the realm of living matter. Thus photosynthesis seemed more directly connected with the phenomena of life than any other known metabolic process.

Since about 1930 overwhelming evidence has accumulated that the photochemistry of chlorophyll involves the cleavage, not of carbon dioxide, but of one O—H bond in water, H—O—H. The assimilation of carbon dioxide is a consequence of this reaction, and not always the only one. Nothing which has been learned since then has contradicted this newer concept.

In retrospect, two things impeded progress: First, too little attention was paid to the laws of physics as they pertain to photochemical reactions, and second, unfortunate choices were made in selecting the plants from which to obtain photosynthesizing, cell-free extracts.

Physical principles could have shown that a simple photosensitized cleavage of carbon dioxide (i.e., decomposition, or *Zerlegung*) is impossible with visible light. The second comment refers to Willstätter and Stoll's work with broken-up cells. *Pelargonium hortorum*, *Cyclamen persicum*, and *Helianthus annuus* are plants from which even today it is difficult to obtain active chloroplast preparations, while spinach (*Spinacia oleracea*) leaves, as bought on the market, generally yield active extracts.

B. Photosynthesis as a Complex Metabolic System

Instead of following the step-by-step development of our knowledge in this field since 1917 (a necessary procedure as long as there was no generally accepted pattern covering the fundamental facts), we shall first describe briefly the evolution of the modern view and in the following sections give the supporting evidence.

As the developments of the last twenty years have confirmed, photosynthesis is a dye-sensitized, photochemical redox process. The sensitizer is chlorophyll, the oxidant is carbon dioxide, and the reductant is water. The process is remarkably efficient in converting light energy into chemical energy.

This chapter is being written at a propitious moment. Several investigations, particularly those concerned with the fate of carbon dioxide have advanced slowly through many years by the efforts of numerous investigators; recently they have reached the point at which they are rather well understood, so that, for purposes of exposition, it is now feasible to have one general scheme which will only need modification as new facts emerge.

The advance of knowledge of photosynthesis during the past forty years is shown by the changes in the over-all equations which, at different times, represented the status of the knowledge in this field.

In Fig. 2, equation (a) is the simplest possible expression of the photochemically induced gas exchange in a green plant. Despite the data accumulated up to 1917 by Willstätter and Stoll and their predecessors, not much more than this could be stated with certainty (cf. 479, 487). The extensive contributions to the kinetics of photosynthesis by Warburg and Negelein (560–566)—such as the clear distinction between photochemical and enzymatic reactions, the effects of poisons or of intermittent illumination, the first attempts to measure the over-all efficiency, etc.—were still compatible with the thought that equation (a) in Fig. 2 represented not only an over-all balance but in a sense also a mechanism.

Twenty years later it had been established that photosynthesis was not a photochemical decomposition of carbon dioxide but rather the consequence of interlocked, dissimilar reactions. An enzymatic carboxylation, equation (b), transforms free carbon dioxide into a carboxyl group. This is followed by the photochemical reduction of the carboxylation product, equation (c). The photochemistry is involved in this second step and consists mainly of the photolysis of water which serves as the ultimate hydrogen donor. Oxygen, therefore, does not originate from carbon dioxide but is formed instead as a waste product, the result of the dehydrogenation of water. In 1917 the term [CH_2O]

1917: $CO_2 + H_2O \xrightarrow[\text{chlorophyll}]{\text{light}} CH_2O + O_2$ (a)

1937: $CO_2 + RH \longrightarrow RCOOH$ (b)

$RCOOH + 2H_2O \xrightarrow[\text{chlorophyll}]{4h\nu} (CH_2O) + O_2$ (c)

1957: $4HOH + 2XY \xrightarrow[\text{chlorophyll}]{8h\nu} 2XH_2 + 2Y(OH)_2$ (d)

$2Y(OH)_2 \longrightarrow 2Y + 2H_2O + O_2$ (e)

$2XH_2 + 2CH_2OH \cdot CHOH \cdot COOH \longrightarrow 2X + C_6H_{12}O_6$ (f)

$CO_2 + C_5H_{10}O_5 \longrightarrow C_6H_{10}O_7 \xrightarrow{H_2O} 2CH_2OH \cdot CHOH \cdot COOH$ (g)

FIG. 2. Forty years of progress in our knowledge of photosynthesis as seen in terms of over-all reactions.

was often taken literally to mean formaldehyde, which had been suggested as the first photosynthetic product by von Baeyer in 1870. By 1937 [CH_2O] stood as a symbol for a part of an unknown carbohydrate, and equation (c) is meant to convey the idea that a carboxyl group is being reduced to an aldehyde group.

A complete change of thought concerning the mechanism of photosynthesis was initiated by van Niel in 1930–1931 (538, 542) when he showed that photosynthesis of green plants and the more complex metabolism of photosynthetic purple bacteria could both be understood as a dye-sensitized redox process.

The question of how free carbon dioxide might enter into a photochemical reaction with water and chlorophyll was answered indirectly with the aid of biochemists working in the field of general metabolism. This happened as early as 1935 and 1936, when Woods (622) discovered formic acid formation from hydrogen and carbon dioxide, Barker (26) the reduction of carbon dioxide to methane, and Wood and Werkman (617–619) the carboxylation and reduction of pyruvate to malate. These carbon fixations were first seen only in microorganisms, but they suggested that a reduction of carbon dioxide may in principle occur in any living cell (532). Later a fixation and reduction of free carbon dioxide was found even in rat liver (144, 546, 620).

With these discoveries, the firm belief that organic substances can arise from carbon dioxide only by the action of light inside the chloroplast was shattered. Thenceforward the problem of photosynthesis divided into two partial problems: the photochemistry of chlorophyll molecules in their long-lived excited states, and the nature of the enzymes responsible for the formation and reduction of an as yet unknown carboxylation product (203).

Such a reduction requires the transfer of four hydrogens from water per carbon dioxide molecule assimilated. It seemed just barely possible (202) that 1 light quantum might suffice for the activation of each hydrogen, or only 4 light quanta for the entire process. The measurements then available of the energy requirements of photosynthesis seemed to support this view (563, 564). The energetics of the process had not been studied critically, and the measured quantum number of 4 certainly fitted the stoichiometry. Soon afterward, however, new measurements were made of the quantum yield (i.e., the number of light quanta required to reduce one molecule of carbon dioxide) which have been confirmed frequently up to this day. They have shown that about 8 light quanta are needed to reduce one carbon dioxide molecule. (The reduction of carboxylic acids and the evolution of oxygen are enzymatic reactions. They closely precede or follow the primary photochemical steps which involve a decomposition of water molecules.)

After the lapse of twenty years, a summary of the essentials of photosynthesis requires at least four equations—(d), (e), (f) and (g) (see Fig. 2). However, in contrast to the fundamental conceptual changes which took place during the first twenty years, the next twenty did not bring about a similar revolutionary advance, but rather a detailed confirmation of these concepts. Much that was hypothetical in 1939 has now become generally accepted knowledge. Equation (d) indicates that the photochemical reaction can proceed only with the aid of certain auxiliary compounds, symbolized by X and Y, which become reduced and oxidized, respectively, while about 8 light quanta must contribute their energy in order that the products, XH_2 and $Y(OH)_2$, be endowed with sufficient free energy to react further as indicated in the following steps:

The oxidized compounds decompose to give water and free oxygen as in equation (e).

The reduced compounds convert the carboxyl group of an organic acid, such as glyceric acid, into the corresponding aldehyde, and eventually to hexose, as shown in equation (f).

The nature of the carboxylation which feeds the main stream of carbon dioxide into the carbohydrate metabolism of the cell has been elucidated in principle, as indicated in equation (g) (32). Of the many carboxylation reactions which became known and were promptly proposed as likely candidates for the hypothetical reaction: $RH + CO_2 \rightarrow RCOOH$, none was more favored in theoretical discussions than the original Wood and Werkman reaction (cf. 532). The research

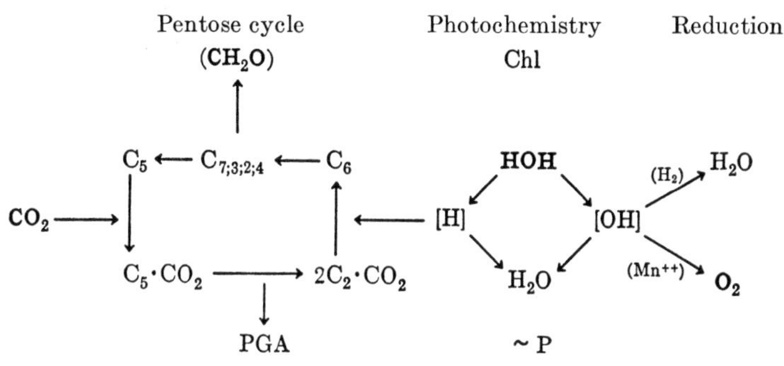

FIG. 3. The mechanism of photosynthesis as a series of interlinked, semiautonomous metabolic systems. PGA is the end product of the carboxylation in the dark. Evolution of oxygen from OH is sometimes replaced by its reduction to water (see text p. 14).

with carbon isotopes finally established a 5-carbon sugar derivative, diphosphoribulose, as the acceptor for carbon dioxide. This reaction yields an as yet unknown intermediate, which in the dark breaks down to give the phosphoglyceric acid mentioned above [equation (g)].

The equations as written above are rather simplified because all the sugars and intermediate carbon compounds react in the cell in the form of phosphate esters (see Section IX).

The true meaning of reactions (d) to (g) can be made clearer in the scheme of Fig. 3, which indicates how those partial reactions are linked together in normal photosynthesis. The scheme in Fig. 4 serves to emphasize that photosynthesis is not the only metabolic consequence of a chlorophyll-sensitized photolysis of water. In looking at the schemes in Figs. 3 and 4, the reader should recall that they do not expound a particular theory but rather summarize what is known and serve as guides for quick orientation among the partial reactions which together constitute the process of photosynthesis. A number of more ambitious theories, purporting to explain in detail and without contradiction the mechanisms of some or of all the reactions indicated, are compatible with these schemes, which will remain useful though the one or other special theory may fail (cf. 436).

According to Fig. 3 at least five separate and semiautonomous partial reactions have been identified. Carbon dioxide enters the system by way of a carboxylation which proceeds without light as an enzymatic reaction in extracts from green plants and even in extracts from non-photosynthesizing, chlorophyll-free organisms. Calvin and Benson discovered, using radioactive C^{14} as a tracer, that the acceptor for carbon dioxide is ribulose diphosphate and that it is regenerated in a special cycle.

During the photochemical reaction the newly carboxylated compound is reduced to form hexoses, from which, by a purely thermal enzymatic process, the C_5 acceptor molecules are re-formed. This transformation among carbohydrates, leading to sugars with carbon skeletons of any length required for the smooth functioning of the cell metabolism was later observed in nonphotosynthetic organisms and in chlorophyll-free extracts from leaves. Thus the concept that the complete mechanism of photosynthesis consists of rather independent metabolic sections has been sustained. In the dark the carboxylation ends with the formation of two phosphorylated glyceric acid molecules, written PGA (215). For several years, stable PGA was looked upon as a normal intermediate and substrate for the photochemical step (476). A precursor, $C_6H_{10}O_7$—equivalent to two molecules of PGA—might be reduced directly to carbohydrate (295). Which of these two possible ways is the main path of the photochemical reduction is not certain; both lead to phosphorylated glucose, C_6 (32).

This cyclic part of the photosynthetic system consists, therefore, of a carboxylation, a reduction, and a rearrangement among several kinds of carbohydrates (see Section IX). Anything which interferes with these reactions inhibits the assimilation of carbon in the light, but not necessarily other activities of the photochemical apparatus. The latter will continue to function as long as there are acceptors for the bound hydrogen (XH) and for the bound hydroxyls (YOH), which are the products of the photochemical reaction (Sections X, XI).

However, carbon dioxide may continue to be reduced in the light, even without a corresponding evolution of free oxygen, whenever the equivalent hydroxyls (OH) are removed in a way which differs from the normal dismutation to oxygen. This can happen when the hydroxyls are reduced again to water with the simultaneous oxidation of certain hydrogen donors. The existence of a separate photochemical production of energy-rich phosphate by illuminated chloroplasts has been proved beyond any doubt (15, 362, and Section XIII).

The carboxylation makes use of a pentose metabolism which does not depend on the photochemistry of chlorophyll. On the other hand, the latter itself survives in chloroplast preparations, independently of the mechanism which fixes carbon dioxide. Hill and later others (see Section XII) showed how artificial hydrogen acceptors like ferricyanide, ferric oxalate, quinone, and certain dyestuffs are easily reduced by illuminated chloroplasts, while the equivalent amount of oxygen is released. For this release of oxygen, a special mechanism is again necessary which requires, among other things, the catalytic activity

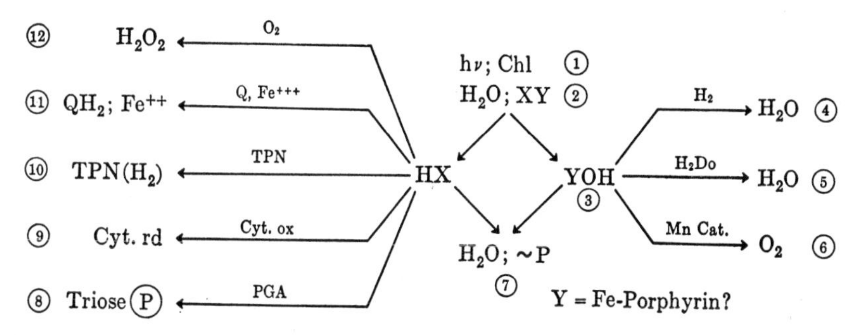

FIG. 4. Summary of photochemical reactions induced by light-excited chlorophyll in living cells and plant extracts which all depend on the photolysis of water (see text).

of manganous ions. The reduction of carbon dioxide, however, does not always depend on this partial reaction. Photosynthetic purple and green bacteria, for example, never evolve free oxygen and, therefore, have to rely on a reduction with special hydrogen donors (Section X). In numerous algae the bacterial type of carbon dioxide fixation can be induced artificially (Section XI).

If the assimilation of carbon is indeed a consequence of the cooperation of several more or less loosely linked specific systems, photosynthesis should be much more variable than had been assumed in earlier times. This is indeed the case, and Fig. 4 is a schematic expression of this variability. The letters "X" and "Y" stand, as in equation (d) of Fig. 2, as symbols for unknown acceptors in the process of water photolysis. XH and YOH are the first products of the photochemical reaction; they may be either a pair of radicals, or may stand for electrical charges which have been separated by the action of light.

Following the circled numbers in Fig. 4, we have: (1) the activation of chlorophyll by light; (2) the production of unknown radicals in pairs. The mechanism of the reaction involving the chlorophyll molecule, the acceptors X and Y, and water is still unknown. What has been designated as "Y" might be one of several iron porphyrins found in the green cell as well as in anaerobic bacteria. This point in the scheme seems logical for such cytochrome-like substances. Reactions (4), (5), (6), and (7) are the various known ways the bound hydroxyl radical can react further. It has the choice of being reduced enzymatically by molecular hydrogen or by organic and inorganic hydrogen donors, by dismutation to water and free oxygen, or by an internal back reaction. The last of these, reaction (7), also involves XH, the reduced hydrogen transfer agent which was formed simultaneously with the bound hydroxyl radical. The existence of such back reactions had been postulated for a long time, but only recently has some information been collected which definitely supports this assumption experimentally. In particular, reaction (7) seems to be one way by which the plants convert light energy into energy-rich phosphate ($\sim$P). This reaction, which is independent of any carbon dioxide fixation, is called photophosphorylation (Section XIII).

Reactions (8), (9), (10), (11), and (12) signify several partly competing reductions which may be observed with living cells or with chloroplast preparations. (8) is the normal reduction of either PGA or of the carboxylated precursor C_6 mentioned above. Reactions (9), (10), and (11) are the reductions of cytochromes, coenzymes, quinones, or iron salts, which have been studied mainly in cell-free preparations. Reaction (12) is the reduction of molecular oxygen to hydrogen peroxide. In case the freshly formed hydrogen peroxide is promptly decomposed by catalase into water and oxygen, the reaction leads merely to an exchange of the oxygen present in water for the oxygen absorbed from the air (Section XII,A).

Of the greatest theoretical interest is reaction (10), the reduction of the phosphopyridine nucleotides (TPN or DPN). By means of reaction (10) all metabolic systems which depend on a supply of reduced coenzyme can now be coupled with the photochemical mechanism (552, 557). Therefore reaction (10) may be part of reaction (8). In some cases it has been reported as part of reaction (7), the back reaction leading to phosphorylation. According to this scheme any one reaction on the left may be linked by way of the photochemical mechanism with any one on the right. In reality all of these possible combinations do not proceed competitively in the same cell. The scheme is a composite one and presents a summary of those reactions which have been discovered, partly with intact plants and intact bacteria and partly with the corresponding cell-free extracts. It is a reminder that the mechanism of photosynthesis begins to look as intricate as that of the better-known processes, respiration and glycolysis. The one common and immutable component is the chlorophyll which initiates the conversion of light energy into chemical energy (see Fig. 124, p. 238).

C. PHOTOSYNTHESIS AS A VERY IMPROBABLE PHOTOCHEMICAL REACTION

The student who has merely learned that the achievement of photosynthesis consists in a reversal of respiration—not only because the final products show this to be the case but because the assimilation of carbon proceeds by similar intermediate steps—and who would be satisfied to know that light delivers the necessary reducing power, perhaps in the form of reduced coenzymes, has learned some of the facts as we now know them but, as yet, has not recognized the crux of the problem.

What sets photosynthesis apart from all other metabolic reactions is its photochemical component. There are very few light-sensitized processes in organic nature, compared with the enormous number of nonphotochemical reactions which together constitute the metabolism of living cells. Among these few light-dependent reactions (phototropism, photoperiodism, growth regulation, and vision), photosynthesis remains unique. It not only initiates, or sensitizes, or directs the course of a very specific cellular activity, but it collects and retains about one-third of the energy available in the light which is absorbed by the pigments in the plastids. Photosynthesis in plants is the one reaction of its kind on earth, and it proceeds, as far as we know, only in the presence of chlorophyll a, the substance symbolized by the structural formula given in Fig. 5. Light absorbed in this molecule is used for the breaking of one bond between hydrogen and oxygen in a molecule of water. In visible light the individual quanta have too small an energy content to perform this reaction in one step. How the photolysis of water is brought about constitutes, therefore, the central problem in photosynthesis (Sections III, IV, and XVI).

As written in reaction (d), Fig. 2, the photochemical reaction looks very much like an ordinary hydrolysis. Of this we have countless examples in the inorganic and organic world, many of them easily reversible and, if catalyzed by enzymes, proceeding very fast. The reversibility means that there is not a great change in energy involved. Mostly the entrance of water and the splitting into two compounds is favored in comparison with the closing of a ring or the synthesis of a new molecule with the removal of one molecule of water. A comparison

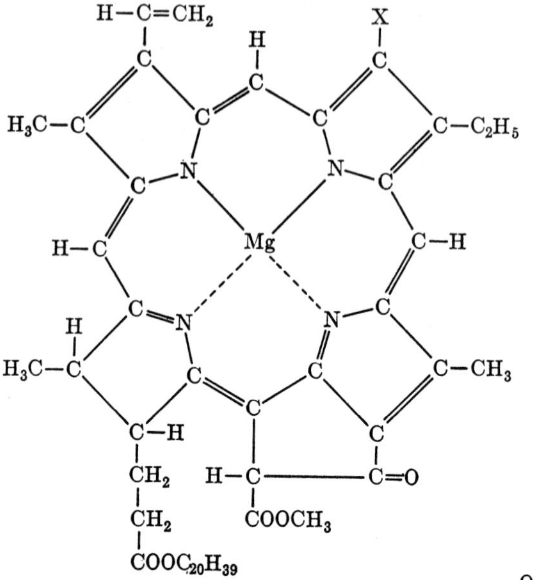

In chlorophyll a, X = $-CH_3$. In chlorophyll b, X = $-C{=}O$ (—CHO, i.e. C double-bonded to O and bonded to H)

FIG. 5. The structure of chlorophylla.

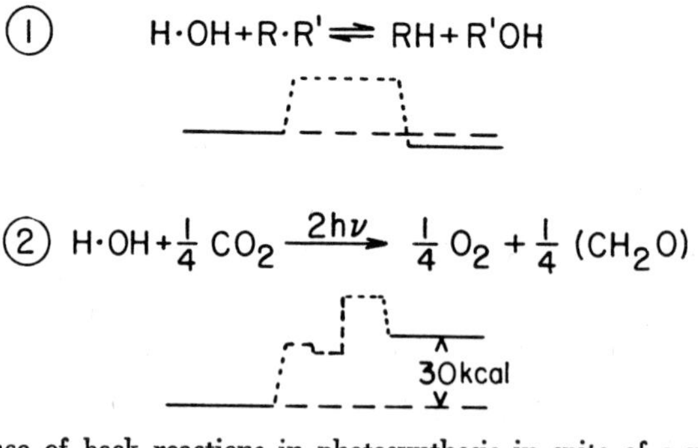

$$\text{(1)}\quad H{\cdot}OH + R{\cdot}R' \rightleftharpoons RH + R'OH$$

$$\text{(2)}\quad H{\cdot}OH + \tfrac{1}{4}CO_2 \xrightarrow{2h\nu} \tfrac{1}{4}O_2 + \tfrac{1}{4}(CH_2O)$$

FIG. 6. Absence of back reactions in photosynthesis in spite of a permanent gain of 30 kilocalories in free energy per water molecule decomposed. Comparison of free-energy changes in reversible hydrolysis (*1*) and photosynthesis (*2*).

between this kind of reaction (with water) and photosynthesis is given in Fig. 6.

The horizontal lines below the left and right sides of the equation represent the free-energy levels. With a typical hydrolysis, these levels are not very different before and after the reaction. In the absence of enzymes a larger activation energy has to be expended in order to pass from the state at the left to that at the right (represented by the dotted "hill" between the levels). The height of the barrier between the two sides determines the reaction rate at normal temperatures.

The next line symbolizes the over-all process of photosynthesis written for one water molecule; the diagram below indicates the corresponding energy change. In contrast to a hydrolysis, the reaction products show an energy gain of 30 kilocalories per molecule of water decomposed. The energy level on the right side is much higher than on the left. If there were no obstacles—no activation energies—between the one state and the other, the products—oxygen and carbohydrate—would immediately reunite and again give water and carbon dioxide. The fact that this does not happen is due to the activation energies necessary to initiate this combustion. In the laboratory we supply this activation energy by means of heat. With so much light energy available, the very first products of the photolysis of water should recombine instantly. Yet we find that the products of photosynthesis are stable and the over-all efficiency high. Therefore, spontaneous back reactions are mostly avoided. This is possible only if activation barriers exist which can be overcome easily in the one direction with the aid of the light energy but not so easily in the reverse direction when each molecule is again at normal temperature. This irreversibility, guaranteed by the activation "hill" drawn as the dotted line in the diagram, must be paid for with some extra calories. And how much more energy is actually expended in order to save and store 30 kilocalories is the main question concerning the efficiency of photosynthesis.

In discussing Fig. 6 we have pointed out that an O—H bond in water may easily be broken in the course of a reaction if the hydrogen and hydroxyl are bound equally strongly or more strongly in their new positions. The energy change is either nil or negative. An entirely different way of cleaving a water molecule is a direct photodissociation into H and OH radicals.

This requires, however, radiation having at least 114 kilocalories per einstein,* corresponding to an ultraviolet wavelength of 260 mμ. Water does not absorb ultraviolet radiation appreciably at wavelengths longer than 190 mμ. A direct photodissociation therefore requires either a still shorter wavelength, or an appropriate sensitizer.

So long as the earth's atmosphere contained no oxygen, short-wave ultraviolet light could penetrate the earth's atmosphere to the surface, and it is generally assumed that 1-quantum photoprocesses initiated the

* The einstein is defined as the energy contained in 6×10^{23} quanta (a "mole" quantum) when the energy of 1 quantum or photon is given by Planck's constant, h, and the wave frequency of light, ν: $N_0h\nu$.

synthesis of organic substances (48, 220, 368, 528). With the appearance of oxygen in the atmosphere, however, by far the greater part of the ultraviolet in the solar spectrum was intercepted by an ozone layer in the upper atmosphere. Thus a direct photochemistry with water

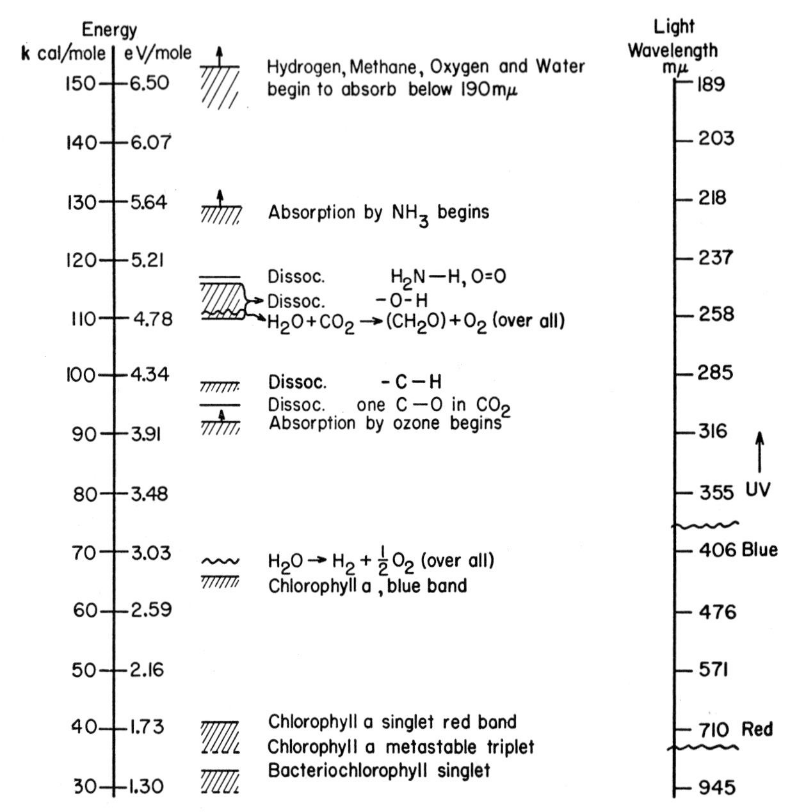

FIG. 7. Energy available per einstein in the ultraviolet and visible light as compared with that required for some fundamental photochemical reactions. The energy available for chemical reactions with the aid of excited chlorophyll always remains below 41 kilocalories per einstein. More than 1 quantum of light is therefore necessary to achieve the photolysis of water.

ceased many millions, or perhaps billions, of years ago. The achievement of the green plant consists in having found a device which circumvents the need for "simple" 1-quantum processes. Photosynthesis is something which lies between the immediate dissociation of the molecule by a directly absorbed quantum of light and the enzymatic hydrolysis which does not provide for any over-all gain in chemical energy.

The scheme in Fig. 7 compares the energy available in ultraviolet radiation and in visible light with that required for certain fundamental chemical reactions. The graphs show three different items: First, the minimum energy for dissociation of certain bonds which occur most often in organic molecules, such as C—H, O—H, N—H, oxygen double, and oxygen-carbon bonds. The energy to dissociate in a one-excitation step any one of these bonds exists only in the ultraviolet region. However, since not only water, but also the molecules of carbon dioxide and hydrogen do not absorb appreciably in the region where the energy of a quantum would just suffice to cause dissociation, an effective photochemistry requires in each case correspondingly larger light quanta.

Because there is no chance for such 1-quantum dissociations to proceed on a large scale (quite apart from the sterilizing effects of ultraviolet on living cells) plants have substituted the visible light absorbed in chlorophyll-like pigments for the direct action of ultraviolet. But here the energy is much too small to achieve by a 1-quantum process the photolysis of water. Chlorophyll a retains 41 kilocalories (or 1.7 volts) per mole in its singlet red band, regardless of whether it has absorbed a red quantum of just this size or a blue quantum with a much higher energy content (about 70 kilocalories). Probably the energy available for chemical reactions by excited chlorophyll is not the 41 kilocalories absorbed, but 31 kilocalories of the triplet state (see Sections IV and VIII). Since the over-all process of photosynthesis results in a gain of approximately 118 kilocalories per carbon atom, at least four absorption acts are required to cover the net thermodynamic debt. In the course of the reaction many chemical bonds are broken and re-formed. The resulting intermediates and final products must be reasonably stable to prevent back reactions (as described in Fig. 6), or the measured efficiency of photosynthesis at very low light intensities could not be as high as it is. Considering the extra energy expended to overcome many thermal activation steps, appreciably more energy will be required than the 118 kilocalories found in the end products.

Experimentally it has been established that between 6 and 10 light quanta are actually needed for the reduction of one molecule of carbon dioxide under optimal physiological conditions (Section VIII). The reason given above renders it extremely unlikely that the theoretical quantum requirement could be much smaller than 8. The good agreement between theory and observation is one of the main arguments against the validity of those measurements which allegedly have shown photosynthesis with 4, or even less than 3, quanta (578).

By their very nature, light quanta arrive as nondivisible packages of energy. As a photochemical decomposition of a water molecule cannot proceed with 1 quantum absorbed by chlorophyll, it will necessarily require at least 2 quanta. This self-evident proposition was first expanded into an "8-quanta theory" by J. Franck as early as 1940 (166). Whenever we find in the literature credible measurements showing somewhat smaller numbers than 8 quanta for the over-all process, they may reasonably be explained by the complexity and diversity of the reactions which follow the photochemical steps. Eight quanta contain an excess of energy. From the triplet state alone, a total of 240 kilocalories are available of which 118 remain stored as chemical energy. Part of the excess energy might be caught as a supernumerary energy-rich phosphate bond. If this is saved it might help to lower the integrated quantum requirement during photosynthesis in the steady state. These cases, however, are rare compared with the very long series of experiments in which the measured number of quanta needed to reduce one molecule of carbon dioxide was never smaller than 8.

II. Materials and Methods

A. Plant Material

Willstätter and Stoll (604) said that in all green plants photosynthesis is fundamentally the same. (The available facts still support this assertion.) Thus any species of plant was believed to be equally valid as a research object if it was suitable for laboratory investigation. During the last thirty years, however, progress has definitely depended on the choice—deliberate or fortuitous—of objects for study with qualitatively different metabolic responses from those of the better-known green organisms. For successful experimentation, it is, therefore, important to become familiar with the physiology of various kinds of plants and to choose some which have not been previously investigated.

The differences between species were better understood after it was found that photosynthesis itself is a system of variable enzymatic reactions likely to be influenced by the entire cell metabolism. We mentioned that the research of Willstätter and Stoll on plant extracts was discontinued because the leaves of the sunflower, etc., did not yield active preparations. This is still true today. The sunflower is one of those plants from which it is difficult to obtain active isolated chloroplasts.

Though leaves are still a favorite plant material for preparative biochemical research, with spinach (*Spinacea oleracea*) and pokeweed (*Phytolacca americana*) far outranking all the others, they are not so practical for accurate kinetic studies. In 1919 O. Warburg introduced the green alga *Chlorella* as a research object (560). All microbiological techniques are applicable to such small cells (51, 69, 379, 392, 431). Many species of the unicellular algae are now being cultivated in the laboratory because, like the higher plants, they have characteristic features which facilitate particular investigations (25, 74a, 96, 130, 158, 384, 386, 387).

When attention was paid to purple and green bacteria, a great step forward was made. In these organisms a true variant of the photochemical process was discovered. It was through the comparison between green algae and bacteria that our understanding of photosynthesis progressed most rapidly in the decade between 1930 and 1940 (Sections X and XI; 273).

In addition to the search for new photosynthetic organisms, mutants have been produced by means of X-ray or ultraviolet treatment. These have been particularly useful in studies on the formation of chlorophyll and other pigments (Sections II and X; 91, 241, 441).

Instead of using genetically mutated strains, it is also possible to grow algae or bacteria under seemingly abnormal conditions so as to obtain strains which again show unusual properties (376–378, 429, 430). The means used can be as simple as a drastic change in the pH of the nutrient medium (133). For instance acid media were found to increase permeability for substances like the aliphatic acids or sodium fluoride (see Section XIV; 41, 576, 577). Growing the culture in the presence of certain poisons may selectively prevent the development of an enzyme or of a pigment without interfering too much with the growth of the culture (Section III,C,2; 98, 99, 195).

Culturing in media deficient in certain elements has long been an established method of research on plant nutrition (38, 417, 421). Using the same method with cultures of algae, important results have been obtained on the need for such nutrients and micronutrients as potassium, manganese, magnesium, vanadium, iron (267, 268), copper, phosphorus, chloride, and boron (274, 382, 460). Since most algae cannot be washed free of any important micronutrients (428), the procedure is to transfer the normally growing, washed cells into deficient media. The elements become diluted by successive cell divisions until the deficiency manifests itself. We therefore call these substances "growth factors." The effect of most of the deficiencies on photosynthesis cannot be reversed in short periods of time, two notable exceptions being the effects of potassium and manganese, first studied by Pirson. This is particularly true of the effect of a manganese deficiency on photosynthesis and respiration which is reversed within a few minutes (Section XI; 413–416).

The simple expedient of growing green algae in the dark with organic substances may lead in certain strains to a loss of chlorophyll (381). Thus, "bleached" algae can be compared with normal ones to see whether certain enzymes remain active once most or all of the active chlorophyll has failed to appear. In this way it was found, for instance, that in some organisms (*Chlorella variegata* and *Euglena* sp.) the carboxylating enzyme disappears with the active pigment. Since each strain of organism responds differently to treatment with

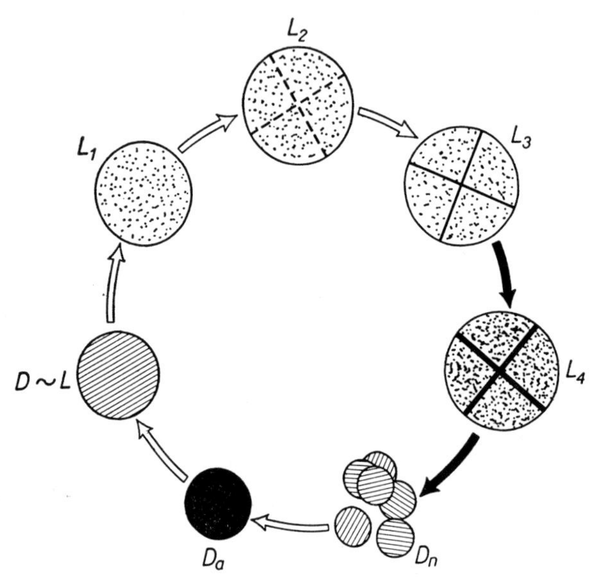

FIG. 8. Schematic representation of the life cycle of *Chlorella*. During the day the small young daughter cells grow first with production of chlorophyll and later mainly with production of general cell material (Stages D_a to L_3). Division occurs during the night (Stages L_3 to D_n). See Tamiya (503), Pirson (422, 423), and Kanazawa (291a).

organic nutrients, many experiments of this kind are needed until it is safe to make a general statement.

Growing algae in large quantities for purposes other than studies of photosynthesis was recently undertaken after the question of algae for food aroused considerable interest (74a, 216, 383, 504).

It is well known that most plants do not easily tolerate uninterrupted strong illumination (385, 610). One reason why unicellular algae, like species of *Chlorella*, *Scenedesmus*, etc., have become so useful in the laboratory is that they grow well when continuously illuminated. Only lately has more attention been paid to the fact that even these primitive organisms have a pronounced life cycle during which metabolic variations can be recognized (see Fig. 8 and 70, 251, 458, 503). Cultivating these algae not only at optimum light intensities, but also in carefully adjusted day and night periods—for instance 14 hours "day" and 10 hours "night"—results in a greater uniformity of the cell material (291a, 393, 415, 419, 423). The cultures then consist mainly of synchronized cells (85), which have the same size, pigment content, and metabolic rates. For certain problems, such as maximum quantum

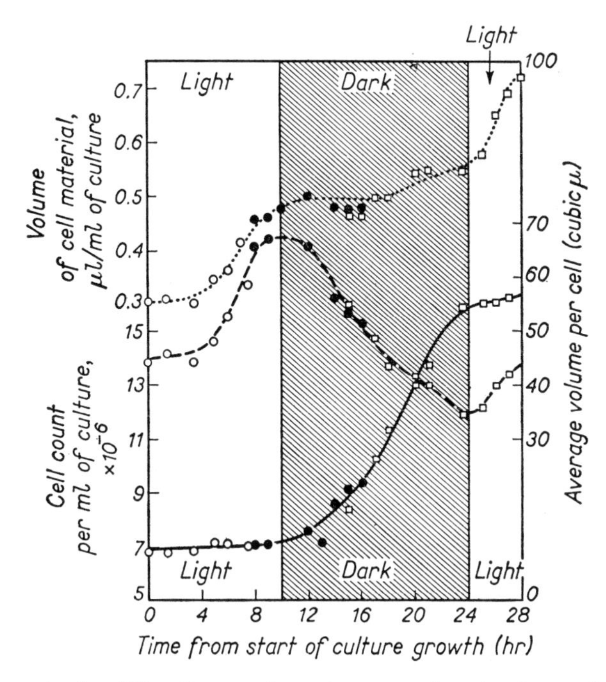

FIG. 9. Growth of a *Chlorella* sp. culture in terms of total volume of cell material (top curve), average volume of single cell (middle curve), and number of cells (bottom curve). According to Emerson; see also (423).

yield, or rhythmical metabolic variation, this may be of great practical importance. Figure 9 compares total volume, single-cell volume, and number of cells as they change in the course of day and night.

B. METHODS

The original procedure of Priestley and other early investigators for analyzing the changes in the composition of the air in a flask containing plants has in one form or another, survived to the present day. The gas exchange of plants has been quantitatively measured by chemical analysis (355, 604), by recording the pressure changes, by following the light absorption of carbon dioxide gas in infrared radiation, by the magnetic properties of oxygen, and by the differences in heat conductivity of such gases as hydrogen, oxygen, and carbon dioxide. Such measurements are often supplemented by the determination of the accumulated end products, which involves the chemical analysis of sugars and other organic compounds.

Among the techniques for measuring photosynthesis by way of its gas exchange, the manometric methods of Haldane, Barcroft, and Warburg have been predominant during the last thirty years (111,

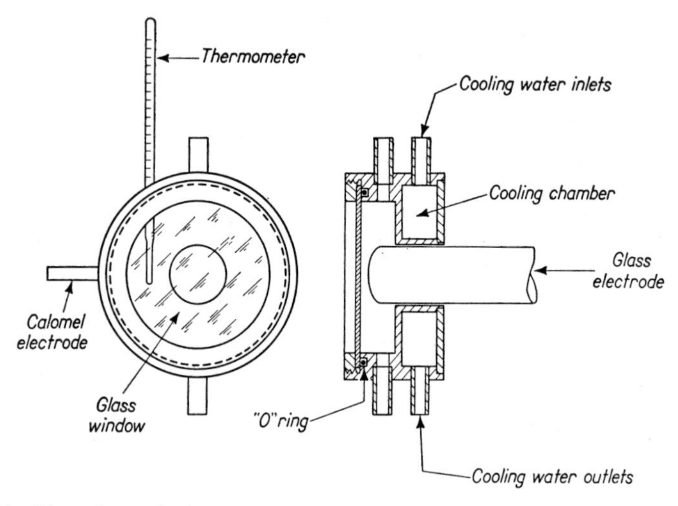

FIG. 10. Glass electrode for quantitative measurement of carbon dioxide exchange of algae suspended in thin bicarbonate buffers. After Gaffron (219) and Rosenberg (444, 445).

527). Interest in the transient reactions of photosynthesis occurring in times shorter than a minute made it necessary, however, to adopt methods more accurate than the classical one. Special investigations by Emerson, Pirson, Meyers, and co-workers of the limitations of manometry have shown that it will give reliable results only where steady-state conditions can be maintained (141, 389). Even the physical lag of the gas exchange between fluid and gas phase—not to speak of the transient phenomena in plants—extends to minutes and varies considerably with the shape and the contents of the vessel.

Thus in recent years the polarigraphic determination of oxygen (53) and the measurement with a pH meter of acidity changes due to carbon dioxide (444) have been elaborated into quantitative methods (see Fig. 10). In combination with automatic recording apparatus, reliable readings can be obtained in a period of only a few seconds—which means that these methods are up to a hundred times more sensitive than is manometry (for examples see Fig. 122 in Section XV on induction periods). Commercial apparatus is now available to measure the oxygen content of a gas stream by the paramagnetism of oxygen, and the content of carbon dioxide by infrared absorption. Though all these instruments may have their special disadvantages, they certainly avoid those which have become so conspicuous in the abortive attempts to follow transient phenomena accurately in conventional manometers of the Warburg type.

The desire to probe into the action of chlorophyll during the photochemical phase has required the construction of optical apparatus and of flash-illumination devices which often constitute a technical research problem in themselves. These physicochemical investigations, mainly optical in nature, such as changes of absorption spectra, of fluorescence, of luminescence, are the only ones which permit a look at the photosynthetic mechanism while it is working.

Thanks to these optical methods, we now have recordings of spectral changes which occur within 10^{-3} or 10^{-4} seconds (Section VI). The data are essentially kinetic in nature and are beginning to supplant the kinetic data on the gas exchange which, during the first forty years of this century, were the mainstay of research in photosynthesis. A substance which seems to fit chemically into a scheme of photosynthesis will nevertheless be unacceptable to the physical chemist when neither its concentration nor its color change in the living cell corresponds to the kinetics deduced from optical observations.

The use of radioactive tracer elements, in particular of C^{14} and P^{32}, has become common practice throughout the field of biochemistry (279, 362, 532). In combination with paper chromatography the tracer method has lead to the results shown in Fig. 69. The unique advantage in following a gas exchange with the aid of several isotopes in the mass spectrometer becomes obvious when we study the examples shown in Figs. 32–35.

The sensitivity of certain special apparatus can hardly be pushed further. For instance, photosynthesis at 10^{-5} atmospheres of oxygen can be followed quantitatively by measuring the quenching of phosphorescence in light-activated pigments adsorbed to silica gel (170, 425). Invisible-light emission is measured with phototubes kept at the temperature of liquid nitrogen (a "quantum counter") (492).

In the treatment of plant material, the advances have been due to the adaptation of methods developed by the biochemists in their search for methods to preserve the activity of labile enzymes. Making cell extracts of temperatures just above freezing and storing them either at temperatures of the order of —20°C or in the dried condition has become accepted procedure (238, 399).

The art of measuring light intensities—incident or absorbed—is treated in special monographs. As applied to problems in plant physiology, however, there are certain difficulties to be solved. The most important of these are the influence of the scattering which light undergoes in nonhomogeneous, turbid media, and the spectral shifts which occur when pigments (whose spectra can easily be determined in clear solution) are found associated with high-molecular proteins and in concentrations which may cause further deviations from the normal (see Section VI).

The majority of experiments on photosynthesis have included only a rough estimate of the high incident intensity, while most of the attention was given to achieving equal illumination in control and experimental vessels. Photosynthetic activity of the cells themselves can often be used to determine whether the light absorbed is near saturation or in the neighborhood of compensation. The light characteristics of algae grown under standard conditions are remarkably reproducible.

Very often it is necessary to work with thin suspensions; the light absorbed is the difference between that falling on the cells and that transmitted and scattered in all directions. The best piece of apparatus to use here is the so-called "integrating" or "Ulbricht" sphere. The vessel containing the algae is situated inside a white-painted container. The scattered, as well as the direct, light produces a general luminosity inside the container which is measured at one point by a photocell. All the light not absorbed by the algae can thus be measured. Only with the aid of this sphere has it been possible to obtain a true picture of the intensity of fluorescence. The green cells themselves are apt to reabsorb fluorescence radiation. This light-filtering effect falsifies the intensity curves as well as the shape of spectral curves (330). To a small extent, this is true even for one single cell, because chlorophyll is so concentrated in the grana.

The changing configuration of a volume of liquid that is being shaken (as must be done if the gas exchange is measured) introduces still further complications. Thus, before embarking on any kind of quantitative investigation, the experimenter should first prepare himself by studying the experiences of others.

There are many devices for measuring visible radiation. They depend mainly on four different principles: The first is the conversion of light into heat on a black surface. This change in temperature produces changes in electrical conductivity which can be recorded. Such instruments as the thermocouple and the bolometer operate on this principle. The second method is based on the release of electrons from an illuminated surface inside a vacuum tube. This "photocell" consists of two electrodes; the cathode is coated with a material which will emit electrons if hit by light quanta, and the photoelectric current is proportional to the intensity of the light. The most sensitive photocell arrangement used so far in plant physiology is the "quantum counter" of Strehler and Arnold (492) developed to measure the light emission of green cells which occurs in the dark after a period of illumination. The third principle is best exemplified by the "solar battery." At the present state of development this is by far the most convenient instrument, since it can be built into many different kinds of apparatus. The fourth is dependent upon a photochemical reaction. A properly chosen dye will sensitize the photodissociation or photooxidation of acceptors whose transformation or oxidation serves as a measure of the light intensity. For many years, uranyl salts have been used; these decompose organic substances under the influence of blue light. Since it was found (197) that porphyrins and chlorophyll can induce the photooxidation of a number of organic and inorganic substances with a quantum yield approaching unity, it has been possible, after proper calibration, to use this reaction as an actinometer. Chlorophyll as sensitizer has an advantage in that its spectral sensitivity is very close to that of the plants.

III. Chloroplast Structure and Constituents

A. STRUCTURE OF THE CHLOROPLAST

It has been known for over sixty years that the chloroplasts in the plant cell are the site of photosynthesis. Studies on the origin, growth, and structure of these inclusions, the plastids, have now become a special chapter in plant physiology (240, 244, 366, 510–515, 544). The reason for this is that synthetic reactions in general seem not to occur in the homogeneous phase of the cell contents, but on the surface of corpuscles such as mitochondria. The electron microscope provided new ways of looking at microstructures and has revealed structural details that were unknown even a few years ago. Figure 11a is a photograph of chloroplasts under high magnification. (Figure 11b is a schematic reconstruction of what the investigators believe they have seen in this photograph.)

The mature, functional chloroplast consists of layers 30–80 A thick resembling a stack of sandwiches or a layer cake. At more or less regular intervals some dark material forms an additional layer between the main lamina. Here is concentrated all the chlorophyll and presumably

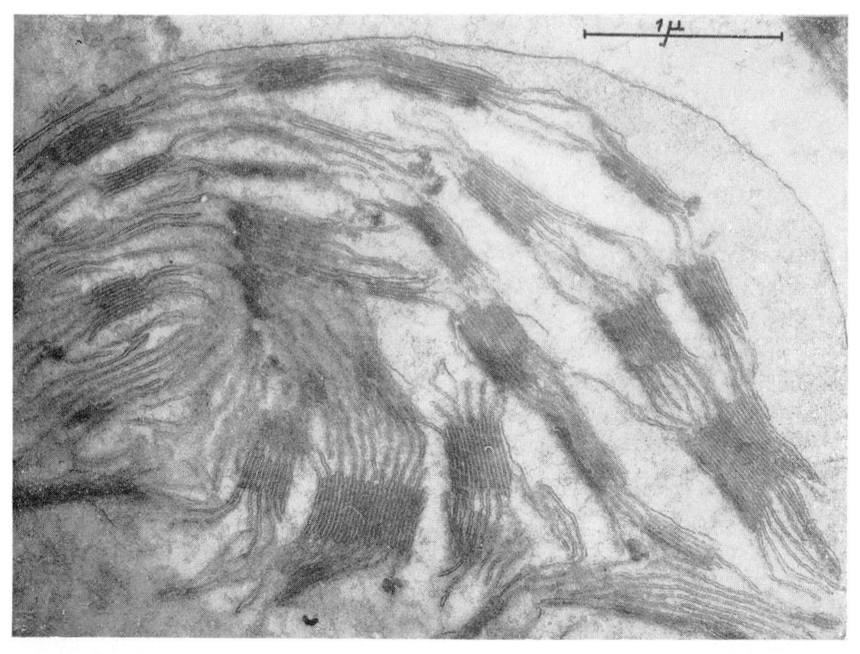

FIG. 11a. Lamellar organization of chloroplasts in barley as seen in the electron microscope. (Original by D. V. Wettstein.)

possibility	granular chloroplast	lamellate chloroplast
1		
2		
3		

FIG. 11b. Schematic representation of possible distributions of "reaction centers" in granular and lamellate chloroplasts. See Thomas *et al.* (515–517a).

the other pigments which are present in the plastid. When the chloroplast is broken apart, these darker regions come out in particle form called "grana." By treating chloroplasts or grana with detergents, the structure of the layers can be unfolded, and it seems as if two of each contain a pigment layer in sandwich form. The chlorophyll is apparently embedded between lipids and proteins. When these stacks are further taken apart, we obtain very thin single elements (see also Chapter I, Volume IA).

As long as attention was focused on the reduction of carbon dioxide as the prime achievement of the light-driven reactions in green plants, the mechanism of photosynthesis seemed to be dishearteningly sensitive toward any interference with the vital properties of the chloroplasts. This feeling has now given way to astonishment at the persistent capacity to evolve oxygen, i.e., to accomplish the photolysis of water, in extracted chloroplast fractions, even after they have been dried, extracted with organic solvent, and reimmersed in water (see Sections VIII and XII).

Not all photosynthetic organisms have chloroplasts. The blue-green algae and the purple bacteria show only local concentrations of pigments which resemble the grana (396, 544). Thus the bigger lamellated structure seems not to be essential for the specific function of the chlorophyll complex. Experimentally this has been confirmed by showing that fractions of chloroplasts still give photosynthetic reactions. By continuing the breakdown process until the capacity for evolving oxygen disappears, Thomas arrived at a lower limit for the particle size which would still do some physiological photochemical reaction. It contained between two hundred and four hundred molecules of chlorophyll. The size of these particles is much smaller than any detail shown on the electron microscope photographs (394).

It is obvious to the eye that plants vary greatly in their degrees of coloring. Some are light green and yellowish and others contain so much chlorophyll that they appear nearly black. The chloroplasts themselves may differ greatly in chlorophyll content. This content seems to parallel the number of lamellar structures seen in the micrographs. Thomas calculated the density of chlorophyll at the lamellar surface found in the grana. Seen that way, the differences which are so clear for the chlorophyll content of the cell as a whole, or in the plastids, nearly disappear. The number of chlorophyll molecules per unit area of lamellar monolayer is remarkably uniform (513). This is an important observation, and the data are given in Table II. Thomas distinguishes between lamellated chloroplasts and grana. The latter name he gives to the bodies found in bacteria and blue-green algae. In

TABLE II

CHLOROPHYLL DENSITY AT LAMELLAR SURFACES IN PLASTIDS FROM DIFFERENT ORIGIN[a]

Object	Type of plastid	Chlorophyll content of a single plastid (grams 10^{-12})	Number of lamellae per granum or grana-free chloroplast	Area of single lamella (μ^2)	Number of chlorophyll molecules per μ^2 lamellar monolayer, 10^5
Land plants—Angiosperms					
Spinacia oleracea	Grana-bearing chloroplasts	1.9	9	0.20	3.1
Hibiscus rosa-sinensis		1.0 (approx.)	15	0.10	2.7
Aspidistra elatior		14.0	26	0.36	11.0
Tulipa sp.		0.07	6	0.06	5.4
Aquatic angiosperms					
Elodea densa	Grana-bearing chloroplasts	2.0	15	0.10	4.0
Green algae					
Mougeotia sp.	Grana-free chloroplasts	67.0	170[c]	1105.0	2.6
Spirogyra sp.		340.0	120[c]	4800.0	4.0
Blue-green algae					
Synechococcus cedrorum	Grana-free chloroplasts	0.26	32[c]	4.3	12.0
Diatoms					
Nitzschia dissipata	Grana-free chloroplasts	0.9[b]	60[c]	10.2	4.0
Bacteria					
Rhodospirillum rubrum	Free grana	0.016[b]	7	0.02	10.0

[a] Data selected from J. B. Thomas *et al.* (515).

[b] Chlorophyll content per cell.

[c] Monolayers.

grana, the coarse structure, the lamellae, are not aggregated in stacks as in Fig. 11. The data of Table II do not contain observations on the most common of our laboratory objects, the algae of the genera *Chlorella* and *Scenedesmus*, probably because they are very hard to break and, if broken, do not release the chloroplasts intact. It would be interesting to see whether the density of chlorophyll in these green algae approaches that in the bacteria and in blue-green algae.

One conclusion of these studies by Thomas *et al.*, is that the chlorophyll molecules are packed very closely. There is barely sufficient room for the molecules to be arranged in the same plane. The areas calculated are, indeed, smaller than necessary for the transfer of energy with 96% efficiency between two pigment molecules such as chlorophyll a and chlorophyll b. The need for such an energy transfer has been postulated on account of kinetic observations and theoretical deductions, while fluorescence behavior gave the main experimental support. It is important, therefore, that direct observation of the structural arrangement inside the pigmented corpuscles does not contradict these ideas, but, on the contrary, confirms them (517a).

The cytology of plastids also has been approached from the evolutionary standpoint. The salient point is that the appearance of structure and of active chlorophyll in the developing cell seem to go hand in hand. Mutants that are defective in photosynthesis were found to have defective structures and vice versa. Interference with the normal development of structure, even if chlorophyll was present, produced cells without normal photosynthesis (610).

One question raised by the fine chloroplast structure is how pigments of such different solubility as carotenes, chlorophylls, and phycobilins are so arranged that an efficient energy transfer between them is possible. The carotenes can be extracted from dried cells or chloroplasts without disturbing the chlorophylls (see Section VIII,C,3). The chlorophylls dissolve rapidly out of living cells by treatment with aqueous alcohols or acetone, and the phycobilins are water soluble only and are extracted, together with their protein moiety, after breaking the cell wall. A kind of crystalline arrangement of the chlorophyll requires that, in at least two dimensions, no other type of molecule interfere with this pattern.

In concluding this short section on the importance of structure, it should be repeated that even the smallest distinguishable parts of the structures seen in the present photographs are much larger than those in the hypothetical photosynthetic unit which we will discuss in Section VII.

B. Chloroplast Constituents

The question whether all enzymes, coenzymes (596), and other factors necessary for photosynthesis (557) are (like the pigments) enclosed in the chloroplast has been debated for some time. Experimentally, this question is difficult to answer, and its significance is doubtful since photosynthesis proceeds very efficiently in cells which do not have chloroplasts. It is obvious that coenzymes and metal ions

TABLE III
Some Substances Known or Assumed to Take Part in Photosynthetic Reactions

Substance	Role	
A. Pigments present in large amounts (visible coloring matter)		
Chlorophyll a; Bacteriochlorophyll a	Main light-energy converting agent	
Chlorophyll b (c,d)	Absorbed energy transferred to chlorophyll a with a yield of	95%
Phycoerythrin		90%
Phycocyanin		90%
Fucoxanthol		75%
Xanthophyll		40%
Carotene β (α)	Protection against photooxidation	
B. Coenzymes and similar factors		
Adenosine triphosphate (ATP); Flavin nucleotide; Thioctic acid (?); Pyridine nucleotides (TPN, DPN)	Factors needed for reduction	
Pyridine nucleotides (TPN, DPN); Adenosine diphosphate (ADP); Vitamin K (or other quinone)	Factors for photophosphorylation	
Vitamin K (or other quinone); Cytochromes (f,c); Catalase (?); Manganous ion (Mn^{++})	Factors for release of oxygen	
Potassium; Vanadium; Iron; Chloride anion	Function unknown	
C. Catalytic proteins		
Reductases	Methemoglobin, cytochromes, flavins DPN, TPN, carboxylic acids, NO_2^-, NO_3^-, N_2	
Oxidases or photooxidases	Cytochrome c, ascorbic acid	
Hydrogenase	Free hydrogen in purple bacteria and adapted algae	
Photodehydrogenases	Fatty acid and alcohol utilization in heterotrophic purple bacteria	
Sulfur-activating enzymes	Photoreduction in purple and green sulfur bacteria	
Phosphorylating enzyme	Photophosphorylation in green plants and photosynthetic bacteria	

may pass freely through membranes which will retain large protein molecules. The method of isolating chloroplasts from green tissue is mainly responsible for the kind of reaction which is afterward found to have remained normal or only slightly disturbed. Enzymes become inactive either irreversibly by denaturation or reversibly by the washing out of cofactors. Identifying and replacing these cofactors have been the main tasks in restoring activity to otherwise undamaged cell-free preparations (cf. 86).

Table III gives a survey of most of the substances—other than catalytic proteins—which were found to play a part in photosynthesis, or at least in some artificial combination of photolysis by chlorophyll *in vivo* with known enzyme systems.

The substances enumerated under *B* (Table III) are familiar to the biochemist from his studies on respiration, fermentation, sugar and fat metabolism. If their function in photosynthesis is not literally identical with that in other metabolic processes, any difference must reside in the specificity of their protein part.

Catalytic proteins specific for the photochemical reduction of TPN (451), of ordinary methemoglobin (110), of cytochrome c, or even for the photooxidation of reduced cytochrome c (396) have been recognized as constituents of chloroplasts, or of plastid-free bacterial cells. It is easy to predict that many more will be found.

1. Light-Absorbing Pigments

Among the pigments listed under *A*, only chlorophyll a (Fig. 5) and the corresponding bacteriochlorophyll a seem to be indispensable. Which of the other colored substances is found in addition in a photosynthesizing cell seems to matter little as far as the essential mechanism of the photochemical reaction is concerned. Chlorophyll b is absent in blue-green, brown, and red algae, in diatoms, and in the green algae of the genus *Vaucheria* (46, 101; see also 246a, 533).

Among the carotenoids only the oxygen-containing members, the carotenols, seem to function as accessory light-absorbing agents (113, 490, 505). Carotene itself, which is nearly always present in normal cells (mostly as β-carotene), appears to be a safeguard against photooxidation. Certain purple bacteria can be made carotene free either by selecting mutants or by growing them in the presence of diphenylamine. As long as anaerobic conditions prevail, carbon dioxide assimilation and growth are normal in these carotene-deficient cells. In air they succumb readily to photooxidation, while the normal cells with carotene seem to be protected against this side effect of light (98, 99, 254).

The concentration of pigments per dry weight of colored tissue (leaves of higher plants, thalli of brown and red algae, cells of unicellular organisms) varies greatly, as does also the ratio of one pigment to another (450, 624). The mechanism of photosynthesis seems not to require any fixed proportion of colored matter to cell plasma nor of one chlorophyll to another, though normal green leaves maintain a ratio of chlorophyll a:b = 2:0.7 (604). In terms of dry weight, leaves contain between 0.2 and 0.8% chlorophyll a; green algae, 0.1–3%. There is a proved correlation between high concentration of chlorophyll and growth at low light intensities (126, 127, 376, 377, see also references in Section II, A). Shade plants are darker in color. Calculated for the chloroplast, the percentage of chlorophyll a and b goes up to 8% of dry matter, and for the grana proper up to 30%. This (highest) concentration corresponds to a 0.2 *M* solution. For purposes of comparison with other catalysts in the chloroplast, it is a simple rule

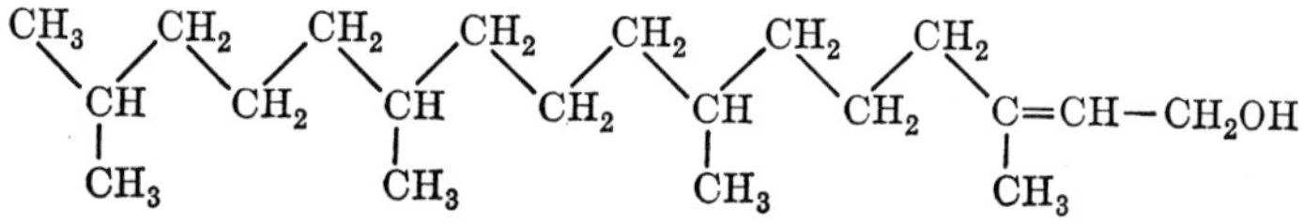

```
CH3   CH2     CH2     CH2     CH2     CH2     CH2
   \ /   \   /   \   /   \   /   \   /   \   /   \
    CH    CH2     CH      CH2     CH      CH2     C=CH-CH2OH
    |             |               |               |
    CH3           CH3             CH3             CH3
```

FIG. 12. Phytol.

to assume a concentration of 10^{-1} *M* of active pigment. Since chlorophyll a has the formula $C_{55}H_{72}O_5N_4Mg$, its molecular weight is 893 and a 0.1 *M* solution contains roughly 0.1 gm per milliliter. More than one-third of the molecular weight applies to phytol, which is attached to the porphyrin ring as a side chain. Except for one double bond and an alcohol group, phytol is a saturated hydrocarbon, an oil of the formula $C_{20}H_{39}OH$ (Fig. 12).

This phytol, which is insoluble in water, gives chlorophyll its waxy consistency. By chemical treatment—or more elegantly, by enzymatic exchange with methyl alcohol—the phytol can be taken off the ring system. The resulting simpler molecule is called a methyl (or ethyl) chlorophyllide. Willstätter and Stoll discovered this reaction by permitting leaves to stand at room temperature in dilute alcohol for a day or two (604). The enzyme chlorophyllase is active under these conditions, and when the reaction has been completed, the chlorophyll has been removed from its place in the lamellar structure and collected inside the cells in the form of small, triangular crystals of chlorophyllide. Except for an increased solubility in lipids, and perhaps proper "anchoring" within the living structure, no special function of phytol has come to light. Phytol also happens to be one of the side chains in natural vitamin K, another constituent of chloroplasts. The function of chlorophyllase is probably to attach phytol to one of the immediate precursors of chlorophyll in the course of its natural synthesis and to the vitamins K and Q (474, 475 and Section VIII,C).

In green cells the amount of total carotenoids is between one-fifth and one-tenth that of the chlorophylls. The xanthophyll fraction can be separated into half a dozen individual chemicals of similar composition, whose particular function is unknown (101, 490).

As to the substances listed under *B* in Table III, photosynthesis appears to have "borrowed" them from other metabolic systems. One line of studies, pursued mainly by biochemists at present, is to prove that the intermediate steps in which these enzymes and cofactors take part in photosynthesis are either identical or distinctly different from the corresponding metabolic reactions in other parts of the cell. Or, in other words, the task is to show whether the synthesis of carbohydrates is the exact reversal of the glycolytic pathway or only similar in principle.

2. *Iron Porphyrins*

A set of reactions certainly unique for photosynthesis is the one leading to the release of oxygen. Except for the splitting of hydrogen peroxide by catalase or the dissociation of oxyhemoglobin, no useful analogy among other metabolic reactions is known. The iron porphyrins (see Fig. 13) found in chloroplasts have, therefore, aroused particular attention for many years. The idea that catalase proper is involved because hydrogen peroxide might be the true precursor to oxygen has been discredited. There is no correlation between catalase content and rate of photosynthesis (132). Poisoning of catalase activity with cyanide does not stop photosynthesis in certain algae, nor has an accumulation of the supposed intermediate H_2O_2 been seen. On the other hand, traces of hydrogen peroxide added to cyanide-poisoned algae are very destructive (rather specifically) for some enzymes in photosynthesis (203).

That cytochromes and cytochrome oxidase occur in plant cells has been known for some time (257–259, 288, 289). With photosynthetic organisms, the question arises whether these catalytic pigments serve exclusively the respiratory dark metabolism of the cell, or whether some among them might be associated with the reactions going on in chloroplasts (506). If cytochromes were found that were not typical respiratory enzymes, and, moreover, could be extracted from chloroplasts, what would be their function? There are several possibilities: they might be a part of the cyclic photophosphorylation system (Section XIII), or of the reaction chain leading to the evolution of oxygen, or both these functions might be combined (see the scheme of Fig. 124). Furthermore, there is the (less likely) possibility that in combination with rather different proteins their potential would become sufficiently low to serve as electron transfer agents on the reducing side of the photochemical mechanism (289).

At present only a few of these questions have been answered. The occurrence of comparatively large quantities of a new cytochrome in

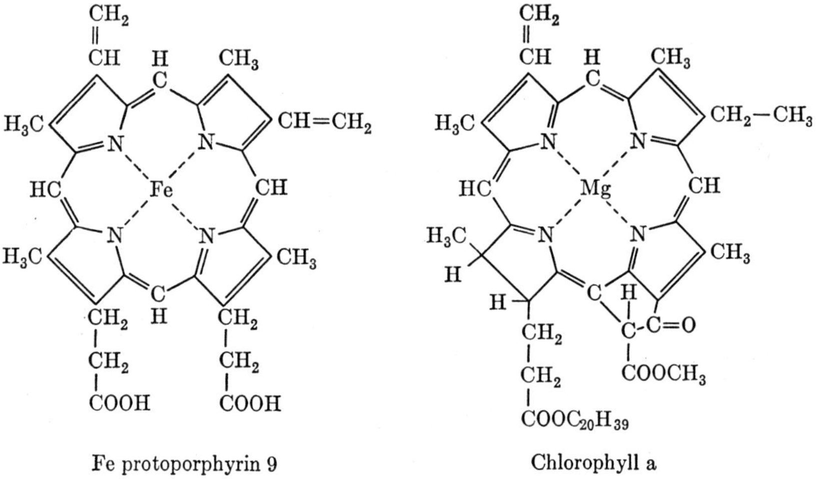

Fe protoporphyrin 9 Chlorophyll a

FIG. 13. Relationship between an iron porphyrin and chlorophyll a.

an obligate anaerobic purple sulfur bacterium, a species of *Chromatium*, proves that this kind of pigment is not necessarily an indication for, or connected with, a typically aerobic metabolism (28, 122, 283–288, 329, 395, 396).

Cytochrome f, found in leaves and green algae by R. Hill (109, 259), very much resembles mammalian cytochrome c but has an oxidizing potential greater by 0.1 volts. Figure 14 shows the absorption spectra of both cytochromes. Cytochrome f has a concentration ten times greater than that of the respiratory cytochromes present there. For lack of any other obvious function—it is not autoxidizable, there is no cytochrome oxidase to fit it specifically—it is assumed to have a function in photosynthesis.

Attempts to see spectral changes of cytochrome c (or of any other cytochrome) during illumination of cells of *Chromatium* have recently been successful enough to indicate some correlation between the kinetics of cytochrome reactions and the rate of photosynthesis (see 89a, and the review in 476).

As said above, in the chloroplast a transfer of energy from one pigment to the other is the rule—and this transfer is most efficient among molecules of similar structure and spectral characteristics. It goes in the direction of the molecule that absorbs (and fluoresces) farthest toward the red end of the visible spectrum. If an iron porphyrin were to receive the light energy in this way it should have an absorption band around λ 700 mμ (cf. 289).

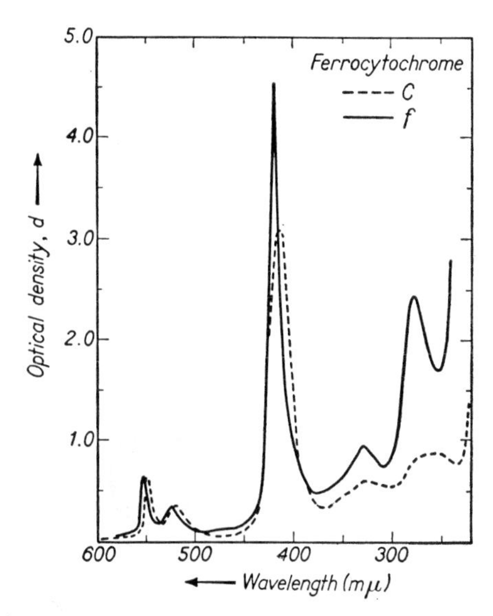

FIG. 14. Absorption spectra of reduced cytochromes c and f. After Hill *et al.* (257, 259, cf. 352a).

Foremost among the unsolved problems is the nature of the substances Xand Y (see the scheme in Fig. 4), the acceptors for the hydrogen and hydroxyl from water. We do not know as yet the exact steps involved in the breaking of an H—OH bond. The hypothesis shown in Fig. 125 below is very persuasive since it fits with the observations which are so far available. There are a few different interpretations possible, but severe theoretical objections to them have not been eliminated, nor are they supported by observations which cannot be explained in some other way. The symbols used throughout this article are the simplest way to describe the problem at the present time (see Section XVI,B,6).

3. *Pyridine Nucleotides and Thioctic Acid*

Current ideas favor TPN as the substance X and one of the special cytochromes as the substance Y, but the reduction of TPN depends on a soluble, heat-labile factor and more steps between the chlorophyll and TPN are likely to be discovered (see Section XII). Thioctic acid, a typical sulfhydryl-group catalyst, was first proposed as the agent instrumental in breaking up the water molecule (32, cf. 217). The theoretical objections to this idea are formidable, let alone the absence of any factual evidence. The more modest assumption that thioctic acid may be an intermediate between chlorophyll and pyridine nucleotides is plausible, but far from proved.

It is remarkable that the chloroplast contains an enzyme specific for the reduction of TPN by a *photo*chemical reaction. Moreover, this enzyme is identical with the factor that catalyzes the reduction of methemoglobin under similar conditions (110, 111). In its reduced form TPN is strongly fluorescent. Hence the changes in light emission of illuminated cells or extracts at the proper wavelength, if observable, should give clues as to the part played by TPN in the course of normal, undisturbed, photosynthesis. (See Brookhaven Symposium 1959, reference on line 8, page 247, and references 116, 117.) Observations of this kind have to be correlated with the more familiar and, to a great extent, definitely established biochemical facts. The detailed papers by Franck and Brugger (Section VI) offer a good introduction to the problems involved.

C. FORMATION OF PIGMENTS

1. *Natural Synthesis of Porphyrins*

How chlorophylls and iron porphyrins are synthesized inside the living cell is only indirectly related to the subject of this chapter (474, 475). But recent studies make it plausible that the proper structure and the active pigments are built up together, and certainly it is important to ask how much of the structure which aids in the synthesis of the compounds is needed to support their ultimate function.

The chlorophylls are closely related to the second most important pigments in living organisms—the iron porphyrin complexes—of which hemin, the blood pigment, and cytochrome are the best known. Chlorophyll has magnesium where the cytochromes or hemes have iron. In addition, chlorophyll has a fifth ring originating from one of the side chains. (See Figs. 5 and 13.) Most likely they are the products of the same evolutionary line. Granick's work (239–243) on the evolu-

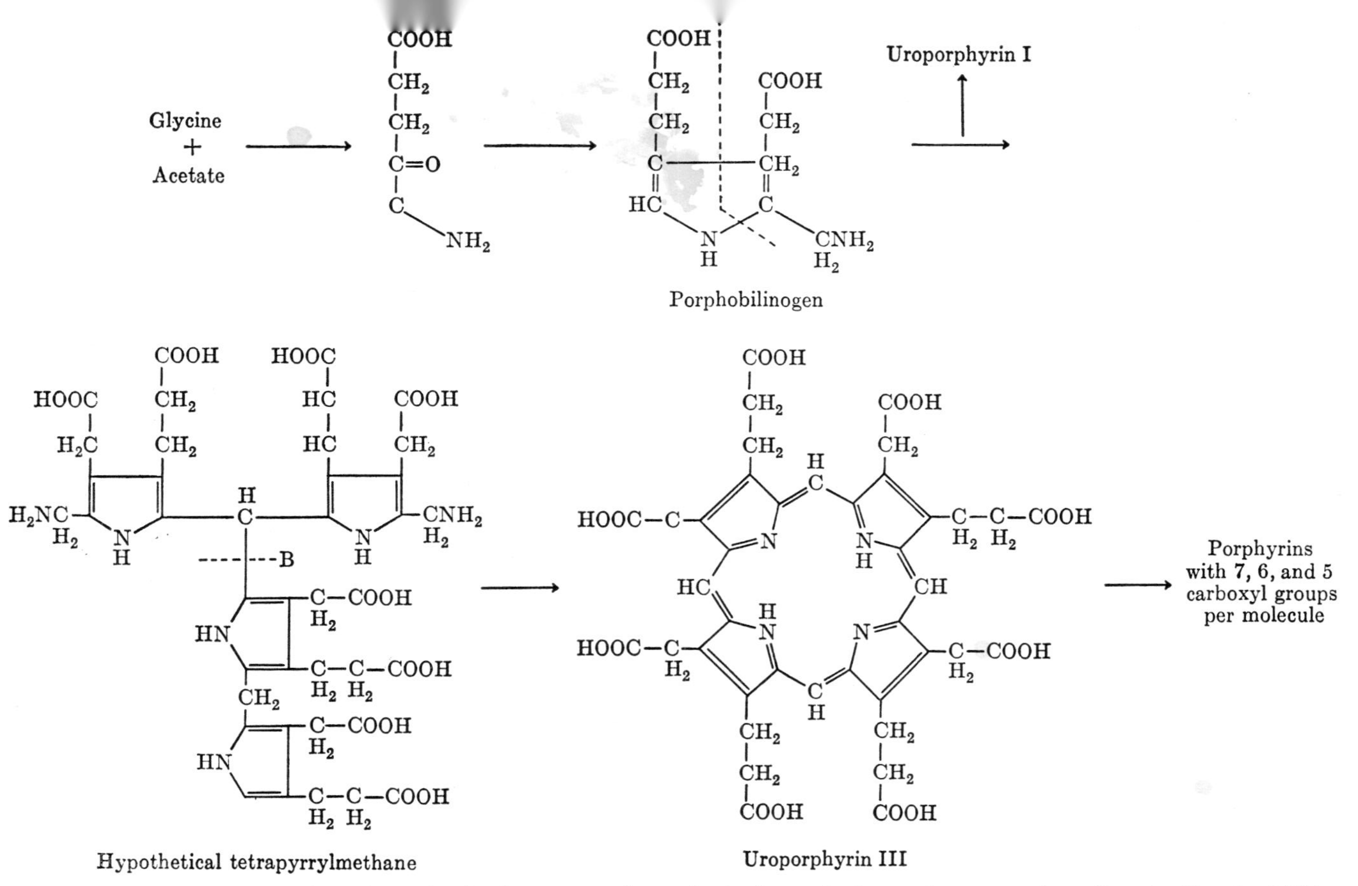

FIG. 15. Natural formation of porphyrins by enzymatic synthesis from glycine and acetate. According to Shemin (461), Granick (241, 242), and Bogorad (50). The second compound is δ-aminolevulinic acid (H_2 is missing at lowest C atom as shown in the formula above).

tion of chlorophyll from porphyrins in algae, as well as Bogorad (49, 50) and Shemin's studies (461) on the biological synthesis of porphyrins, have made this a near certainty. The effort of chemists to synthesize these complex molecules has been long drawn out and is an admirable contribution in chemical research; the way nature achieves the same end is astonishingly simple and direct. Figure 15 shows the steps of porphyrin synthesis, so far established, as they follow each other within the living cell. Though these reactions are all catalyzed by enzymes, it is of interest that they may proceed *in vitro* quite spontaneously. The synthesis of chlorophyll proper—the steps leading from porphyrins or porphyrin precursors to the magnesium complex—have been studied by Granick. The evidence for this was obtained from mutant algae which had been discovered in heterotrophic media after irradiation of the parent strains with ultraviolet light or X-rays (243).

Further studies of the enzymatic steps in the natural porphyrin synthesis revealed a ring formation on the level of the reduced pyrroles to give porphyrinogens, colorless substances with spectra similar to those of the individual pyrroles. The four pyrroles are bound together by $—CH_2—$ (methylene) bridges, instead of the $—CH=$ (methene) bridges in the finished porphyrins. As long as they are not dehydrogenated to porphyrins, the porphyrinogens are unable to bind metals. In this way the shortening of the side chains by decarboxylation, etc., is possible before the choice is made to insert either an iron or a magnesium atom (50).

Iron deficiency causes chlorosis in plants and algae and leads to the accumulation and actual excretion of porphyrins in purple bacteria (329). That iron should be necessary to incorporate magnesium into the porphyrin complex seems paradoxical. The most characteristic feature in chlorophyll molecules, the 5-carbon ring in the formulas in Figs. 13 or 5, requires for its formation an iron-containing catalyst. Once the nature of this fifth ring had been established, the properties of the free C-H group in this ring attracted the attention of chemists and biologists. Theory and experimental evidence point to a heightened reactivity of the hydrogen on this particular carbon atom (compare Fig. 125, Section XVI). For a discussion of chlorophyll formation from the point of view of evolution, see references 220, 368, and 528.

2. *Biosynthesis of Carotenoids*

Much has been published on the abundance and number of carotenoids in microorganisms, plants, and higher animals (237a). It appears to be simpler to make a list of the organisms devoid of carotene (certain fungi, for instance) than to enumerate the types of living cells in which they do occur. New derivatives of the many known carotenoids are continually being discovered, and the conditions which lead to their formation in plants are just now being studied (cf. 91). About their general physiological role, little is known. What has been learned concerns very specific functions—their role as photoreceptors in phototaxis, in vision, and in photosynthesis.

Normally the carotenoids and chlorophylls appear together in the new plastids of the growing plant. In those plants that require light for the final steps in chlorophyll formation, the analysis of seedlings grown in darkness has shown that some carotene is formed independently of any photochemical activity. On the other hand there are white albino mutants of sunflowers which have no carotene in their cotyledons but produce some chlorophyll a in weak light. Neither the etiolated leaves nor the blue-green, carotene-free varieties show any sign of photosynthesis. As long as chlorophyll is present in the mutants, more light induces photooxidation with subsequent bleaching. Among the several mutants of *Chlorella* (cultivated in media containing sugar) which showed themselves unable to form the usual pigments, one is of interest because, as in flowering plants, no normal pigments are formed in darkness, but they appear when the cultures are exposed to light. A special sensitivity of the carotenes formed in the dark (higher saturated molecules, phytoene, phytofluene, etc.) toward pure blue light could be demonstrated in this case. Claes found that blue light causes certain *cis-trans* isomerizations (cf. 91). Valuable as these experiments are in giving clues to the biosynthesis of the carotenes, they do not as yet permit conclusions as to their role in photosynthesis. The first revealing experiments in this respect were those mentioned above by Griffiths and associates, with a bacterial mutant which continued to reduce carbon dioxide though it did not contain the normal complement of carotenoids (245). We shall return to this in Section VI. The same result could be obtained with bacteria (*Rhodospirillum rubrum*) in which, by the Goodwin method of poisoning with diphenylamine, the carotene synthesis had been suppressed (99, 194). Biosynthesis of chlorophylls and of carotenes can proceed independently. Figure 16 shows how cell mass and chlorophyll content continue to increase quite parallel to one another in presence of diphenylamine (DPA), while production of carotenoids stops soon after the poison has been added to the growing bacteria.

Figure 17 shows how the typical absorption band of carotenes fails to reappear after removal of the poison when carotene-free *Rhodospirillum* (*Spirillum*) *rubrum* is illuminated during later incubation in air. In the dark the bacteria resume growth, as well as synthesis of carotenes, and become normal again—that is, resistant to illumination in air.

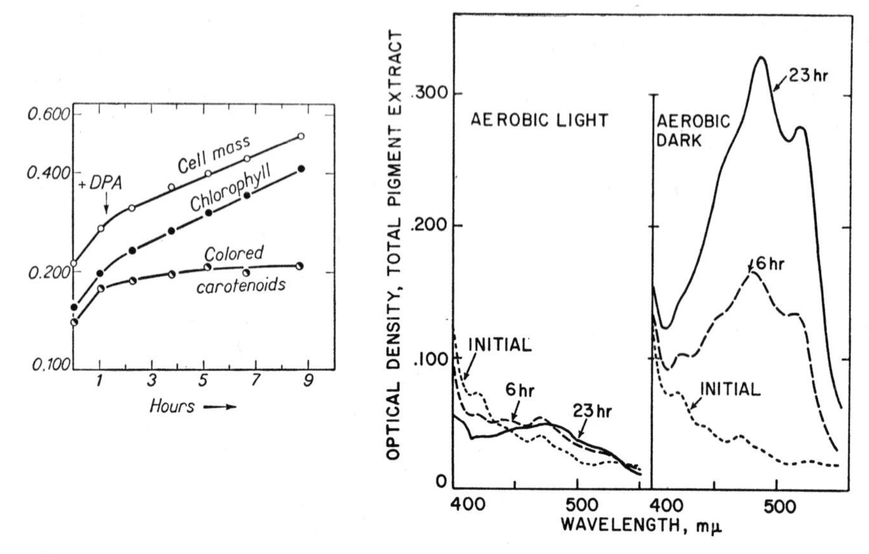

FIG. 16. (Left) Specific inhibition by diphenylamine (DPA) of carotene synthesis in anaerobic cultures of *Rhodospirillum rubrum.* Bacteria continue to grow at a diminished rate and produce the normal amount of chlorophyll. Cell mass: $OD_{680\ m\mu}$; chlorophyll: milligrams per 100 ml of culture; carotenoids: $OD_{485\ m\mu} \times 2$ (98, 99).

FIG. 17. (Right) Resynthesis of carotenoid pigments by cells in buffer after removal of DPA. *Rhodospirillum rubrum* can resynthesize its lost carotenes by continued aerobic culture in the dark. In the light the cells suffer from photoxidation.

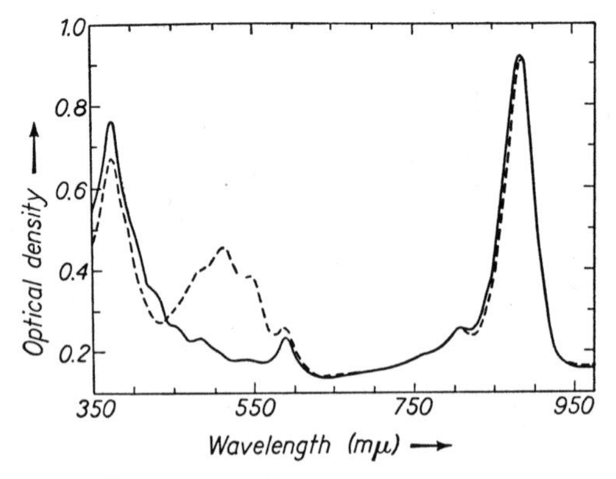

FIG. 18. *In vivo* spectrum of normal cells of *Rhodospirillum rubrum* (dashed line) and of cells grown in the presence of 7×10^{-5} *M* diphenylamines (solid line). DPA-treated *Rhodospirillum rubrum* cells have lost only the carotenes from their complement of pigments (98, 99).

Figure 18 compares the spectra of *Rhodospirillum rubrum* grown anaerobically without and with diphenylamine.

A case of such a separation between the role of carotenes and photosynthesis was also seen in a strain of the green alga, *Chlamydomonas* (89). Thus for the chemical processes of photoreduction of carbon dioxide and the photolysis of water, the carotenes are not indispensable. Their role as light-sensitive pigments and as possible aids in the release of oxygen will be discussed below. While green cells, as typical aerobic organisms, require the presence of oxygen for chlorophyll (and carotene) synthesis, the biosynthesis of both types of pigments is suppressed during aerobic and heterotrophic growth of *Rhodospirillum rubrum*. Light does not overcome this effect of oxygen. The problem is a complex one because it is known that aerobic and heterotrophic growth in the dark suppresses pigment formation in the green algae *Euglena viridis* and *Chlorella variegata*.

IV. Chemistry and Photochemistry of the Chlorophyll Molecule *in Vitro*

Without a thorough knowledge of chlorophyll chemistry it would be difficult to understand the pigment's action within the chloroplast, since chlorophyll—particularly chlorophyll a—seems to be indispensable for photosynthesis. A century of botanical research has not disclosed any type of cell which, in the absence of chlorophyll, achieves a storing of light energy. Consequently it is hard to believe that chlorophyll functions in the living cell only as a sensitizer as it does (like many other fluorescent dyes) in a variety of known photochemical reactions *in vitro*. We quote R. Livingston (345):

"It is the primary act, the capture of light energy for chemical purposes, which makes photosynthesis the most important and the most fascinating of biological processes. Even if every enzyme, with its attendant substrate, product and coenzyme, which enters into the biochemical cycles of the living plant were known, we might still be completely ignorant of the primary process which distinguishes photosynthesis from other biological processes. There is no known straightforward way by which the nature of the primary act can be determined. In fact, there are very few photochemical reactions of complex molecules in solution whose primary act has been unequivocally determined. In view of the difficulty of the problem, it appears worth while to investigate many different photochemical and spectroscopic properties of chlorophyll in solution, in synthetic and natural aggregates of chlorophyll molecules and in the intact cell."

Fifty years of chemical research in the field of hemins and chlorophylls, initiated in the grand style by Willstätter and Stoll (603) and continued by Fischer and his numerous collaborators as well as by Conant and by Stoll and Wiedeman (488) finally established the structural formulas of the chlorophylls extractable from plants and from bacteria. Figure 5 above shows the structure of chlorophyll a. Chlorophyll b has the keto group

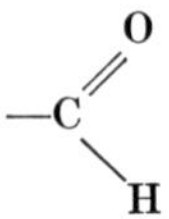

in place of the methyl $—CH_3$ next to the ethyl side chain.

The small deviations in composition among the chlorophylls are perceived most easily as differences in their color, or, more precisely, in

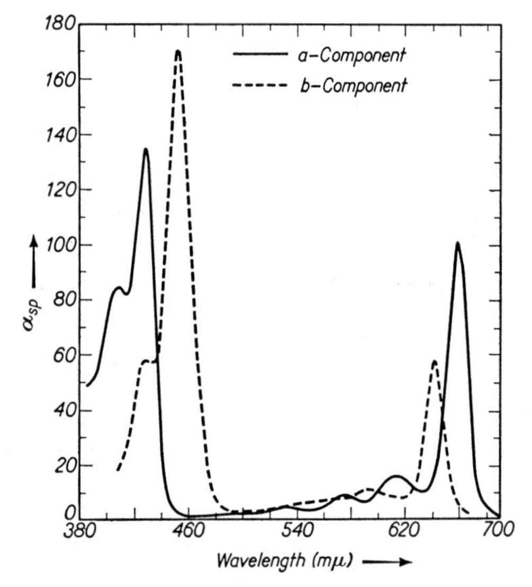

FIG. 19. Absorption spectra of chlorophyll a (solid line) and chlorophyll b (dashed line).

their absorption spectra, which are shown in Fig. 19. Chlorophyll a is blue green to the eye, and b is yellow green. The $\rangle C=O$ group in chlorophyll b is sufficient to shift the peak of the red absorption band by 300 Ångstrom units to shorter wavelengths, that of the blue band by about the same distance to longer wavelengths. The absolute position of the main absorption bands in chlorophyll molecules shifts somewhat with the solvent in which they are being studied (19, 448).

As chemicals, the two chlorophylls, a and b, are so nearly related that hardly a difference exists between them in their behavior toward ordinary chemical reagents. Their spectral differences, however, are conspicuous and have been analyzed in detail. Chlorophyll does not belong to the class of pigments (like methylene blue or the flavins) which can easily and reversibly be reduced in the absence of oxygen to a (mostly colorless) "leuco" form and which subsequently return to the more deeply colored form on contact with air. Strong chemical treatment ($Pd + H_2$) reduces chlorophyll, like other porphyrins, stepwise to the level of porphyrinogens (cf. 50). Of much more interest are the reversible photochemical reductions in the presence of ascorbic acid, discovered by Krasnowsky, which will be discussed below (320, 322, 324).

Dissolved in alcohol, chlorophyll undergoes autoxidation, called "allomerization." About one molecule of oxygen is taken up by each chlorophyll molecule. The result, however, is not *one* but at least *three* oxidation products, having still a typical green color (264, 488, 490).

Treatment of an alcoholic solution of chlorophyll with alkali momentarily produces a brown color ("phase test"). The word "test" has been introduced because the reaction indicates that no "allomerization" (oxidation) has taken place, since autoxidized chlorophyll does not give an intermediate brown discoloration with alcoholic alkali. A great number of studies have been made of the spectral changes involved. So far no connection between these chemical reactions and the function of chlorophyll in the living cell has been established. To quote Strain (490): "Chlorophylls are remarkably labile substances, each pigment being capable of existence in two or more isomeric forms. Living plants contain only one isomeric form of each pigment but once the pigments have been extracted additional isomers are rapidly produced." And "When leaves are killed with anesthetics or by grinding oxidative and hydrolytic reactions contribute to the formation of some dozen or more green pigments that can be isolated by chromatographic methods. None of these alteration products has ever been observed in carefully prepared extracts of fresh plants."

The bacteriochlorophylls are similar but more reduced, containing two more hydrogens, presumably in the pyrrole ring II, and one more atom of oxygen. Instead of the vinyl side chain $—CH{=}CH_2$, there is an acetyl group $—CO—CH_3$. When extracted with alcohol they autoxidize faster than the green chlorophylls. Simultaneously, hydrogen peroxide is formed (233–235).

Figure 20 shows, diagrammatically, how the conjugated ring systems in the porphin skeleton changes with stepwise reduction from protochlorophyll to chlorophyll to bacteriochlorophyll (436).

The magnesium in the chlorophylls is easily removed in acid solutions. The magnesium-free substance is called pheophytin and shows an olive-yellowish color.

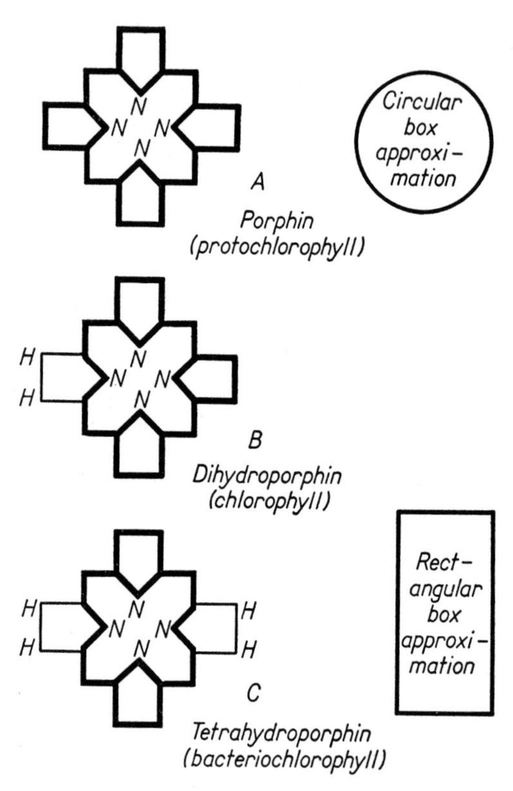

FIG. 20. Porphin, dihydroporphin, and tetrahydroporphin conjugated ring systems. After Rabinowitch (436), p. 1794.

One fact which may have a significance for the problem of photosynthesis is a peculiar affinity of chlorophyll for water. Dissolved in absolutely dry benzene, chlorophyll shows no fluorescence. Traces of water—it is sufficient to open the flask containing the dry chlorophyll solution to the air—restore the fluorescent state of chlorophyll. Methanol and some "bases" have the same effect. The magnesium-free pheophytins do not show this dependence of fluorescence on the presence of an "activator" (343, 344).

In the living cell, chlorophyll acts as a catalyst. It is not consumed in the process of photosynthesis. Whatever changes it may undergo must be completely reversible. *In vitro* only the light-induced chemical changes approach this requirement of easy reversibility (cf. 320) and for this reason the latter appear to be more important for our problem than is the general chemistry of porphyrins.

The interaction between molecules and light quanta (=photons) is a chapter in the science of molecular physics and spectroscopy. We shall mention here only a few fundamental observations which contribute to the understanding of the laws governing the behavior of photoactive plant pigments (174, 175, 177, 180, 341, 345, 446).

Light quanta (photons) are absorbed as units or not at all. The intensity of spectral lines (absorption or emission), or, in molecules, rather broad bands, is a measure of the probability that a light quantum corresponding in its energy content to that particular region of the spectrum will be absorbed (and cause the displacement of an electron in the molecule) or will be emitted (upon the return of a displaced electron to its former place). The energy changes involved in absorbing or emitting a quantum are usually noted as the amount of energy that would be absorbed by one mole of the reacting substance—that is by 6.02×10^{23} molecules. $N_0 h\nu = 6 \times 10^{23} h\nu$ is a mole quantum, or one "einstein." The energy in one quantum is given by $E = h\nu$; ν, the frequency of the radiation, is given by a relation between wavelength, λ, and c, the velocity of light: $\nu = c/\lambda$. Figure 7 contains a scale showing the energies corresponding to ultraviolet radiation and visible light. The absorption of one quantum by a molecule raises the energy content by that much above the energy it had at the moment of absorption.

In a condensed system—a pigment solution, for instance—the average energy of all pigment molecules is determined by the temperature. Individual molecules vary greatly in their energy content, and only a few at a time are "hot" enough to undergo chemical reaction if an opportunity presents itself. Therefore, chemical reactions increase in rate with rising temperatures. A molecule that has absorbed a photon is called an "excited" molecule. It represents in a sense a very hot molecule and is, in this condition, ready to take part in a chemical reaction which will not occur among the normal nonexcited ones. The light-excited molecule need not wait for the rare chance of a corresponding thermal excitation, and its own reactivity is therefore independent of temperature. The lifetime of this excited state, however, is very short. Unless another molecule, the likely reaction partner, collides with the excited molecule during the latter's lifetime, or has already been associated with the pigment before the light absorption occurred, the chance for a chemical reaction will be gone. Other events will have dissipated the energy between the moment of excitation and the encounter with the next reactive molecule.

The different events which may happen as a consequence of light excitation are schematically explained in the series of equations of Table IV and in the diagram in Fig. 21.

The facts symbolized by this diagram are based on physical, not biological, observations. The indicated relationships are valid for any conjugated organic photochemical molecular system and, therefore, also for the chlorophyll complex in the living cell.

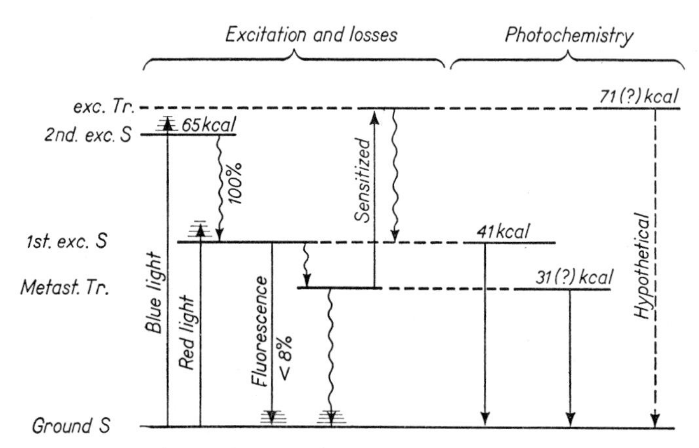

FIG. 21. The different energy levels in the chlorophyll molecule from which energy might be drawn for photochemical purposes. Energy-poor red light absorbed in the band at around 680 mμ (compare Fig. 19) produces the first excited singlet state. Energy-rich blue light absorbed in the band at around 430 mμ produces the second excited singlet state. The wavy lines mean unspecific heat losses. The energy of the first excited singlet can produce the metastable triplet state at a loss of about 10 kcal. This internal conversion into the triplet state competes with fluorescence, heat losses, and photochemistry (see text and Table IV).

The diagram in Fig. 21 is of the type generally used to indicate energy levels and transitions in light-excited molecules. Here it shows the three levels of excitation to which the chlorophyll molecule is lifted by the absorption of light quanta in the visible spectrum and the steps by which this energy is subsequently either lost or put to work in photochemistry. Blue light excites the second singlet state at a level of 65 kilocalories (kcal). Part of this energy is always lost as heat within 10^{-11} seconds, while 41 kcal are retained in the first excited singlet state. The latter level is reached directly by absorption of red light. Its lifetime is approximately 10^{-9} seconds. From here the energy may disappear in several ways—either as heat, as fluorescence, as chemical action, or by transition to the metastable triplet state (see Table IV). The fluorescence yield is directly proportional to the actual lifetime of the excited state (161). The more ways there are for the dissipation of the excitation energy, the less the chance that it be re-emitted as fluorescence. The heat loss during the internal conversion into the triplet state is over 10 kcal (reaction 8, Table IV). The remaining 31 kcal (or less) are available for chemical work during a time lasting up to 10^{-2} seconds. If photochemical action is excluded, about 92% of the energy of the singlet state is lost as heat, and 8% is re-emitted as fluorescence. Unless some chemical effect occurs—"quenching" (341, 346)—the triplet state itself disappears by dissipation of the energy into heat or by radiation in the infrared region (phosphorescence). While in the triplet state, the chlorophyll molecule may receive a second quantum of light which then produces an excited triplet state at the level of about 71 kcal (reaction 11, Table IV). In condensed systems this second excitation has an appreciable chance to occur by way of the transfer of energy from the singlet state of another nearby chlorophyll molecule (163, 347). Both the singlet state and the triplet state of chlorophyll are known to promote photochemical effects *in vitro*. In principle this should also be possible for the excited triplet state, but so far no true case of this kind has been demonstrated. The photochemical action with 71 kcal is at present merely a very interesting hypothesis (178). In the living cell the chances for photochemical use of the 41 kcal of the singlet state are small, because of the short lifetime of 10^{-9} seconds. With the sacrifice of at least 10 kcal by internal conversion into the metastable triplet state, the chances for a photochemical reaction are increased a million times, owing to the much longer lifetime (197, 346). Because the successful photochemical effect in cells stores energy, it diminishes the heat losses and living algae remain cooler while doing photosynthesis than dead ones. Indeed, a calorimeter has been successfully used to determine the efficiency of photosynthesis (5, 354, 436). Several hypotheses have been proposed to explain how the plant may make use of the three different energy levels shown in this scheme (57). A big chemical step following the absorption of two light quanta and the excitation of the triplet would solve—by a purely physical mechanism—the problem of having to use the energy of more than one light quantum for breaking an O—H bond. There is no evidence available that this actually happens (335–337). Other hypotheses postulate a cooperation between singlets and triplets, while the simplest assumption would be that photosynthesis makes use only of the metastable triplets which live long enough to allow for all kinds of energy migrations and chemical changes (455a).

Figure 22 shows the absorption spectrum of the metastable state of chlorophyll a in pyridine (335). The dotted line is the ordinary spectrum. The comparison shows how thoroughly the color of chlorophyll is "bleached" by excitation. The bleaching light was an extremely bright flash of 2 μsec duration. The bleaching was perfectly reversible. About 90% transformation was achieved. In a concentrated solution the lifetime of this triplet state is not much longer than 10^{-7} seconds.

TABLE IV

SOME REACTIONS OF LIGHT-EXCITED CHLOROPHYLL[a]

1. Excitation	$Chl + h\nu \rightarrow Chl^*$
2. Sensitized excitation	$Phy^* + Chl \rightarrow Phy + Chl^*$
3. Fluorescence	$Chl^* \rightarrow Chl + h\nu$
4. Heat loss	$Chl^* \rightarrow Chl$
5. Collision-quenching	$Chl^* + O_2 \rightarrow Chl + O_2$
Self-quenching	$Chl^* + Chl \rightarrow 2Chl$
6. Chemistry	$Chl^* + AH \rightarrow ChlH + A\cdot$
	$ChlH + A \rightarrow Chl\cdot + AH$
7. Ionization	$Chl^* \rightarrow Chl^+ + e^-$
8. Conversion into triplet state (long lived)	$Chl^* \rightarrow Chl^t$
9. Chemistry, direct	$Chl^t + AH \rightarrow ChlH\cdot + A\cdot$
10. Chemistry, sensitized	$Chl^t + A \rightarrow Chl + A^*;\ A^* + BH \rightarrow AH\cdot + B\cdot$
11. Double excitation	$Chl^t + Chl^* \rightarrow Chl^{t*} + Chl$

[a] Chl stands for chlorophyll; Phy for phycoerythrin, as an example of any other light-absorbing pigment from which chlorophyll may receive energy. In most cases the photochemistry will lead to the formation of radicals—either of a pair such as $AH\cdot + B\cdot$, or of a biradical when a bond is opened in one molecule. The stabilization of these radicals either by recombination or dismutation is the most likely consequence of the photochemistry. The reactions shown above are only a sample among numerous variations which have been proposed in the literature. Chl* means the singlet excited state and Chl^t the metastable triplet state of chlorophyll.

Reactions (1)–(10) in Table IV have been observed with chlorophyll and chlorophyll derivatives *in vitro*. It has not been shown that all of these reactions occur also *in vivo*.

Reaction (2), the sensitized excitation or energy transfer, is important in plants because it is the way by which many other pigments contribute to photosynthesis. Fluorescence, reaction (3), has a lower yield in plants (3%) (331) than in solution (15–25%). This means that other processes interfere more *in vivo* than *in vitro* with the excited state, thus diminishing the fraction of light energy which has a chance of being re-emitted. Simple unspecified losses, reactions (4) and (5), cannot be large because the efficiency of photosynthesis is unusually good. Thus reactions (6), (7), or (8) must be the main path into which the light energy is channeled.

Chemical effects originating from the singlet level, reaction (6), have little chance of succeeding because of the short lifetime. Since the fluorescence originates from this excitation level, presence or absence of a chemical reaction that is draining away or leaving the energy in this

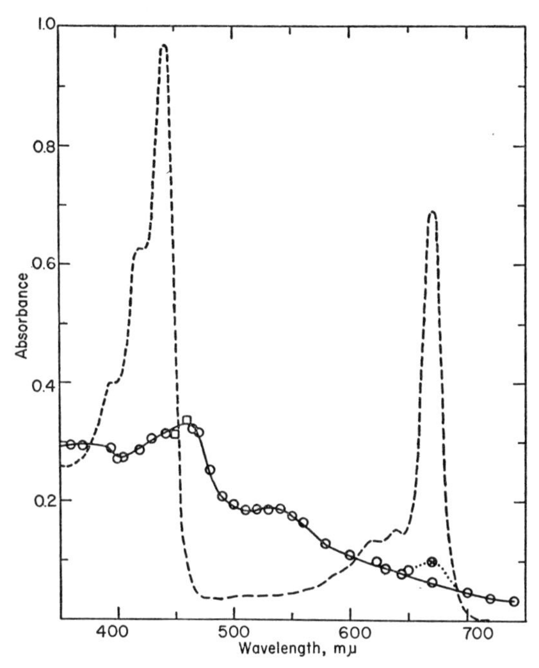

FIG. 22. Absorption spectrum of metastable state of chlorophyll a in pyridine (solid line). Dashed line, normal absorption spectrum of chlorophyll a. Abscissa, wavelength in mμ from 350 to 750. Ordinate, absorbance from 0 to 1.0. From Linschitz (335–337).

state should give correspondingly strong changes in fluorescence. These have not been seen. Fluorescence changes are very much smaller.

Reaction (7), ionization, is very probably the source of a long-lasting but very weak afterglow (luminescence).

Reaction (8), conversion into the triplet state, makes possible excellent yields in chemical reactions *in vitro* (197) and therefore is assumed to be vital for the success of photosynthesis. The triplet state can promote synthetic reactions which require less than 30 kcal. The chemical change may occur directly with chlorophyll participating as a chemical catalyst, or the energy may be transferred again (with some loss) to another molecule which now reacts as a chemical agent (so-called sensitized photochemistry) (cf. 6, 71).

Reaction (11) is Franck's hypothesis, designed to circumvent the difficulty of collecting the energy of the two quanta necessary to transfer hydrogen from water by distinct chemical steps. Here some 70 kcal could be delivered at once.

Photoactive pigments in solution are mostly fluorescent to a degree visible to the unaided eye—that is, the quantum yield is at least 1% (237). Porphyrins as a class and their magnesium or zinc complexes are fluorescent. Their complexes with heavy metals like iron or copper are not fluorescent and are also not photochemically active. The best-known example is hemin. The fluorescence yield is a measure of the lifetime of the first excited singlet (161). In hemin it is so short—the energy is so quickly dissipated—that no fluorescence is detectable.

In the chlorophylls a and b the excited singlet state lasts for about 10^{-8} seconds. The electronic excitation energy can be exchanged between chlorophyll molecules in solution at distances up to 50 A. In solutions containing both chlorophyll a and b the fluorescence of b is quenched by a and that of a is sensitized by b. This phenomenon of sensitized fluorescence is of greatest importance in the living plant (171). Interaction between excited chlorophyll molecules and other substances can be seen as a quenching of the fluorescence (346, 347).

During certain *in vitro* experiments, Livingston *et al.* observed recently that carotene quenches the metastable state of chlorophyll in solution. This effect of carotene parallels, therefore, the already known quenching by molecular oxygen.

In all those cases where a photochemical reaction proceeds with a good yield and yet no large change in the fluorescence yield can be observed during the reaction, it is generally assumed that the reaction originates from the metastable triplet state after the internal conversion (see Fig. 21 above). An example is the chlorophyll-sensitized oxidations of certain organic compounds [thiourea, aliphatic amines (197)] which proceed with a quantum yield of nearly 100%.

In the absence of oxygen and reactive compounds, chlorophyll is remarkably stable against illumination. But in organic alcoholic solutions or in pyridine very rapid reversible changes in the spectrum have been found upon illumination with strong light flashes (Fig. 22; 336, 337, 446).

During and after World War II, a group of Russian scientists headed by A. A. Krasnovsky pursued investigations on photosynthesis. Their interest centered on those chemical reactions of chlorophyll which could, perhaps, have significance for the natural process; they (rightly) considered any reversible photoactivity important enough to be studied extensively. They found that in organic media, particularly pyridine, the coenzyme I (DPN) could be reduced by ascorbic acid in the presence of illuminated chlorophyll. Oxygen has to be absent to prevent ordinary photooxidation (320, 322). Illuminated chlorophyll itself is reduced by ascorbic acid to a reddish-colored substance. The interpretation of the reaction with DPN is that chlorophyll transfers the hydrogen from ascorbic acid to DPN. These reactions are (partly) reversible in the dark. They should be remembered in connection with certain experiments on the photochemical carbon dioxide fixation by extracted chloroplasts in the presence of TPN and ascorbic acid (Sections XII and XIII).

What makes the observations less valuable, from our point of view, as models of the specific role of chlorophyll in the cell is that they are in no way unique for chlorophyll. They can easily be copied by reactions with other fluorescent dyestuffs and therefore are not as specific as the *in vivo* chlorophyll reactions themselves seem to be. Furthermore, to transfer hydrogen from ascorbic acid (a strong reductant) instead of from water is, energetically, much less difficult. In the course of these investigations a particular influence of the magnesium in chlorophyll was observed which is of interest. The magnesium-free compound, the pheophytin, becomes reduced much faster than chlorophyll itself. Conversely, the magnesium compounds are aerobically oxidized much faster in organic media in the light than the magnesium-free porphyrin derivatives.

The Russian investigators also confirmed that illuminated chlorophyll may produce radicals because it can sensitize the polymerization of chemical monomers. Krasnowsky's observations have been confirmed, in the main, by other scientists (402, 529, 530). It is noteworthy that some theoretical considerations of the Russian workers are identical with the conclusions reached by scientists elsewhere. For instance, they too assume a metastable, long-lived state in order to understand the efficiency of photosynthesis. They also mention the possibility of a double excitation by two successive light-absorption processes in order to facilitate the collecting of sufficient energy for the photolysis of water.

Most observations of the photochemical behavior have been made with dilute chlorophyll solutions *in vitro*. Sensitized fluorescence—the transfer of energy from one pigment molecule to another—which plays such an important role in the living cell is not easily produced in these dilute solutions. This may be one reason why energy-storing photoreactions practically never occur *in vitro*. Nevertheless, all that we know about singlet and triplet states and their lifetimes, about fluorescence, absorption spectra, and the usual photochemical reactions—the reversible bleaching, and so on—have been the result of research on chlorophyll *in vitro*.

It is comparatively easy to extract the active pigments from the living cells. Green leaves and algae release the chlorophylls and most of the yellow pigments by treatment with wet ethanol, methanol, or acetone (604). Many marine red algae yield their phycoerythrin simply upon immersion into distilled water (46, 321). To purify the extracted pigments without changing their natural configuration is, however, rather difficult. Studies of the optical properties of these pigments, particularly of the chlorophylls, have been going on for nearly a hundred years (19). Figure 19 shows one of the numerous spectra of the chlorophylls a and b that have been published. The position of the main absorption band shifts with the solvent, with the aggregation of the chlorophyll molecules, and with the adsorption out of solution onto surfaces of large molecules or of undissolved materials. Most effects due to aggregations consist in a shift of the spectrum toward longer wavelengths. The comparatively minor difference between spectra in solution and in the living cell—the position of the peak of the red band of chlorophyll a at λ 660 mμ in solution and λ 680 mμ in the chloroplast—has been much considered. However, absorption measurements *in vivo* are rather difficult (see below) and no interpretation of great theoretical interest has so far been given for this difference. On the contrary, the absence of a major difference in color between extracts and the living cell provides a good argument against certain proposed mechanisms of photosynthesis (525a).

Chlorophyll absorbs light quanta from the near ultraviolet, around 360 mμ, to the red where the absorption ends, approximately between λ 680 and λ 700 mμ (see Fig. 19). A shift of great theoretical importance is that which distinguishes green plant chlorophyll from bacteriochlorophyll (234). The latter has its long-wave peak at about λ 880 mμ. Thus bacteriochlorophyll in the living bacteria absorbs red and infrared light to which the cells of green plants are transparent. (See Fig. 23, cf. 436.)

Behind the proper light filter the human eye adapts itself to light between λ 700 mμ and λ 800 mμ. With the aid of such a filter it is possible to look through a chlorophyll solution which is so concentrated that it appears black and opaque in normal daylight. The lack of absorption at the end of the visible spectrum has been used by plant physiologists to handle plants which served as dark controls in certain experiments on the effect of light on the growth of plants. Only recently has this trust in the meaning of the chlorophyll absorption spectrum been shaken by the discovery of other pigments, present in very small amounts, and absorbing between λ 740 mμ and λ 760 mμ. These new pigments turned out to be mostly, if not exclusively, responsible for the phenomenon of photoperiodism (cf. 251).

The ecological consequence of the different colors in plants and purple bacteria is that it is possible for purple bacteria to grow very well under a dense cover of green and blue-green cells that absorb practically all daylight. Theoretically, the interest lies in the attempt to

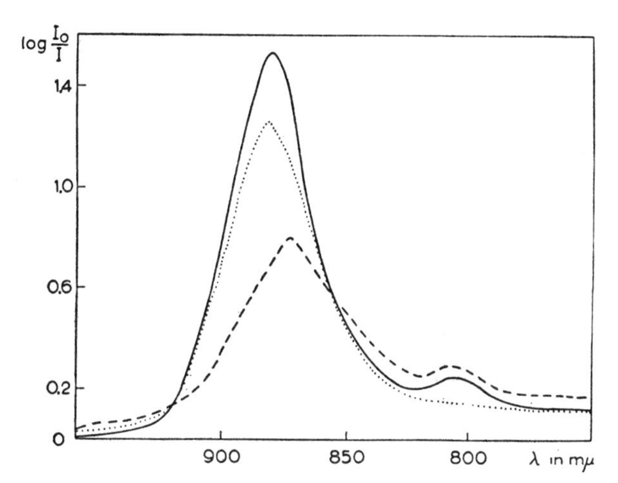

FIG. 23. Long-wavelength absorption band of bacteriochlorophyll in *Rhodospirillum rubrum.* The solid line indicates the spectrum of the colloidal extract; the dashed line, the same spectrum some minutes after the addition of ferric chloride (10^{-3} moles/l), and the dotted line, this spectrum after the subsequent addition of ascorbic acid. From J. C. Goedheer *et al.* (235).

correlate the smaller energy available in infrared light quanta with the fact that purple bacteria are unable to liberate oxygen, though the entire mechanism of photoreduction in bacteria and photosynthesis seems otherwise to be the same (see Section X).

For a detailed discussion of the spectra of chlorophyll and its derivatives—including the weak absorption in the far infrared—see Rabinowitch (436, p. 1793) and Holt (264).

The fluorescence spectrum of chlorophyll—that is, the red glow we see in alcoholic solutions—begins with a strong band having a peak at λ 672 mμ. This band is therefore very similar to the red absorption band. The spectrum continues, however, much farther into the red, with a second peak around λ 730 mμ (see Fig. 55, Section VI). Because so much of the fluorescence and absorption spectra overlap, light emitted by an excited chlorophyll molecule has a good chance of being absorbed by another chlorophyll molecule, particularly in dense solutions and certainly in the chloroplasts where the concentration is of the order of tenth molar. In dilute solutions, roughly every fourth absorbed light quantum reappears as a quantum of fluorescent light. In the living cell, however, the fluorescence yield does not surpass 3%—and until recently it was assumed to be only a tenth of that value (331, 514, 582).

Finally, we should mention that light emission from the first singlet excited state is not invariably caused by a preceding absorption of a light quantum. The necessary excitation may also be brought about by oxidation reactions (155), as they occur in a mixture of aldehyde, alkali, oxygen, and chlorophyll in methanol. In this case the light emission is called chemiluminescence. Plants emit a faint light for many minutes or even hours in the dark after they have been in the light (492, 497). This is not a fluorescence, nor a phosphorescence from the triplet state, but a delayed light emission which in several publications has been called a chemiluminescence. The name implies that certain reactions—presumably back reactions between reduced and oxidized products of photosynthesis—of a purely chemical nature are the energy source for the light emitted. Since this interpretation has become questionable, the name chemiluminescence has been changed to either "afterglow" or simply "delayed light emission."

V. Influence of External Factors on the Rate of Photosynthesis

A. LIGHT

1. The Light-Intensity Curve

The classical way to get the first, basic, information on the light-mediated metabolism of a photosynthetic organism, leaf, tissue or chloroplast preparation is to measure the increase of the rate of photosynthesis with increasing light intensity. The plot of such data gives a curve like the one shown in Fig. 24, which is called an intensity, or saturation, curve. In a purely photochemical reaction—let us say a simple, irreversible photodissociation of a substance whose concentration is kept constant—the rate of the reaction is directly proportional to the light intensity. It will remain so up to extremely high intensities, because it requires—even in a dilute solution—a lot of light to dissociate all light-absorbing molecules simultaneously (e.g., in 10^{-8} seconds) (see Section VII).

With photosynthesizing cells, the rate of carbon assimilation also increases in a linear fashion with the light intensity, but at higher intensities the rate curve begins to bend and at a certain point becomes parallel to the abscissa. This means that all light above this intensity is wasted, i.e., that the cells have become light-saturated. Obviously, the photosynthetic output is restricted by some factors other than light intensity alone. This has been known since at least 1905, when F. F. Blackmann drew attention to this limitation of the rate of photosynthesis at high light intensities. These other factors are the chemical, enzymatic, nonphotochemical, so-called "dark," reactions. They comprise reactions which produce the substrate to be reduced by the

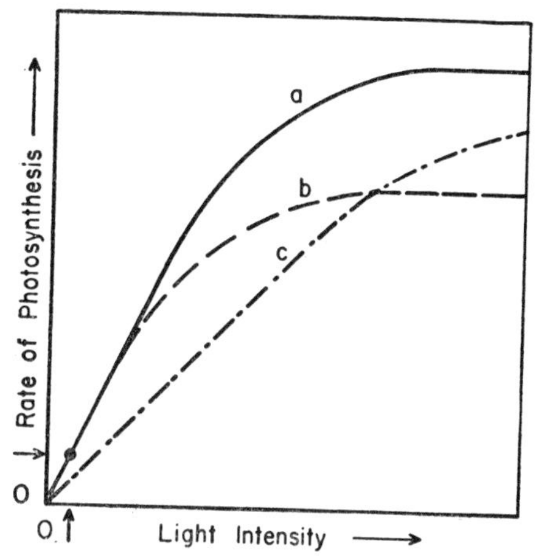

FIG. 24. Rate of photosynthesis as a function of light intensity: *a*, normal course of curve (compare Fig. 26); *b*, course as seen with carbon dioxide deficiency, or cyanide poisoning, or at low temperature; *c*, course seen with chlorophyll deficiency, narcotic poisoning, or inhibition of oxygen evolution. Short arrows indicate point (black dot) at which respiration is compensated by light.

activated chlorophyll complex and those which remove and stabilize the reduction products.

By means of a light-saturation curve, one can find the maximum light intensity at which the enzymatic dark reactions still satisfy the demands of the photochemical process. Up to this point the curve is approximately linear. Light begins to be wasted as soon as the substrate or the products of the light reaction are not moved fast enough to keep pace with the primary photochemical effects.

The absolute values for light-saturation vary greatly with the species of the plant under observation, with the way a particular plant has been grown (high or low chlorophyll or enzyme content), or with the experimental conditions (temperature, presence of inhibitors) (103, 126, 127, 130, 388, 390, 472).

Every light curve for photosynthesis thus shows two regions—a light-dependent one and a light-independent one. Reactions involving the chlorophyll complex will determine the over-all rate of photosynthesis if the light intensities are so low that all nonphotochemical processes are fast by comparison and are kept waiting upon the photoproducts. From this it follows that the characteristics of the photochemical process must be explored at low or moderate light intensities, whereas those of the enzymatic processes are more easily seen in intense light. Take the effect of temperature on photosynthesis, for instance. It is quite different in high and in low light (127, 436, 623). Photochemical processes are known to be rather insensitive to temperature changes because the light absorbed gives to the absorbing molecule a reservoir of free energy far surpassing that which is needed for the usual activation energies in chemical reactions at room temperature. Thus temperature changes between 0° and 100° can hardly contribute to the effect of light itself. Accordingly, the rate of photosynthesis at low light intensities is not much improved by raising the temperature—although, of course, the chlorophyll mechanism can be damaged by heat. On the other hand, the light-saturation rate of photosynthesis will increase with a rise in temperature, like any other chemical or enzymatic reaction, until heat damage occurs; this, in most plants, begins above 40°C.

The saturation rate also responds to changes in the concentration of substrates (e.g., CO_2 partial pressure) or of enzymes. (The latter can be varied either by growth conditions or by applying specific inhibiting poisons.) Plants need less carbon dioxide at low light than at high light; the depressing influence of smaller concentrations of a poison like cyanide vanishes in comparison to the rate in unpoisoned controls if the test is made at low light intensities, equivalent to low rates of photosynthesis. Numerous examples of light curves are described by Rabinowitch (436, Vol. II, pp. 965–1016).

Warburg was the first to show that this distinction between light and dark reactions also becomes apparent if strong light is given in intermittent short periods instead of continuously. If excess light is given only for a moment it may use up the entire supply of substrate (e.g., RuDP, see Section IX). But the empty substrate pool will be refilled during the dark periods between flashes. The result is a "saving" of light energy. On the other hand, the integrated, over-all rate of photosynthesis in flashing light cannot be faster than that which the enzyme system is capable of delivering—that is, the saturation rate (129, 385).

The plotting of light-saturation curves has, through the years, proved to be a very useful device for a survey of those conditions in the plant which will determine the outcome of certain experimental tests. In most cases it suffices to compare the rates at one low and one high intensity in order to see whether the phenomenon under observation affects its photochemistry or some of the many enzyme systems which we now believe to be involved—for instance those of the Calvin-Benson cycle (see Section IX). The initial slope of the photosynthesis versus intensity curve indicates the photochemical efficiency. It is proportional to the quantum requirement (see below). The level of the curve at light saturation is an over-all measure of the enzymatic capacity of the entire system. Each part of the curve can be influenced independently (472). If, for example, one-half of the chlorophyll molecules would, for some reason, become inactive, the initial slope would be halved. This does not preclude the possibility that the rates eventually reach the same saturation level (curve *c*, Fig. 24). On the other hand, any factor which interferes with one of the enzymatic systems in the carbon cycle is likely to lower the maximum output.

In general, one can say that photosynthesis increases from the very beginning of the light curve linearly with illumination. Particularly, the absence of a sigmoid shape at the very lowest light intensities is theoretically important. This proves that even a very slow succession of light quanta can be used efficiently, and it follows that the intermediates produced by each single absorption act must either live long enough to await the arrival of the next quantum, or that there must be a mechanism or structure which permits the transfer of energy received by widely separated chlorophyll molecules to one reactive center. The energy pulses will then arrive at this center in quick succession, though each particular chlorophyll molecule may have to wait many minutes until it has a chance to absorb the next light quantum. What is meant by a "sigmoid" light curve of a photochemical reaction can be seen in Fig. 25, which is given here as a contrasting example. It plots the mating behavior of *Chlamydomonas* sp. in relation to light intensity. Low-intensity illumination has no effect at all on the copulation behavior, because the photoproducts, being used up faster than they are produced, never reach a certain threshold concentration (162).

This type of test reveals how the influence of external factors falls into two classes. Low temperature, deuterium oxide (heavy water), lack of carbon dioxide, poisoning with cyanide, and deficiency of vanadium all have the same effect of depressing mainly the saturation rates (curve *b*, Fig. 24). On the other hand, lack of manganese, lack of coenzyme Q, or poisoning with hydroxylamine (NH_2OH), menadione (2-methyl-1,4-naphthoquinone), *o*-phenanthroline, DCMU [3-(3,4-dichlorophenyl)-1,1-dimethylurea, an herbicide], or phenylurethane, all depress the yield of the photochemistry in the linear portion of the curve (curve *c*, Fig. 24) (see Section XV).

Present knowledge allows us to locate the first group of effects in the carbon dioxide fixation mechanism; the second group, in the mechanism leading to the evolution of oxygen. This division is, however, not

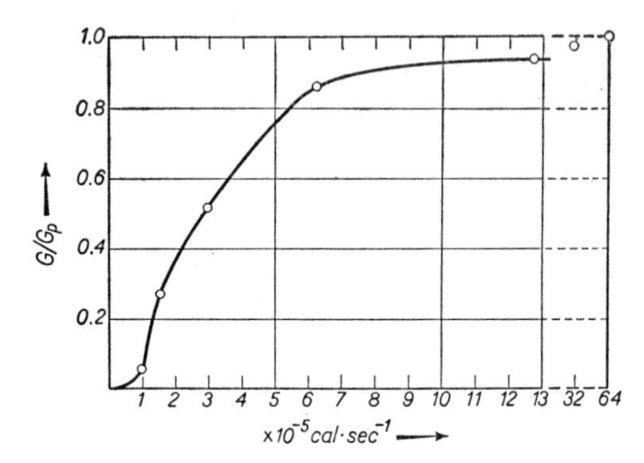

FIG. 25. Sigmoid shape of the curve showing copulation in *Chlamydomonas* sp. as a function of light intensity. Abscissa, light intensity. Ordinate, ratio of the number of activated gametes to the number of potential gametes. After Förster (162).

always clear cut, because certain agents or conditions may influence more than one set of enzymes at a time.

2. *Photooxidation*

If the light intensity is increased much above the saturation point, many more chlorophyll molecules are excited than can contribute to useful, normal reduction processes, and side reactions become noticeable. The reductive power of the product of photolysis is gradually diverted to other acceptors (167, 318, 375, 482). At first, conditions are still physiological in that they remain reversible—the effects of high light intensity in the presence of saturating concentrations of carbon dioxide remain comparable to those found at low intensities when carbon dioxide is limiting the rate or is missing (131, 218). With still higher light intensities, abnormal photochemical reactions take over. These are particularly conspicuous when oxygen is present (296, 471, 482, 616). Not only does oxygen compete as an acceptor for the photolytic hydrogen, but plain photooxidation of the type familiar from experiment with ordinary dyes—in other words, a completely unspecific reaction—begins to play a role and the damage done to the cell becomes irreversible. For a theoretical discussion showing why photooxidation is practically absent during normal photosynthesis, even under restricted inhibited conditions, see Franck (167, 436). The protective role of carotenes is discussed in Section VI,C.

3. *Compensation of Respiration and Other Effects of Weak Illumination*

More interesting than the effect of extremely strong light is that observed with very weak illumination.

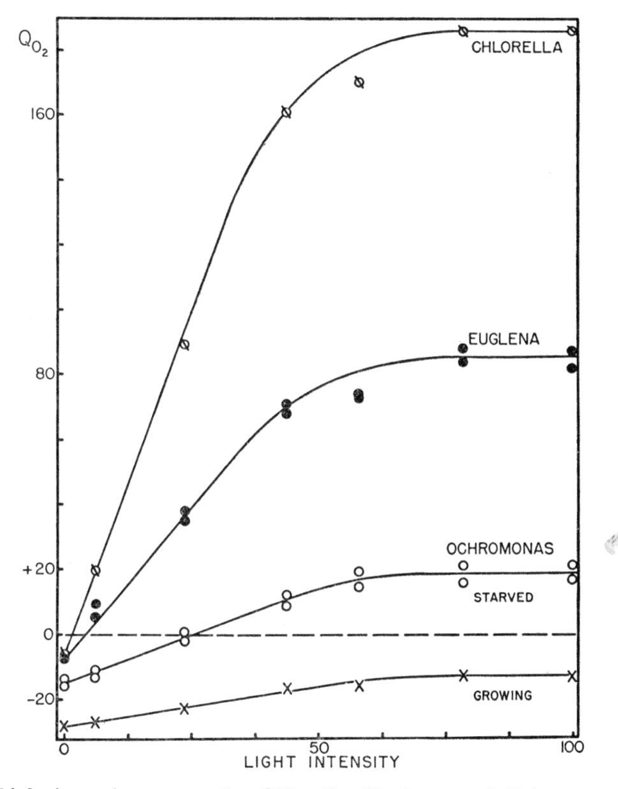

FIG. 26. Light-intensity curves for *Chlorella*, *Euglena*, and *Ochromonas* according to Brown and Weiss (62). *Ochromonas malhamensis*, a flagellate saprotrophic protozoan, produces so little chlorophyll that in strong light its photosynthesis barely suffices to compensate respiration (compare Fig. 24).

The mark on the lower left of the curve in Fig. 24 indicates the "compensation point." Its position is determined by the rate of respiration (see Section V,E,1). Starting from complete darkness, the effect of light is first to balance, more and more, the respiratory gas exchange, until the latter is just compensated. Only above compensation do we find a net gain in carbon fixation due to light (see Fig. 26).

The literature reports two sets of light-intensity curves. Mostly the measured points extrapolate neatly backward to zero rate at zero intensity. But some light curves were seen to deviate from linearity around the level of the compensation intensity. The curve suddenly becomes much steeper below the compensating level and, since the slope is a measure of the photochemical efficiency, light appears to be much more efficient (up to twice as much so) while compensating respiration than in fixing free carbon dioxide. This was discovered by Kok (315, 316) with algae (Fig. 27) and later confirmed by van der Veen, using tobacco (*Nicotiana tabacum*) leaves (536). Emerson and Chalmers (139), as

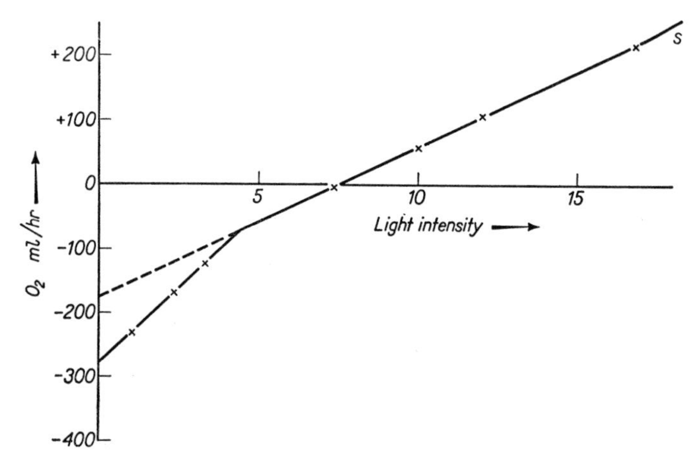

FIG. 27. Break of the light intensity versus rate curve below the compensation point. *Chlorella* grown in Knop solution. After washing, resuspended in a medium containing NH_4^+; pH = 7.0. Gas phase: air plus 5% CO_2. γ assumed to be 1.0; sodium light. Kok (315, 316).

well as Brackett *et al.* (52), who looked for this effect, did not find it, yet there is no doubt that the yield of chlorophyll fluorescence also changes in this region (see Fig. 52, p. 99). It seems now that as yet undefined conditions in the algae determine whether or not a "Kok effect" will be noted.

Strictly speaking, we have two compensation points in the gas exchange: one for oxygen and one for carbon dioxide. They will coincide only if both the respiratory and the assimilatory quotients are unity or if the same mixture of substances is respired as is being synthesized. Usually this condition is not entirely fulfilled.

We must point out that the counterbalancing by light of the total respiration of the cells in a given volume of a *dense* suspension is, obviously, not the compensation we are discussing here. Those cells which are shaded by others receive hardly any light at all and only respire, while others in front show a high rate of photosynthesis above the true compensation point. True compensation must be studied in thin suspensions or with thin leaves where the cells do not shade each other much. A shaded cell receives less light and its metabolic condition corresponds to a lower place on the light-intensity curve.

Anything that affects the rates of respiration or photosynthesis independent of the opposing reaction will shift the compensation point upward or downward on the light-intensity scale. In *Scenedesmus* sp., for instance, cyanide inhibits respiration much more strongly than photosynthesis. In the poisoned algae less light is needed to reach the compensation point (203).

Kok's observation that below the compensation point less energy is needed to compensate for the disappearance of an oxygen molecule absorbed in respiration than for the release of it as free gas above the compensation has stirred up anew the discussion of the reactions which are involved here. Since we know that coenzymes can be reduced photochemically, explanations are not difficult to invent (Section XII). As early as 1920, Warburg (561) had observed that in *Chlorella* sp. the compensation reaction is insensitive to cyanide. He remarked that this speaks in favor of a photochemical reduction of some precursors of carbon dioxide in place of that of the free respiratory carbon dioxide after its formation. This is still the best explanation, since it fits with current knowledge of the inhibition of reversible carboxylations by cyanide.

Light so weak that it does not even suffice to compensate respiration is not without some, perhaps decisive, influence on cell metabolism. We do not mean the phototropic responses, which are well known. Kandler discovered that under anaerobic conditions a little light is sufficient for the incorporation, the transport, and the storage of glucose into the cells of *Chlorella* sp. (293); in complete darkness this will not happen at all unless oxygen is present, i.e., unless respiration functions. His explanation is that some photophosphorylation proceeds in very dim light and that the assimilation of glucose from the environment depends on this supply of energy-rich phosphate bonds (compare Chapter 4 of Volume II for the role of energy-rich phosphate bonds in absorption and transport).

Equally intriguing is the observation that the very short, strong flash of light (10^{-4} seconds) after a long anaerobic period in complete darkness promptly causes the release of the expected amount of photolytic oxygen from *Scenedesmus* or *Chlorella* cells when the reduction is that of a "Hill reagent" (namely quinone), but that nothing measurable happens if the cells are normal and ready to begin photosynthesis. A very dim background illumination, too weak to compensate respiration, is all that is needed to make this first flash as effective for photosynthesis as for the reduction of quinone (179) (see Section VII).

Related to this may be the effect of light on the growth of *Chlorella vulgaris* in glucose-containing media. In darkness glucose supports only a very low rate of cell proliferation. An added light dosage, so small that it will support no growth in the absence of glucose, causes a large increase in growth rate (38).

These three examples of the special effect of dim light—absorption of glucose, elimination of an inhibition of oxygen evolution after an anaerobic dark period, and the stimulation of heterotrophic growth—may well be traceable to the same cause: photophosphorylation (see Section XIII) and involve the general ways in which the cell can make use of energy stored in this form.

B. Temperature

The temperature limits for photosynthesis in the intact cell are given on the one hand by the damage of the essential structure due to freezing (disruptive crystal formation) and on the other hand by the heat denaturation of enzymes or structural proteins. In terms of degrees these limits vary for each plant species or even for nearly related mutants of the same strain. Certain conifers remain green and their needles viable despite the severest winters. The blue-green algae found in hot springs grow at temperatures of 80°C.

An unusual amount of work has been invested in measuring the rate of photosynthesis in relation to temperature. Except for the fact that two types of reactions exist—those having a high temperature coefficient typical of many enzymatic reactions and those having one approaching unity, indicating the predominance of photochemical steps—not many results are available that can be suitably generalized. One consequence of the double nature of photosynthetic reactions is the shift of the compensation point at low or medium light intensities with temperature, for the rate of respiration rises faster than that of light-limited photosynthesis. An extensive discussion of the complex problems involved is given by Rabinowitch (436, pp. 1211–1254).

C. Carbon Dioxide Concentration

Among the external factors which influence the rate and efficiency of photosynthesis, such as light, temperature, humidity and carbon dioxide, the last is, of course, the most important, since it is the substrate to be transformed into living matter. Low as the concentration of carbon dioxide is in normal air (0.03–0.05% of an atmosphere), it evidently suffices to keep the cycle of carbon going. At this concentration the plants are capable of absorbing carbon dioxide with considerable speed (121, 196). Since we have a cycle of carbon, it means that at present, down to this limit of 0.03 atm, the plants on earth utilize all that is being produced by the decay of organic matter, by combustion, and by respiratory reactions in living cells. For the scientist, the question of how the rate of photosynthesis depends on the concentration of carbon dioxide available to the plant is, of course, of great interest.

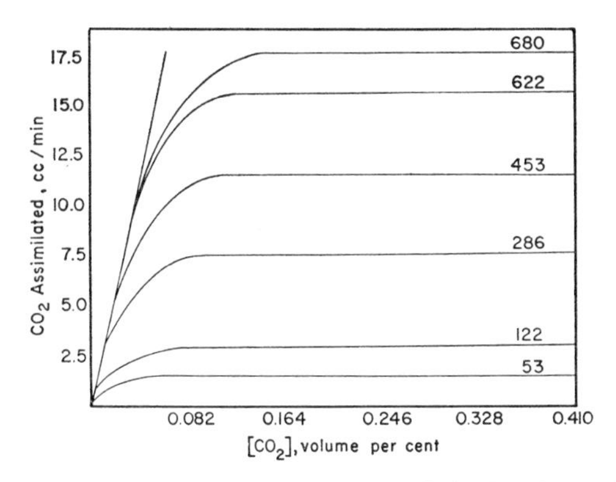

FIG. 28. Carbon dioxide assimilation curves of whole *Triticum* (wheat) plants at increasing light intensities. From Rabinowitch (436), p. 896, after Hoover, Johnston, and Brackett (1933). Parameters in Kerg/cm²/sec.

Since 1919—that is, long before the specific nature of the carbon dioxide-fixing reaction had been elucidated—this question has been studied in great detail (405–409, 560, 566) (see Figs. 28 and 29). Very often the measurement of the rate of photosynthesis as a function of carbon dioxide concentration gave answers which did not agree with the majority of earlier results. Thus the question of how much carbon dioxide is needed to saturate photosynthesis, or at what low concentration the plant is unable to show a net gain in carbon assimilation, has remained controversial (131, 445, 481, 485, 600) (see Fig. 31).

Before the more biochemical analysis of photosynthesis, careful kinetic studies of gas exchange rates in intact cells were the only way open to investigate the role of carbon dioxide. With the new knowledge, the old data are easier to understand. The discussion of this problem can be shortened if we consider that the rate of the enzymatic carboxylation is bound to vary not only with the species of the plant observed, but also with the conditions to which the plant has been subjected and accustomed during the time preceding the experiment. There is such a thing as enzymatic variation or adaptation. We cannot expect therefore to answer the question: "Which is the lowest carbon dioxide concentration still capable of maintaining the production of sugars?" or "Which concentration saturates photosynthesis?" by quoting a few exact and uniform figures. Light intensity, chlorophyll content, the concentration of the very products of carbon fixation and similar factors complicate the issue. In nature all plants have to operate

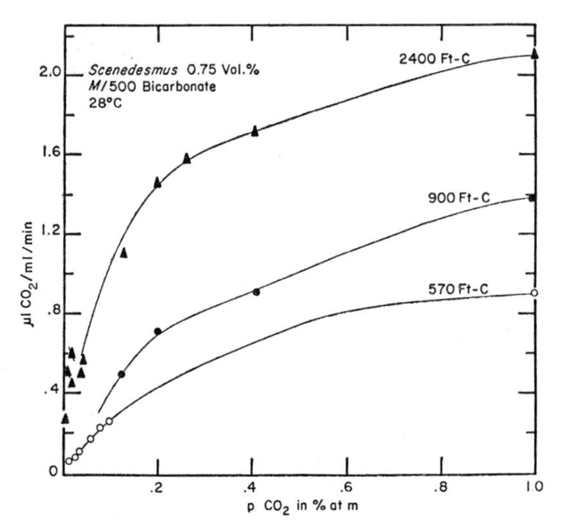

FIG. 29. Carbon dioxide saturation curves at different light intensities for *Scenedesmus* sp. as determined with a pH meter. Saturation at about 1% carbon dioxide.

with the average amount of carbon present in air, which is 0.03%; but in the laboratory most plants, particularly the favorite strains of algae, are usually grown in a stream of air enriched with carbon dioxide; 4–5% CO_2 in air is the gas mixture most often used for cultures of *Chlorella* or *Scenedesmus*, and it is not yet known whether this influences the capacity of various carboxylating enzymes.

Probably all plants photosynthesize faster in the presence of more carbon dioxide than is available in ordinary air; and some plants are known to give better and better rates until carbon dioxide concentration in the surrounding gas mixture reaches about 1% (13). Adaptation to very low carbon dioxide concentrations has been shown by Österlind to occur in *Scenedesmus quadricauda.* He compared rates of photosynthesis at different times after the cells had been kept at a particularly high or low concentration of carbon dioxide or of dissolved bicarbonate (340). Figure 30 is an example which shows how the ability to utilize low concentrations of carbon dioxide varies with the pretreatment of the plant material after exposure to acidifying conditions (50% CO_2). The rate of photosynthesis at low CO_2 partial pressures is first very much lower than normal, but increases in the course of an hour after the algae have been transferred to a slightly alkaline medium (cf. 436). The maximum rate at about 1% CO_2 remains unaffected.

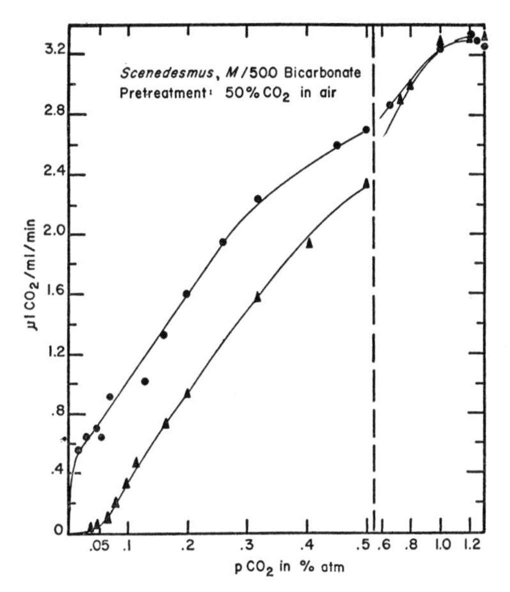

FIG. 30. Adaptation to low carbon dioxide partial pressures. *Scenedesmus* in 2×10^{-3} *M* bicarbonate. Lower curve: algae pretreated with 50% carbon dioxide and washed. Upper curve: same algae after 1 hour at pH 8.7.

The entire question of carbon dioxide influence will be studied differently in the future, since we have now progressed to the point where several carboxylation reactions have been discovered which may be coupled with the primary photochemical process of the chlorophyll complex. The question has become more specific and concerns the nature of the various carboxylation enzymes. The influence of carbon dioxide resolves into the analysis of the variability of these enzymes and their affinity for their substrates in cell-free preparations.

Among these carboxylations, the addition of carbon dioxide to ribulose diphosphate is pre-eminent. It is the only one discovered so far that leads to a substance which may very well be the substrate of the photochemical reaction in photosynthesis, namely phosphoglyceric acid: RuDP + $CO_2 \rightarrow$ 2 PGA. It will therefore be discussed especially in Section X. With respect to carbon dioxide partial pressure and rates of photosynthesis it also fulfills the requirement that it should proceed spontaneously in the direction of synthesis rather than of decarboxylation. It is an exergonic reaction, so far found to be irreversible. This explains why plants are able to proceed with photosynthesis at the low

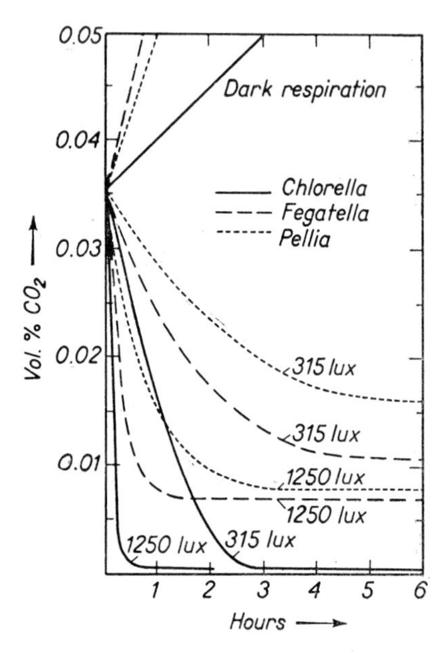

FIG. 31. Time course of changes in the concentration of carbon dioxide within a closed volume of air. In the dark, respiration produces carbon dioxide. In the light, *Chlorella vulgaris, Pellia epiphylla,* and *Fegatella conica* are able to decrease the carbon dioxide content far below that of ordinary air. The equilibrium between carbon dioxide production and consumption in the light is a function of the light intensity and of the species of plant used for the experiment. From Egle (121).

carbon dioxide partial pressure found in air. In a closed vessel illuminated *Chlorella* sp. is capable of lowering the carbon dioxide concentration below 0.001 volume % (see Fig. 31) (121).

It should be mentioned that the life of green plants, as far as carbon dioxide is concerned, is not solely determined by the specific properties of the carboxylating enzyme of photosynthesis. Certain metabolic intermediate stages in all living cells seem to depend upon the presence of some free carbon dioxide (457). It is well known that nonphotosynthetic organisms suffer great disturbances in their growth if carbon dioxide is rigorously removed. The phenomenon is usually interpreted as a consequence of an excessive decarboxylation of organic acids which play a role as catalysts in the glycolytic and respiratory cycles (76). A biotin-carbon dioxide complex is required for the synthesis of fats.

The question of the saturating concentration for photosynthesis is further complicated by the fact that carbon dioxide becomes an inhibitor or poison as soon as its concentration surpasses the physiological range. Again, various plants differ considerably in their tolerance toward an excess of carbon dioxide; for instance, the leaves of higher plants are more sensitive than the laboratory-grown algae (23, 340, 404, 483). The experimenter should keep in mind that the enhancing and the poisoning effects of carbon dioxide may both be present. In order to compare and evaluate rate measurements, or quantum yield determinations, or induction phenomena, one has to know at which concentration of carbon dioxide these measurements were made and to what extent the particular carbon dioxide concentration chosen influences the metabolism as a whole.

A related question is whether aquatic plants will admit bicarbonate ions through their membranes, so that bicarbonates can contribute directly to photosynthesis. If there is such a direct participation of bicarbonate it is certainly small in range and size. The respective experiments are complicated by two factors: the influence of high pH (alkalinity) of the medium on permeability and the necessity of balancing properly the relationship between sodium and potassium ions. Particularly, blue-green algae, like species of *Nostoc,* suffer easily from lack of potassium ions (4, 96, 349, 405–409, 445, 483, 575; see also discussions in 158 and 436). (Reference may be made to Chapters 1 and 4 of Volume II for the principles that govern the relative absorption of ions and neutral molecules.)

The vast amount of work on carbonic anhydrase—the enzyme which catalyzes the equilibration between carbon dioxide and carbonic acid in aqueous solution—also inspired investigations on whether such an enzyme plays a role in the mechanism of carbon dioxide fixation in green fields. Certainly this enzyme is of great importance for the carbon dioxide exchange in the lungs of vertebrates. A carbonic anhydrase has indeed been found in many plants, but what its function actually is there has not been established with certainty. If a hydration of carbon dioxide inside the cell is a prerequisite for its combination with the carboxylation enzyme, it would be understandable that an enzyme is necessary to keep this initial step going at the rate required by photosynthesis at high light intensities. Waygood and Clendenning made a special study of this problem (590).

D. WATER

While it is easy to vary experimentally the concentration of carbon dioxide or of oxygen, to change the temperature or the light intensity, it is difficult to interfere with the water supply of the plant in a way that would make it possible to ascribe the effect found unambiguously to changes in the photochemical mechanism. It is possible to dry out living cells slowly and to register reversible and irreversible damage to various metabolic reactions or to follow changes of the fluorescence yield; but so far not much definite knowledge has been gathered in this way.

More successful have been experiments in which ordinary water was either tagged by adding some heavy water (D_2O) or tritium oxide (T_2O), or in which water was exchanged for nearly pure deuterium oxide. In intact cells deuterium oxide depresses the saturation rate—the enzymatic reaction—and seems not to interfere with the photochemical behavior.

Why the photolysis of water should not respond to a replacement of its substrate by deuterium oxide in Craig, Pratt, and Trelease's experiment with the whole cell, whereas it does so when the reduction of ferricyanide or dyestuffs (Hill reaction) is studied in heavy water remains to be answered. Even here it has not as yet been possible to pin down any simple step as the one into which water enters as a reactant (372, 426, 427).

E. OXYGEN, AEROBIC AND ANAEROBIC CONDITIONS

1. Influence of Respiration and of Oxygen on Photosynthesis; Light Respiration

Oxygen influences photosynthesis in three ways. First, there is respiration and its relation to photosynthesis. Green plants are aerobic organisms, and the oxygen of the air enters into their metabolism by way of respiration. The substrates of respiration are, in general, the products of photosynthesis. More important, the intermediates of glycolysis and respiration may interconnect with the photosynthetic mechanism. We can therefore expect that respiration constantly influences photosynthesis. Second, oxygen may substitute for carbon dioxide and become reduced, in the same way as Hill reagents are reduced. Third, oxygen can directly quench the excited states of chlorophyll and thus diminish the yield of photosynthesis at the source (299, 346, 561).

Of the greatest interest is the effect of respiration on the level of intermediary metabolism. Both respiration and photosynthesis produce the same reactive metabolites: phosphopyruvate, phosphoglycerate, ATP, reduced coenzymes, etc. If there is a completely free interplay—a rapid exchange of these substances throughout the cell, regardless of their origin—the relative rates of respiration and photosynthesis should determine the direction of this mutual influence (357).

It has been, and still is, common practice to ignore respiration and its probable effect when dealing with photosynthesis at maximum rates, that is, when the light metabolism is ten to thirty times faster than the respiratory metabolism in the dark. Under these conditions respiration may even become inhibited through the action of light. If, in excess light, the coenzymes engaged in the stepwise degradation of carbohydrates are forcefully kept in the reduced state, the coenzyme-catalyzed oxidation steps—the decarboxylations—cannot proceed (see Sections IX and XI). Calvin and Weigl did observe that C^{14}-labeled intermediates of photosynthesis did not enter the citric acid cycle as long as the light was on (590).

Matters become, however, very complex—at least in theory—when the light intensity is low, e.g., around the compensation point. Here the photochemical reactions proceed not much faster, or even slower, than does respiration. Will there be mainly a physical compensation, a balance of independent gas exchanges, or a true reversal of the respiratory and glycolytic intermediate steps? Will the rate, as well as the respiratory quotient, change because now, instead of endogenous reserve material, newly formed carbohydrates become available for respiration? How should one correct the observable light effects for respiration under these circumstances? These questions have loomed large in the discussion on quantum yields because the latter are measured at low light intensities. If the experimenter wishes to make any corrections for respiration presumably going on during the time of exposure to light, he could hardly do any better until recently than to measure the rate of respiration before and after a certain light period, hoping that an interpolation between these two values will produce truer results than a correction based on speculating how respiration might have run during the time the light was on. In starved cells, in those that have been kept respiring in the dark until most of the endogenous reserve has been used up, the increase in respiration produced by even a few minutes of light is easy to see afterward. But this is not the main problem. The question is, whether the photochemistry will, through its intermediates or through the reduction of coenzymes, speed up respiration in the light to an unexpected degree (176). Warburg (578) believes he has evidence that light does just that. A back reaction with molecular oxygen supposedly consumes two-thirds of the original photoproducts. The energy of this light respiration is stored in a chlorophyll-carbon dioxide complex which, for this reason, can decompose into carbohydrate and oxygen upon the absorption of one single quantum (576, 577) (see Fig. 62 and the equations on page 135, Section VIII,E).

Obviously this mechanism cannot work unless the light respiration proceeds at twice the speed of the visible, steady-state rate of photosynthesis. *A priori* this seems somewhat improbable, and it is therefore gratifying that it became possible to eliminate this hypothesis by direct observation. Brown *et al.* made use of a mass spectrograph and of the oxygen isotope O^{18} to follow the course of respiration while photosynthesis was in progress (63, 64, 66). The result of these definitive investigations is that the respiratory uptake of oxygen continues more or less undisturbed by the progress of photosynthesis in the same cell. Figures 32–35 are examples of simultaneous measurements of photosynthesis and respiration in the light with the aid of a mass spectrometer. Mass 44 $= CO_2$; mass 32 $= O^{16}O^{16}$; mass 34 $= O^{16}O^{18}$. The oxygen in the gas phase contains O^{18}, that in the water or in the plant tissue only O^{16}. The experiment of Fig. 32 shows the oxygen exchange in a tobacco leaf. In the dark, oxygen of mass 32 and of mass 34 are both taken up in respiration. Their ratio in the surrounding atmosphere remains constant. In the light, oxygen of mass 32 is rapidly evolved from water, thus completely masking its uptake in respiration. But the oxygen of mass 34 is seen to continue to be absorbed at the same rate. After the light period the ratio of partial pressures of O_2^{34} to O_2^{32} has changed. The closed system now contains more O_2^{32}. But from then on the ratio remains constant. Both oxygen isotopes are again respired in the same proportion.

Figure 33 illustrates a similar experiment with a blue-green alga, *Anabaena* sp. and reveals a doubling of the rate of respiration in strong light but much less of a light effect when the intensity is lowered. (The slope of the curve for mass 32, indicating photosynthesis, is less steep on the right side.)

Figure 34 shows an experiment with *Chlorella* sp. The light was given in 2-minute intervals, the method which Warburg *et al.* used to demonstrate in manometric experiments the existence of a light respiration which they calculated to be two-thirds as fast as photosynthesis. No trace of this can be detected here.

Figure 35 shows the time course of carbon dioxide exchange, together with that of the two forms of oxygen in *Chlorella pyrenoidosa*. Neither continuous light, nor intermittent illumination with 1-minute periods, disturbs the rate of oxygen uptake while photosynthesis proceeds at four times the rate of respiration.

It is futile to try to explain the absence of the expected fast back reaction by postulating an immediate and quantitative reabsorption of two-thirds of the photochemically liberated oxygen (as has been done to discredit Brown's experiments). The oxygen of the air is actually seen to enter the cell as usual. Therefore it should be available for the back reaction, at least partially, when the latter proceeds in strong light at thirty times the rate of the normal dark respiration. To say, on the other hand, that it is not the free oxygen, but some precursor, which reacts back, means that the only salient point of the discussion has been abandoned. Internal back reactions between, say, XH and YOH, are an integral part of the hypothesis of the photolysis of water and are therefore far from a novel idea. Neither here nor in any other case where this postulated back reaction was sought, could it be found (218, 441). In the one case which produced some sort of evidence for its existence, namely, manometric measurements of photosynthesis in intermittent illumination with periods lasting about 1 minute, it has been definitely established that the method is inadequate. Induction phenomena overlapped by a physical lag of the gas exchange between gas and liquid phase suffice to interpret Warburg's data (see Section II and ref. 141). An unchanged rate of oxygen uptake in the light, however, does not guarantee an undisturbed respiratory metabolism (315, 484). Illuminated green cells often do not release the carbon dioxide which corresponds to their uptake of oxygen in respiration. The effect of light on the carbon dioxide evolution in respiration can be instantaneous (219, 436). This is no contradiction to the experiments of Brown, since we know that oxygen in respiration is reduced to water along a pathway which is entirely different from that of the dehydrogenation of metabolites leading to the release of carbon dioxide. The fact that the coenzymes are being reduced photochemically does not mean that they are prevented from proceeding along their usual way on the oxygen side, where they transfer their hydrogen to the flavins, etc. Light, in a way, then produces a "short circuit," and it depends on where the rate-determining step is located whether we see an increase, a decrease, or no effect at all on the rate of oxygen uptake in the light.

It was a source of wonder how light, through photochemistry, could so completely "catch" the carbon dioxide released by respiration. The present way of looking at the problem—by the inhibition of the decarboxylation—makes this compensation effect a good deal more plausible. There still remains the fact of spatial separation between

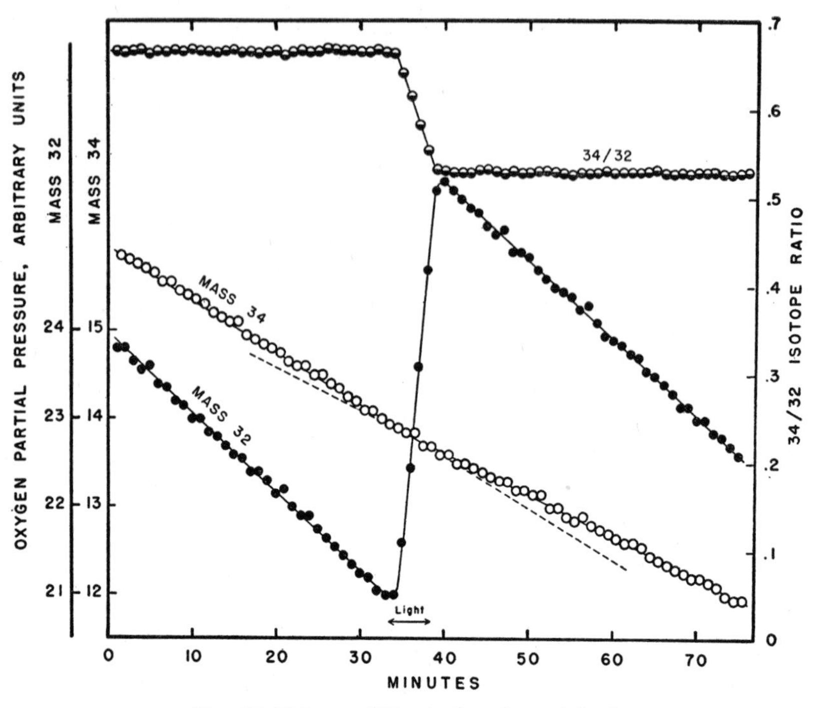

FIG. 32. Tobacco (*Nicotiania tobacum*) leaf.

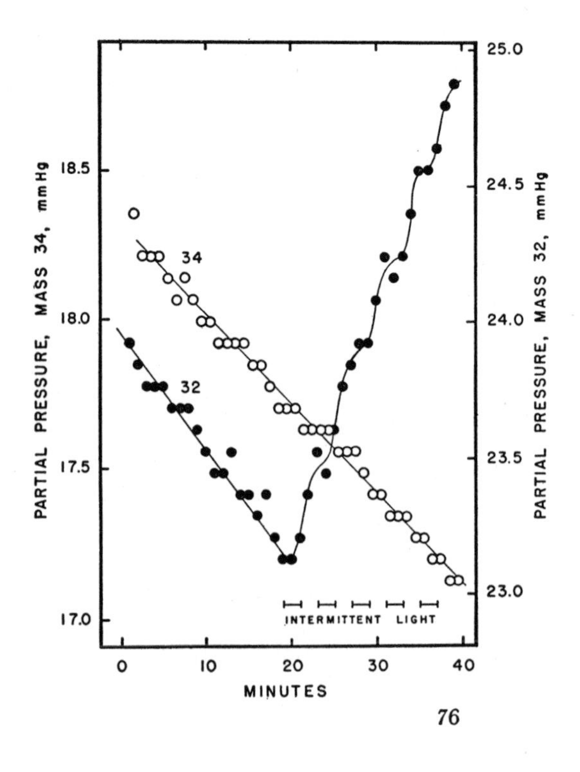

FIG. 34. *Chlorella* sp. Compare Fig. 62.

FIGS. 32–35. Respiration during photosynthesis as recorded with a mass spectrograph. Photosynthesis evolves oxygen from water having mass 32. The same normal oxygen is contained in air and absorbed in the dark. In addition, air contains oxygen of mass 34 which is not present in the water. The curve for mass 34 shows that respiration continues undisturbed in the light at the same rate as in the dark. After Brown *et al.* (63, 64).

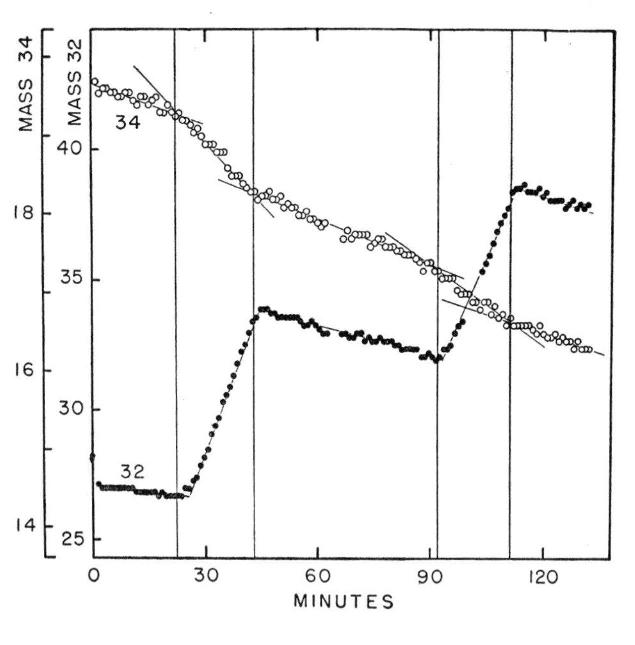

FIG. 33.
Blue-green alga
Anabaena sp.

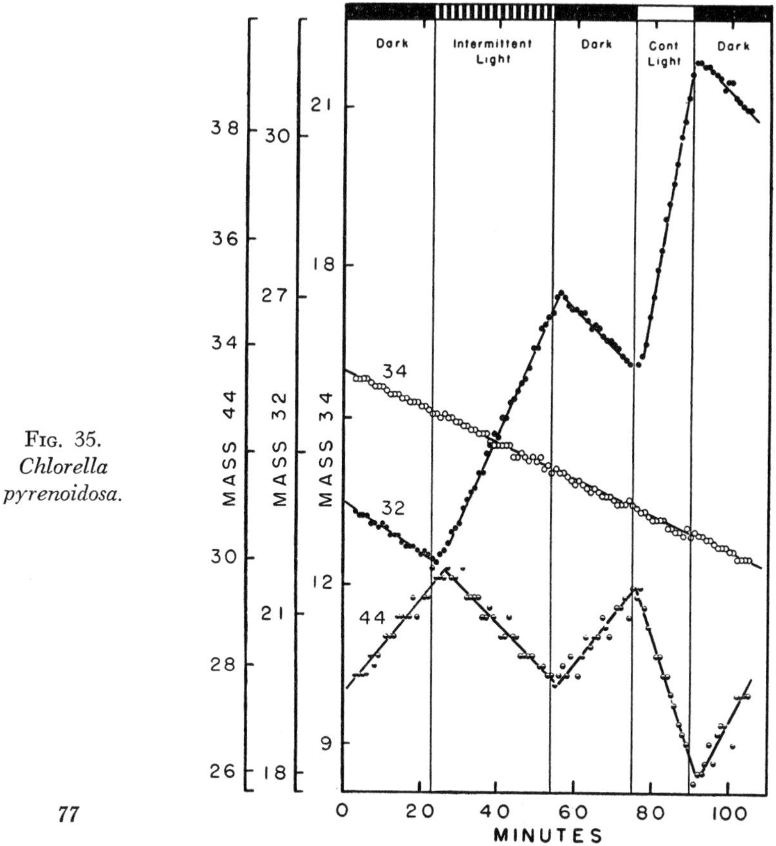

FIG. 35.
Chlorella pyrenoidosa.

the plastids, the mitochondria, and the cell surface—places where an independent respiration might proceed. This is indicated by the fact that respiration of added glucose is cyanide sensitive in *Chlorella*, while that of endogenous material produced by photosynthesis is not (125).

There are plants which are predominantly photosynthetic and carry

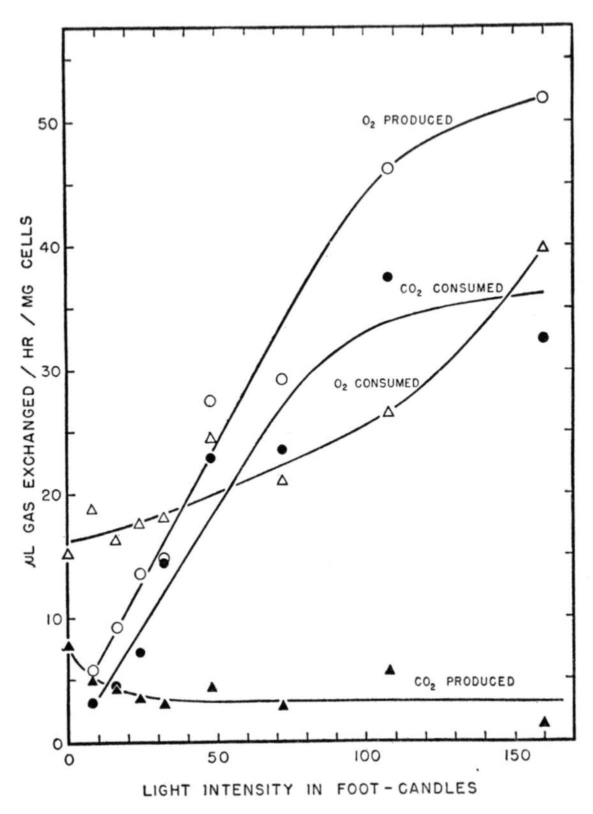

FIG. 36. The effect of light intensity on the gas exchanges of starved *Ochromonas malhamensis*, based on spectrophotometric data obtained by using two isotopic forms of carbon dioxide (masses 44 and 45) and two isotopic forms of oxygen (masses 32 and 34). After Brown and Weis (62).

on little respiration. An example is *Anacystis nidulans*, a blue-green alga recently investigated by Myers (386, 387, 533). Here the correction for respiration in the light hardly presents a problem. On the other hand, the chrysophyte flagellate *Ochromonas malhamensis* is mainly a heterotrophic organism endowed with some minor photosynthetic power (see Fig. 26) (391, 556). Its respiration is large and variable. Figure 36 shows what Brown and Weis found, using the mass spectrometer to analyze the simultaneous consumption and production of two gases, when starved *Ochromonas malhamensis* were subjected to increasing intensities of light. Oxygen consumption more than doubled, carbon dioxide production declined, and the assimilatory quotient was near unity only at medium intensities—between 30 and 50 foot-candles. This is an example of metabolic complications which can hardly be detected by recording merely the over-all gas pressure changes as in the usual manometric method.

2. *Anaerobic Conditions and the Alleged Need of Oxygen for Photosynthesis*

After discussing the various effects of oxygen, we have now to ask what happens if oxygen is removed and the cell is required to photo-

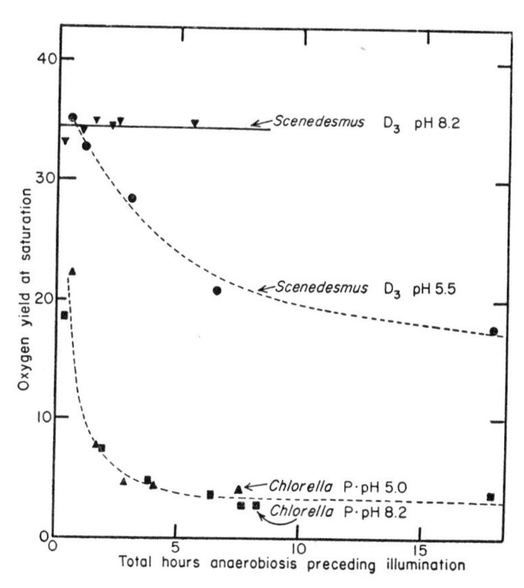

FIG. 37. Inhibition of photosynthesis at saturation light intensity as a function of the time of anaerobic incubation in the dark and the influence of pH. *Chlorella* is extremely sensitive; *Scenedesmus*, sensitive only in acid media (2).

synthesize with carbon dioxide in pure nitrogen, hydrogen, or helium. Experiments of this kind are beset with difficulties because it is theoretically impossible to maintain completely anaerobic conditions in an oxygen-evolving cell. Furthermore, only the noble gases can truly be considered to be metabolically inert. There are the nitrogen-fixing blue-green algae and purple bacteria, as well as numerous strains of photosynthetic organisms capable of utilizing hydrogen under anaerobic conditions (Sections X, XI).

The best approximation to stable anaerobic conditions despite continuous strong illumination was achieved in the experiments of Allen. The oxygen evolved by a few cells suspended in a stirred droplet of water was constantly swept away by a stream of (moist) nitrogen. The partial pressure of this oxygen amounted to less than 10^{-6} mm Hg, and the concentration of oxygen maintained by the plant in the immediate neighborhood of the cell could be shown to correspond to less than 1/40,000 of an atmosphere—much below the partial pressure necessary to initiate respiration. Under these conditions photosynthesis of the alga *Scenedesmus obliquus* frequently reached a rate of 40 cell

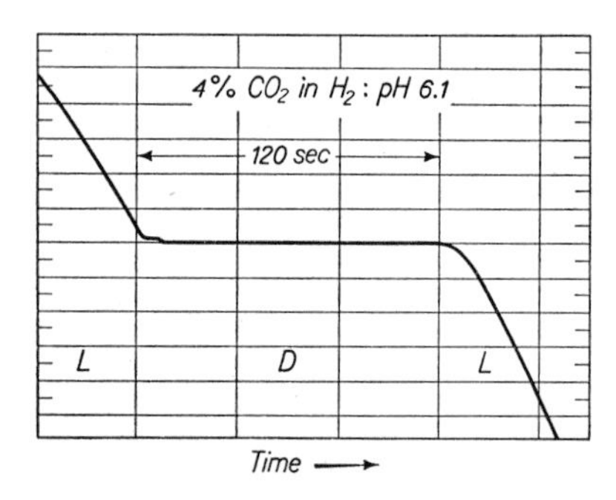

FIG. 38. Photosynthesis under anaerobic conditions (H_2) at high light intensity and high carbon dioxide concentration (4% CO_2) recorded as pH changes. *Scenedesmus* D_3 suspended in *M*/500 bicarbonate. Time scale: 40 seconds between vertical divisions. pH increase between upper left and lower right from 6.10 to 6.15. Absence of pH changes during 2 minutes of darkness (*D*) between light periods (*L*) reveal complete absence of respiration without subsequent inhibition of photosynthesis (218). Compare Figs. 62 and 122.

volumes of oxygen, higher even than the corresponding rate in air (Fig. 37). Evidently, oxygen is not necessary for photosynthesis—or more precisely for the functioning of those partial reactions which lead to the evolution of oxygen. That carbon dioxide can be reduced photochemically under strict anaerobic conditions in certain green plants is known from the experiments on photoreduction (Section XI). Allen's findings corroborated a number of earlier observations (2). The same conclusion must be drawn from an experiment designed to check Warburg's idea of a back-reaction with oxygen as part of the photosynthetic mechanism (see Section VII, Fig. 62). Figure 38 is a recording of acidity changes produced by illuminated *Scenedesmus* in bicarbonate buffer under helium. Two minutes of darkness interrupt a period of fast photosynthesis. The light metabolism stops, and after the pause, during which nothing happens, resumes its course with the least of disturbance. Compare this figure with those in Section XV (Fig. 122, a and b) showing similar experiments under aerobic conditions.

The question is often raised: How high is the oxygen tension at its point of origin in the algal cell? Could there not be a significant retention and reconsumption on the spot? Two sets of experiments speak very much against this idea. First, we have Brown's mass spectrometer experiments (63, 64) (Figs. 32–35). They would be very difficult to understand in their entirety if there were not a very rapid exchange and equilibration between internal and external gases in these microorganisms. Second, a persistent and gradual inhibition of oxygen evolution in a stream of nitrogen seen in *Chlorella* depends on the length of a preceding anaerobic dark period (2). If oxygen, once its evolution by light has begun, were retained and used preferentially for internal oxidations, the results shown in Fig. 39 should not be obtained at all (602).

This brings us to the problem of the reversible inhibition of photosynthesis after anaerobiosis in the dark—the very problem whose incomplete treatment has been responsible for the confused state of the literature about the likely role of oxygen in photosynthesis.

First of all, it should be pointed out that a sensitivity against lack of oxygen is not a characteristic of the photosynthetic mechanism as such but of the plant being studied. This is shown in Fig. 37. The steady rate of oxygen evolution at saturation light intensity declines rapidly in *Chlorella* with the length of the preceding anaerobic incubation independent of the pH. It falls off slowly in *Scenedesmus obliquus* at pH 5.5, and not at all at pH 8.2. Already Willstätter and Stoll (604) stated that they could confirm earlier observations on the capacity of the chloroplasts (in intact leaves) to start with an evolution of oxygen immediately upon illumination, even after many hours of anaerobiosis in the dark. Yet they focused their attention, and much experimental effort, on the fact that in certain plants this was not the case. Here they found photosynthesis to be completely inhibited—at least in the beginning. With continued illumination such plants either recovered spontaneously and resumed the fixation of carbon dioxide, or did so—provided they were not permanently damaged—only after the nitrogen had been replaced by air.

This means that green plants are aerobic organisms. It can be expected that strict anaerobiosis leads to a number of abnormal effects, such as the accumulation of fermentation products (like lactic acid), or the shift from an oxidized to a reduced state of certain cellular catalysts, or the disappearance of intermediates needed to maintain a cyclic process. In short, the plants begin to asphyxiate—some slowly, some faster. One of the earliest symptoms may be the conspicuous failure of photosynthesis to start off as usual upon illumination after an anaerobic treatment, as had already been pointed out in 1935 (201). However, Willstätter and Stoll searched for a special explanation because they looked upon photosynthesis as a mechanism separate and insulated from other reactions in the cell. In 1918 little was known about intermediary metabolism, and their interpretation was not then considered strange. They concluded that a certain small amount of molecular oxygen, bound dissociably inside that mechanism, was essential to its function. Because the observations proper are easy to confirm, some later investigators accepted or even enlarged upon this obsolete hypothesis (300–302). On account of their very special theory of photosynthesis, Warburg and Burk (570–574) (see Section VIII) were forced to assume that, without a reoxidation of two-thirds of the reduction product by molecular oxygen, photosynthesis is unable to continue—hence the inhibition under anaerobic conditions. This hypothesis is still being maintained (578) despite the experimental demonstrations by Brown (63, 64), Allen (2), Gaffron (201, 218, 219), Kok (314, 317), Whittingham (602), and others that the postulated light respiration simply does not exist (29, 441).

It has been known since 1935 that algae of the genus *Scenedesmus* are among those plants that can evolve oxygen normally after protracted periods of anaerobiosis in the dark (201). But these and all other experiments until the work of Franck and associates suffered from the fact that the oxygen, once its evolution had begun in the light, was allowed to accumulate. This restored aerobic conditions, started respiration, and relieved the inhibition. The experiments shown in Figs. 37 and 39 were done with a tiny amount of cells in a stream of nitrogen.

Obviously, the length of the anaerobiosis determines the concentration of fermentation products, and these have, therefore, been held responsible for the peculiar inhibition.

Assuming that the problem still merits some interest, such possibilities as photoreduction with endogenous hydrogen donors (Section XI) or back-reactions like the cyclic phosphorylation (Section XIII) should also be considered as factors causing the sigmoid shape of the family of curves shown in Fig. 39.

In summary, it can be said about the influence of oxygen on photosynthesis that complete absence of oxygen may, but need not, produce peculiar metabolic alterations; that its presence gives rise to various side reactions, such as (a) the direct quenching of the singlet and the metastable excited states of chlorophyll; (b) direct reduction to

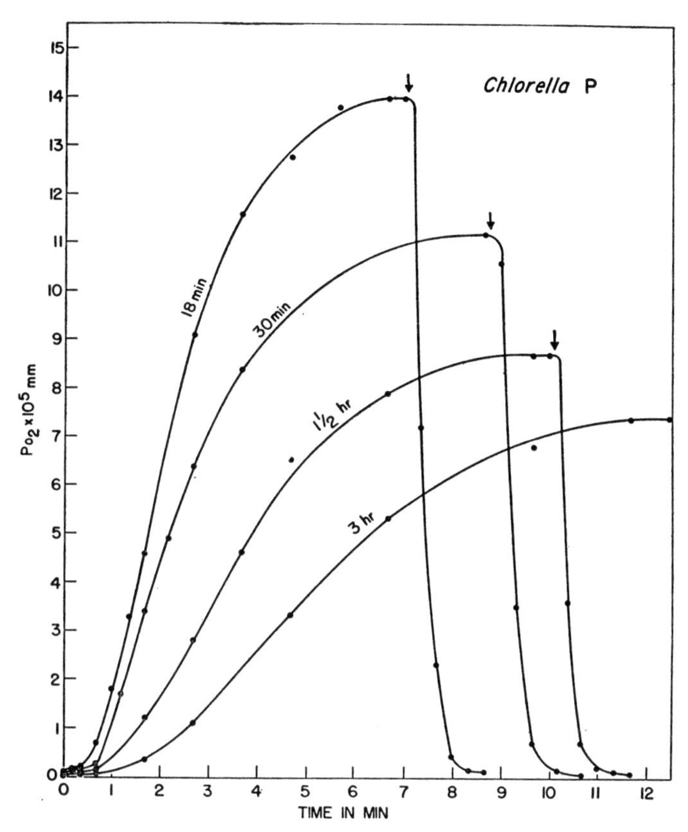

Fig. 39. Rate of photosynthetic oxygen evolution by *Chlorella pyrenoidosa* in a stream of nitrogen after anaerobiosis in the dark. Time marked on curve refers to length of dark incubation preceding the beginning of illumination at zero time. Anaerobic pretreatment not only prolongs induction periods, but progressively diminishes the saturation rate. According to Allen (2).

hydrogen peroxide (see Section XII); (c) intrusion of respiratory intermediates into the photosynthetic mechanism; (d) chlorophyll-catalyzed enzymatic photooxidation (396).

VI. Absorption, Fluorescence, and Luminescence in Living Cells

A. Absorption and Action Spectra *in Vivo*

The only way to determine whether a pigment present in a living cell is responsible for a photochemical reaction is to compare the amount of light absorbed by that pigment with the rate of the observed reaction. The very first example of this type of experimental analysis was the observation, nearly a hundred years ago, that only the green parts of plants were capable of photosynthesis and that other strongly colored organs, like flowers, did not respond in the same way to illumination. The discovery of quite a number of different pigments in the chloroplasts complicated the problem, and today the optical analysis of photochemical events in the living cell has become a complex and refined technique (19, 46, 101, 115, 118, 120, 475, 490).

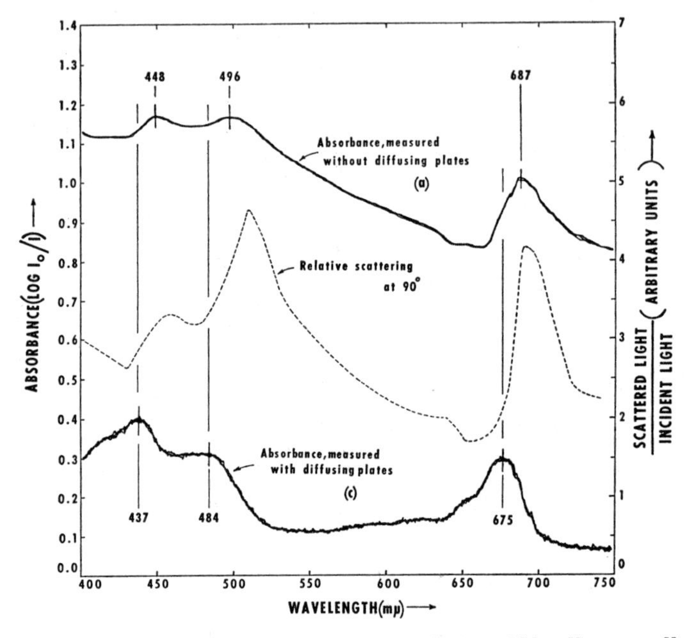

FIG. 40. Shift of the absorption spectrum of living *Chlorella* sp. cells due to scattering. Curve *a*: Measurements without a device to minimize distortion. Curve *c*: Measurements with a diffusion plate inserted between sample and recording photocell. After Latimer (330).

The student of botany will soon notice, when he compares curves of absorption spectra taken by different investigators from the same kind of living cells, that (contrary to the experience with extracts) they rarely seem to agree. This unhappy condition arises, on the one hand, from the fact that there is as yet no standardized way of plotting the observations, and, on the other, from the fact that different methods give diverse results. The main cause of variation is the scattering of the light by the outer walls and the surface inside of the illuminated plant material (330, 436, 437, 446, 462, 534).

We cannot go into the details of this problem, but Fig. 40 is an example of the differences encountered in measuring the light absorption of *Chlorella* sp. when the influence of scattering is large or small. The upper curve (*a*) is taken without the aid of a device to minimize the distortion produced by scattering, the lower one (*c*) with a "diffusion plate" inserted between sample and recording photocell. The middle curve shows how scattering at 90° from the incident ray varies with wavelengths.

Figures 41–44 are examples of investigations done for the purpose of finding out whether pigments other then chlorophyll are photosynthetically active. The procedure consists of comparing the absorption

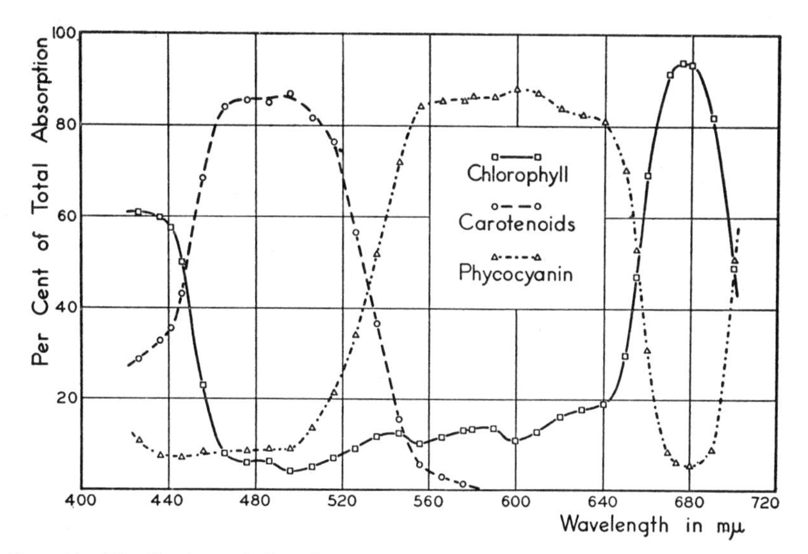

FIG. 41. Distribution of the absorption of light among the pigments of a blue-green alga, *Chroococcus* sp. From Emerson and Lewis (136, 137).

spectrum of the living cell with its action spectrum and evaluating the share of the various pigments in producing the latter. An action spectrum is obtained by measuring photosynthesis (or photoreduction) induced by light of a narrow spectral range and known intensity and repeating these measurements from one end of the spectrum to the other (46, 137, 247, 564). The best light sources are lamps giving the monochromatic emission lines of mercury, sodium, or cadmium. For the regions where there are no good spectral lines, either filters or monochromators have been used. The light should have equal incident intensity in einsteins and not be too strong, since what is to be measured are the relative efficiencies of the pigments—the photochemical yield of the systems (see Section V,A,1). The cell suspension (or the leaf) should be so thin that most of the light passes unabsorbed. Only when all these conditions are fulfilled (several kinds of corrections are necessary) will deviations between absorption spectra and action spectra tell us how much (or how little) the several carotenes, fucoxanthols, phycocyanins, phycoerythrins, and the two or three chlorophylls, contribute to the photochemistry.

As a rule, any light quantum absorbed by an organic pigment molecule produces the same chemical effect (if any), regardless of its

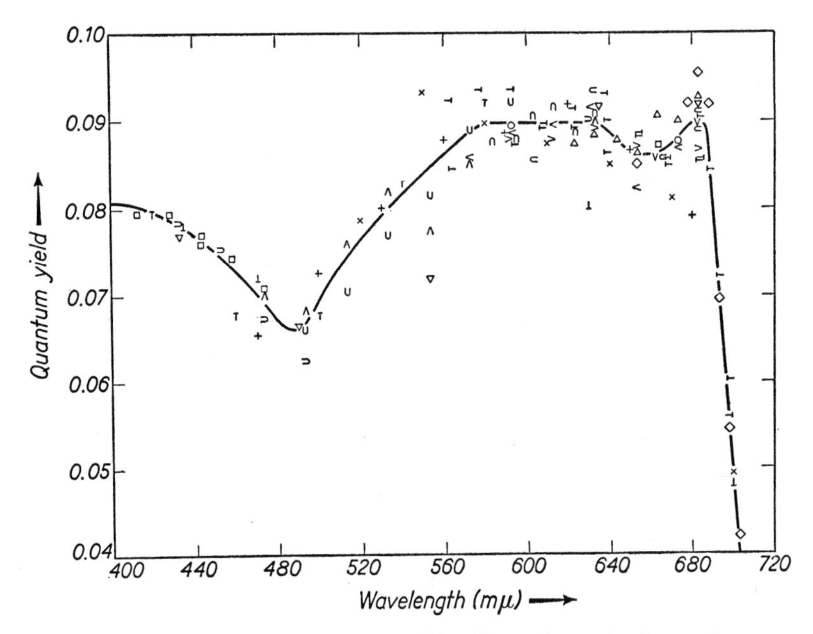

FIG. 42. Efficiency of light absorbed by *Chlorella* sp. determined over the range of the visible spectrum. Emerson and Lewis (137).

energy content. An exception we shall deal with later is the smallest quanta, barely absorbed, at the long wavelength limit of the absorption spectrum of chlorophyll in algae (138). We expect, therefore, that the efficiency of each quantum will remain constant throughout the chlorophyll absorption spectrum. Emerson and Lewis (137) did careful comparative measurements and found that this is indeed the case. Looking at Fig. 42 we see, however, that there is an appreciable loss of efficiency in blue and green light. This is the region where the carotenoids absorb light strongly, while the green chlorophyll absorbs green light least. The carotenoids take up most of the light entering the cell and leave little for the chlorophyll. Yet calculations showed that not all the light absorbed by the carotenoids could have been lost (cf. 564). This result proves two things: that unless we work in a region where only one pigment, e.g., chlorophyll, absorbs, the photochemistry becomes difficult to evaluate and, second, that in these algae the carotenoids are either a mixture of efficient and inefficient sensitizers or that all carotenoids give a low yield when they function as accessory photosynthetic pigments (see Table III).

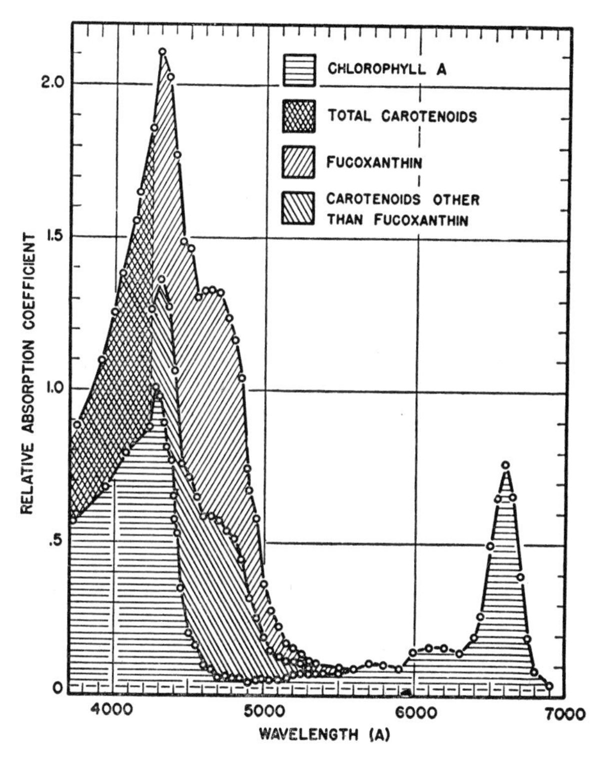

FIG. 43. Absorption due to different pigments in diatoms. Acetone extracts from *Nitzschia closterium*. Top curve: all pigments. Middle curve: chlorophyll a and carotenes, or fucoxanthin, respectively. Lowest curve: chlorophyll a (113).

Brown marine algae and diatoms seem to grow quite well in light of a color that is mainly absorbed by the yellow and brown pigments (Fig. 43). Engelmann in 1884 and Montford in 1934 therefore insisted that nonchlorophyllous pigments must contribute to photosynthesis. Since Montford's rather qualitative work the question has been thoroughly investigated in various laboratories (46, 113, 136, 373, 505). To determine how the absorbed light is distributed among plant pigments is a difficult research problem in itself. A complication is that a mixture of all the extracted pigments has a color that differs from that of the intact cell. Each of the pigments suffers a spectral shift when liberated from its binding site in the cell. And the degree of change is not the same for each pigment. There are indications that a fraction of the carotene originally bound to protein may change its color drastically, the absorption peak going from 550 mμ *in vivo* to 450 mμ *in vitro*. Thus, this substance is red inside the cell and yellow when dissolved in organic solvents.

With the exception of chlorophyll a, the other chloroplast pigments (including chlorophyll b) are active only as sensitizers, as accessory pigments (see Section VI,F). The energy absorbed by all of them is transferred to chlorophyll a, and it depends on the degree of "coupling" whether the final quantum yield is good or not. The transfer is nearly 100% efficient for chlorophyll b, less so but in varying degrees for the other pigments, and it depends also on the species of plant investigated. All this explains the apparent deviation from the rule that an absorbed light quantum which causes the excitation of chlorophyll a should produce exactly the same effect regardless of its color (energy content) (114, 115, 188).

The same experiments were repeated with the photoreducing purple bacteria. Absorption spectra, fluorescence, action spectra, analysis of pigment content—all gave results of the kind reported above and therefore support the same conclusion. In some botany text books there are still statements to the effect that chlorophyll absorbs mainly in the red and that, consequently, red light is necessary for photosynthesis. Nothing could be more erroneous (245, 508, 509).

B. Inactive Chlorophyll in Growing Cells

In most green, brown, and blue algae, the peak of chlorophyll absorption coincides very neatly with a corresponding peak of the action spectrum. In 1950, while studying several species of vigorously photosynthesizing red algae (*Porphyra* spp.), Haxo and Blinks discovered that this peak in its action spectrum was conspicuously missing, while the absorption peak for chlorophyll was present as usual (see Fig. 44). This meant that light absorbed directly by chlorophyll was relatively less effective than light absorbed by phycoerythrin and the other pigments (247). Fluorescence studies (see below) showed again that the light energy absorbed by the accessory pigments was transferred to chlorophyll a, because the latter was responsible for the red fluorescence.

A chlorophyll-independent photochemical system therefore is *not* the cause of the inefficiency of directly excited chlorophyll in red marine algae. Several explanations are presently under consideration

(69, 183). Any part of the pigment system which is inactive reduces the photochemical efficiency. *A priori* one cannot say that inactive fractions of an otherwise active pigment do not exist in growing cells. The case of the red algae is, however, the only one known where the fraction of "inactive" chlorophyll must be large.

Some Russian scientists pointed out that a change between monomolecular and aggregated chlorophyll, which they believe they have observed, may account for such shifts between active and inactive chlorophyll (558). Blinks and Haxo showed that the proportion of inactive chlorophyll may change according to the ways the algae are

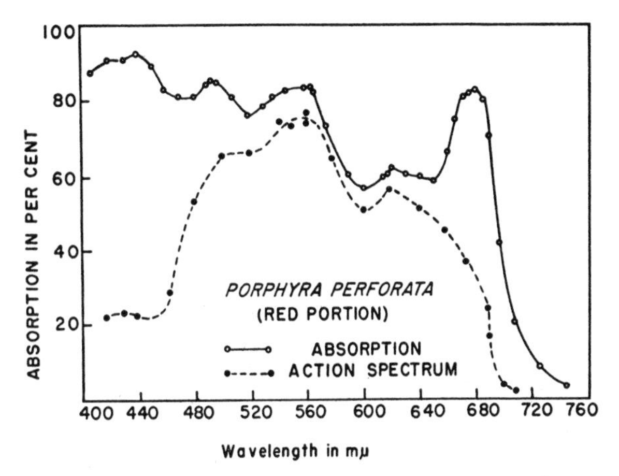

FIG. 44. Absorption spectrum and action spectrum in a red alga (*Porphyra perforata*). The greater part of the light absorbed by chlorophyll is not used for photosynthesis. From Haxo and Blinks (cf. 46).

grown. The most interesting feature of these experiments is that the color of the light is important for adaptation. In algae left to photosynthesize in red light, the yield due to chlorophyll increases, but the algae also become definitely greener. Under the name "chromatic adaptation," similar phenomena have from time to time been described in the literature (436). (For the most recent studies, see 57a, 246a, 624.)

We know that the transformation of chlorophyll from protochlorophyll proceeds in steps, and the greening of a plant precedes noticeably its capacity for photosynthesis (474, 475). Thus, a proper association of the pigment with protein may be necessary; this in the red algae has not gone to completion (321). The theory of the photosynthetic unit (Section VII,B) conceives that only a small fraction of the absorbing chlorophyll is truly chemically active. Thus, it may not be contradictory that a high percentage of chlorophyll is inactive in cells which, like the red algae, assimilate carbon dioxide efficiently with the aid of accessory pigments.

Emerson and Lewis (137) in their studies of quantum yields at different spectral regions observed long ago (1943) that at the very end of the chlorophyll absorption, where it rapidly decreases toward the infrared, the quantum yield declines faster than expected. Here light is definitely absorbed by the cells, yet produces little photosynthesis. Duysens (115) found that the same limitation holds for light emission. The smallest quanta still absorbed by chlorophyll a do not give rise to the usual fluorescence. Recently, Emerson *et al.*, observed that the light between λ 680 and λ 700 mμ, which by itself is so ineffective, is not lost for synthetic reactions provided that it is supplemented with light of some shorter wavelengths [not necessarily blue, red light at λ 644 mμ will do it (138, 142)]. Whether this has any relation to the observations in red algae, mentioned above, remains to be seen. In case the light with the larger quanta is absorbed by some pigment other than chlorophyll a, let us say chlorophyll d or phycoerythrin or phycocyanin, we may speak of the "cooperation" of two pigments. Such cooperation can, however, be interpreted in at least two different ways: either on the basis of the different chemical actions induced by the respective pigments, or, more simply, by making a more precise distinction between the excitation levels reached with small quanta in deep red light and the normal first singlet of chlorophyll a, which requires somewhat larger quanta. If such a physical explanation is the correct one, it would mean that photosynthesis does not proceed as long as only low-level triplet states are excited by light. They must be supplemented by excited singlet-state energy (183).

C. Specific Reactions of β-Carotene

For a long time no cases were known of plants which did not contain carotene but yet were capable of assimilating carbon dioxide photochemically. Consequently, it was generally assumed that carotene played some role in photosynthesis, other than that of an occasional light-absorbing accessory pigment. Furthermore, in spectral regions where carotene absorbs most strongly, abnormal light effects were seen which could not be attributed to the action of chlorophyll. For instance, Emerson and Lewis found that blue-green light of the wavelength λ 480 mμ produced a transient increase in respiration which was different from that due to any accumulation of normal photoproducts (137). There is the possibility that not carotenes but flavins (though they are present only in very small amounts and account for only a small fraction of the total light absorbed) may exert some photochemical action by way of a catalytic chain reaction which is responsible for a temporary speed-up of oxygen consumption.

In 1957 Stanier *et al.* encountered a new strain of purple bacteria which is devoid of the typical carotenes. This strain grew very well, as purple bacteria do, by means of photoreduction under anaerobic conditions. The same was true for *Rhodospirillum rubrum* when grown carotene-poor in the presence of diphenylamine. Diphenylamine is a specific inhibitor for cellular synthesis of carotenoids. Figure 18 is a comparison of the absorption spectra of *Rhodospirillum rubrum* grown normally and with diphenylamine present. This inhibition is reversible, and rapid synthesis of carotenoids takes place in the dark when the diphenylamine-treated cells are washed and resuspended in buffer (see Fig. 17). The two strains of bacteria—the genetically carotenoid-free one, and the one grown in the presence of diphenylamine—belong to those that can also live aerobically. But the purple bacteria, without the normal complement of carotenoids, had become sensitive to oxygen in the light. While they continue to grow in the light, under anaerobic conditions, illumination in the presence of oxygen leads to bleaching, prevents the resynthesis of the missing carotenes, and brings about the destruction of the bacterial chlorophyll.

One of the important properties of any photosynthetic system must be a certain resistance against photooxidation in the presence of oxygen. Stanier and co-workers believe, therefore, that the main role of carotenoids does not so much concern the reduction of carbon dioxide, but the *protection of the chlorophyll mechanism against free oxygen* (98, 245). Photochemists have long been familiar with sensitized autooxidations, and with the effect of small additions of substances, as antioxidants, which counteract oxidation and thus protect the oxidizable compounds. The idea of carotenes as antioxidants implies that they react preferentially with activated oxygen. Perhaps their role as protective agents is not the sole function of the carotenoids. It is clear in view of Stanier's experiments, that the carotenoids do not play a direct part in the photochemistry proper. This is confirmed by the fact that photophosphorylation also proceeds normally in fragments from carotene-free *Chromatium* sp. (see Section XIII).

D. Observing the Primary Process *in Vivo*

Studies on action spectra reveal which pigments take part in photosynthesis, but they do not tell exactly what happens in or near the molecule after a light quantum has been absorbed inside the chloroplast. The physics and chemistry of illuminated pigments in nonliving systems provide the basic knowledge of the reactions to be expected in the living cell (see Section IV), but proof can come only from the direct investigation of the primary process.

There are four ways open to investigate the events which follow the light excitation of the pigments associated with the green plastids. One is to look for color changes by recording the appearance or disappearance of absorption bands in the spectra of the light-absorbing pigments and of oxidoreduction catalysts, such as coenzymes, flavins, and cytochromes; this is a method familiar to every biologist.

The second is to analyze the intensity changes, as well as the color, of the light re-emitted from illuminated living cells—in other words, to study fluorescence (cf. 237).

The third method is rather recent. Arnold and Strehler discovered an extremely faint light production by green plants, which persists (in contrast to fluorescence) for a comparatively long time in the dark, after a period of illumination. The intensity of the light produced by plants in the dark is about one-millionth of that which induces photosynthesis. This luminescence, or "afterglow," is measurable only with very sensitive "quantum counters," but once the machine has been assembled the luminescence can be studied in relation to the metabolism of the cell, just like the fluorescence or the absorption spectra (10, 497, 520).

The fourth method is to search for loose electrons or free radicals by means of electromagnetic resonance. Only recently has this become a research tool in photosynthesis. In principle this method is well understood. The task here (just as in the three methods mentioned above) is to correlate unequivocally the recorded signals with certain known or assumed events in the chloroplasts (84, 447, 477). Since photochemical effects of any kind will always produce radicals or ionizations (402), a specific success of this approach is still to be demonstrated (529–531).

While a hand spectroscope was sufficient to enable Keilin to detect the cytochromes in yeast, the physical aids needed to discover and register color changes in the working photosynthetic pigments of plants are quite formidable, and years of construction work requiring extensive knowledge in physics usually precede the observation and publication of new data concerning the "reversible bleaching" of chlorophyll or of other pigments in the course of photosynthesis.

1. Color Changes in Photosynthesizing Cells or Chloroplasts

Attempts to see the chlorophyll at work, as it were, by watching for a change of color under conditions of rapid photosynthesis, probably go back several decades. From experiments *in vitro* it is known that a reversible bleaching of dyestuffs occurs in the course of photosensitized chemical reactions (335, 336, 345, 436). A bleaching of chlorophyll in the light by typical reducing agents like ascorbic acid is mentioned above (320).

The principle of the method is this: With very weak light, too low in intensity, supposedly, to disarrange the metabolism obtaining in the dark while the cells are respiring or fermenting, the transmission either of one special spectral region or of the entire spectrum of the cell from ultraviolet to the infrared is recorded. Then these cells are irradiated strongly with either white, or monochromatic light; this treatment ("bleaching") may produce measurable changes in the "dark" transmission spectrum. The difficulties of excluding the "bleaching" or "actinic" light from interfering with the measuring light are overcome, either by means of complementary light filters and monochromators or by the device of "bleaching" with extremely short light flashes and then observing the result in the pauses between the flashes. In the first case, one may bleach, for instance, with blue light and observe its effect on the red chlorophyll band, or bleach with red light and follow the changes which occur as a consequence of this treatment at a shorter wavelength. The intermittent or "flash" illumination method gives greater freedom in the choice of the color of the bleaching and measuring light, but it requires an even more elaborate apparatus.

Illuminated cells not only absorb, but also emit, light instantly (fluorescence) and afterward in the dark (delayed light emission). It is not always easy to deal with these additional complications. Mostly, the apparatus used to observe changes in absorption can be modified to measure also the intensities and spectra of the light emitted by living cells. Figures 45–47 below are examples of the results obtained by these optical methods.

The method which records changes during continuous illumination permits one to use lower intensities and therefore is more within the physiological range. Extremely bright flashes may, by the excess of light energy not used for photosynthesis, produce bleaching effects which do not occur normally (see Section V). Working with continuous illumination should certainly give a truer picture of the change from the dark steady state into the light steady state for all pigments involved in, or affected by, the photosynthetic reaction. The flash method has already revealed that the reversal in the dark of some of the reactions produced by light is very fast. Thus there will always be some difference between the results obtained by these two experimental approaches. On the other hand, the moments of transition from light to darkness and vice versa—the induction period and the after effects—can be of special interest, and for these kinds of observations the flash method is very useful.

Having an instrument to record spectral changes is, in itself, not sufficient to determine what is going on in the cell. The spectral meas-

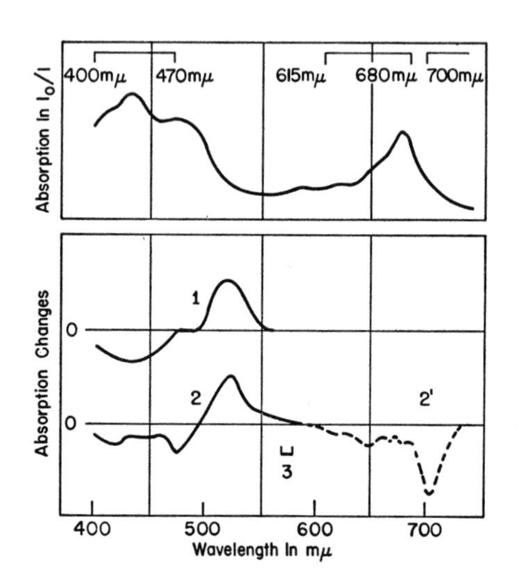

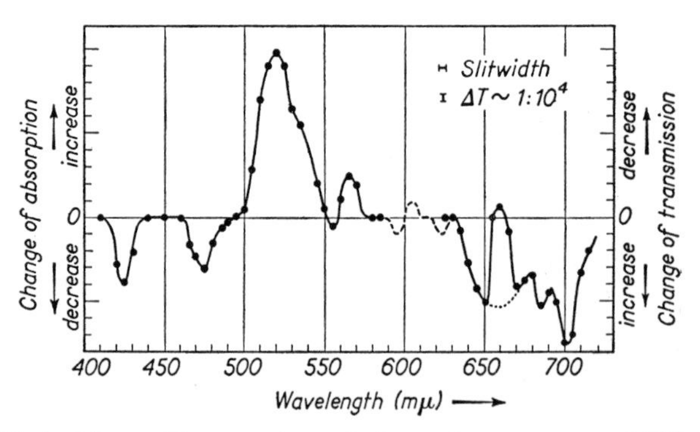

FIG. 45. (Top) Schematic comparison of absorption spectrum of *Chlorella* sp. and location of changes induced by short, strong flashes of red light. Upper curve: normal absorption spectrum. Lower curve: Absorption changes increase (upward) or decrease (downward) about 0.1% of original absorption shown above. From Witt, in press.

FIG. 46. (Bottom) Changes of absorption induced by strong light flashes in *Scenedesmus* sp. Average of four experiments. Flashtime, 0.5 msec; dark time, 60 msec; observation time, 4 msec. From Kok (319).

urements ought to be combined with simultaneous or corresponding measurements of metabolic changes. What we have called changes in absorption are, of course, noted as the differences between the dark and light conditions. If these are plotted for all the spectral regions studied one obtains the so-called difference spectra, and the task is now to correlate the peaks and valleys of such difference spectra with the known or expected behavior of the pigments present in the cells. (For a critique of methods and results, see 118, 446, 476.)

Reversible changes in the absorption spectrum of green algae have been recorded (and confirmed) by various authors (88, 89, 100, 319, 496, 498, 611) at the following wavelengths: λ 420, 480, 520, 555, 650–680, and 705 mμ. The direction of the change in optical density varies

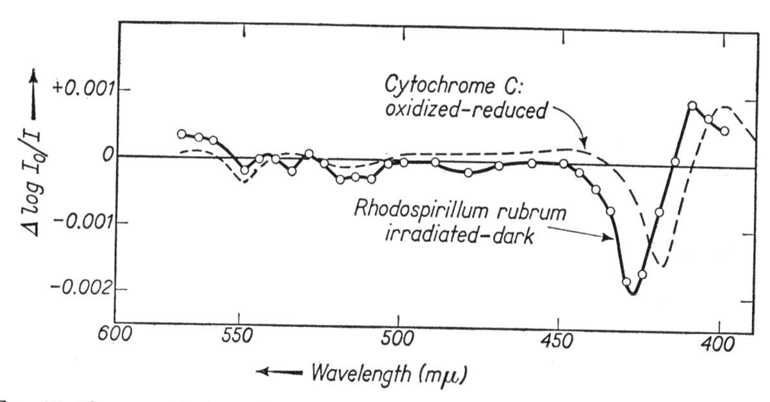

FIG. 47. Changes of absorption at λ 425 mμ induced by irradiation of *Rhodospirillum rubrum*. Effect is similar to the difference in absorption between oxidized and reduced cytochrome c. From Duysens (118).

with the method of observation. The (most conspicuous) change at λ 520 mμ is positive when seen during illumination (Kok) and negative a moment afterward in the dark (Strehler). The same inversion holds true for the changes at 480 and 650 mμ which are negative in direct illumination (bleaching) and positive in the Strehler method, where a stream of algae is strongly illuminated before it passes measuring light beams. Figures 45 and 46 show such difference spectra.

A special study of the kinetics of the appearance and disappearance of these spectral changes (mainly at λ 515 mμ and 475 mμ) was made by Witt (611–614). Employing extremely short, strong light flashes, he was able to distinguish three phases in living *Chlorella*.

The first photochemical part is faster than 3×10^{-5} seconds. A subsequent, light-induced change continues in the same direction if the light flash is made to last longer; this other phase does not occur in chloroplasts. In the dark the spectral changes are reversed in about 0.01 second (see Figs. 48 and 49). The second photophase and the recovery in the dark are temperature-dependent reactions. The initial

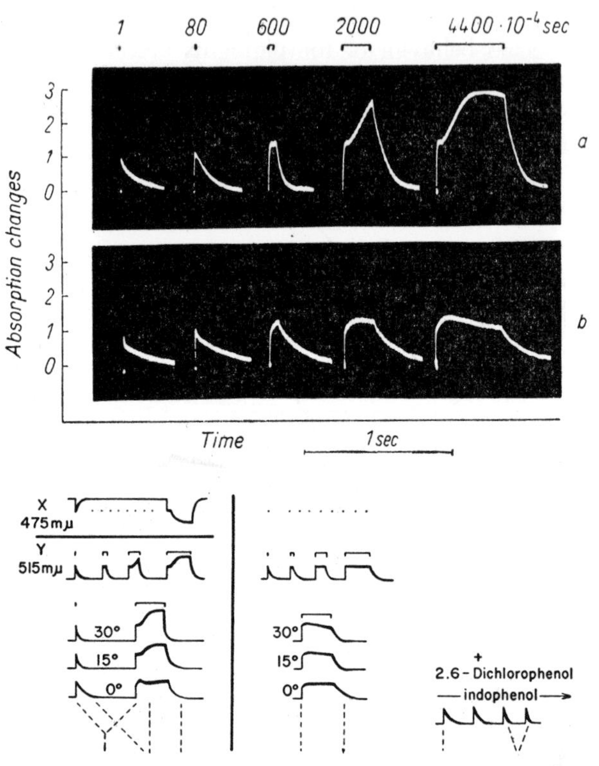

FIG. 48. (Top) Absorption changes at λ 515 mμ, (a), in *Chlorella* sp. cells, (b), in spinach (*Spinacia oleracea*) chloroplasts induced by intense light flashes lasting between 10^{-4} seconds and 1 second. Oscilloscope recording. From Witt (611, 612).

FIG. 49. (Bottom) Schematic summary of results obtained by Witt's method. *Chlorella* sp. cells, left; spinach chloroplasts, right. Flashes lasting longer than 5×10^{-4} seconds evoke an additional slow spectral change in the same direction in intact cells, not in chloroplasts. This secondary rise is temperature sensitive, as is the back reaction in the dark after the flash. 2,6-Dichlorophenolindophenol greatly accelerates the back reaction in chloroplasts, while quinone does not. From Witt *et al.* (611, 614).

fast spectral change is not. The magnitude of the effect observed is hardly more than a tenth of a per cent (1/1000) of the total absorption.

The extremely rapid spectral changes must be attributed to the primary excitation process. All others might be induced chemically as a consequence of the photoreaction. Besides the chlorophylls and the various accessory pigments, there are metabolic catalysts such as cytochromes, flavins, and pyridine nucleotides in the cell which are known to change color according to their oxidation-reduction level (89, 116, 117). The task is to distinguish between direct and indirect spectral changes (88, 498).

The changes in the spectra of purple bacteria (87) due to illumination in the infrared and recorded for the visible regions around λ 420, 430, 530, and 560 mμ are being attributed, at least in part, to the oxidation or reduction of cytochromes, of which purple bacteria contain a considerable amount (115, 118, 400) (see Section III). If typical

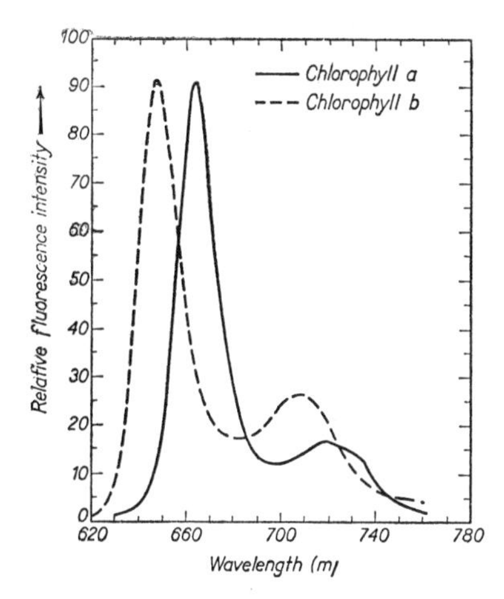

FIG. 50. Fluorescence spectra of chlorophylls a and b.

cytochrome absorption bands change in intensity with aerobic or anaerobic conditions and respond relatively slowly to illumination, the probability is certainly high that the observed changes are indirect (115, 352a).

2. *Fluorescence of Chloroplast Pigments in Vivo*

The fluorescence of leaves was discovered by Stokes a hundred years ago and has been mentioned or studied more often with the improvement of the methods for observing and measuring weak radiation excited by a much brighter incident light. Figure 50 shows the spectral distribution of the fluorescent light emitted by the two chlorophylls.

Measuring fluorescence is difficult not only for the more trivial reason that adequate light filters have to be used to separate the reflected and scattered rays of the incident radiation from the emitted one but mainly because of the corrections to be applied for the loss by scattering and reabsorption of the emitted light inside the cells themselves. A measurement of the fluorescence yield is important in order to calculate the lifetime of the first excited singlet state under the conditions of active photosynthesis. This value tells us the time available for an energy transfer from the excited molecule to other pigment molecules within the chlorophyll complex. The newest measurements by Latimer (331) set the yield at about 2.7%, which is about one order of magnitude higher than was first reported. By comparison, it should be mentioned that the fluorescence yield in dilute solutions of other pigments

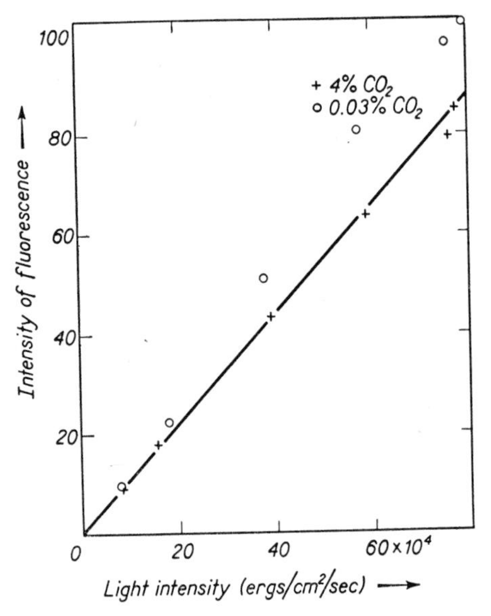

FIG. 51. Intensity of fluorescence versus incident light for wheat (*Triticum* sp.) at 4% and at 0.03% carbon dioxide. From Wassink *et al.* (582).

(like fluorescein), can reach 90% of the light absorbed, and that chlorophyll a dissolved in ethyl ether yields about 30%. Under the simpler conditions of pure solutions, the fluorescence intensity is strictly in proportion to the incident radiation. This is not true for the metabolizing living plant because the physical properties in the neighborhood of the chlorophyll system change with the nature and concentration of the photoproducts. This is the reason why different stages of the process of photosynthesis have an influence upon the amount of light which is re-emitted (67, 580) (see Figs. 51 and 52).

Systematic studies of chlorophyll fluorescence and of the other pigments associated with the green plastids began with Kautsky's discovery in 1928 of a startling induction effect (300–302). Looking through a red filter, he saw that the fluorescence of a green leaf suddenly exposed to blue light rose very rapidly to a maximum, and then slowly decayed in the course of a minute or two to a steady value. The course of this change is shown in Fig. 53. For a simple demonstration

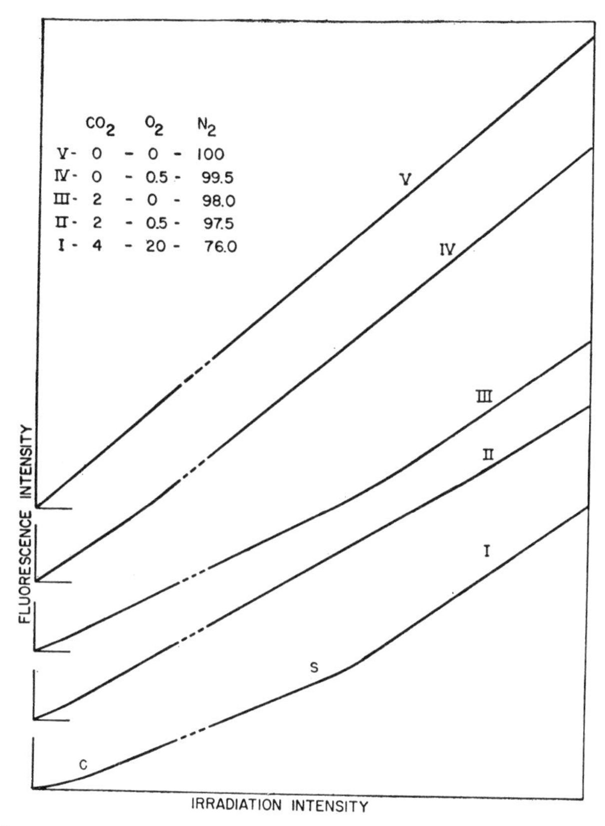

FIG. 52. Fluorescence intensity as function of irradiation intensity in *Scenedesmus* sp. The yield remains constant in pure nitrogen. It increases at the compensation point, *C*, and at saturation, *S*, when the algae are photosynthesizing in air. After Brugger (67).

it is even better to shade half of the leaf in the beginning and to remove the cover when the fluorescence of the first half has declined. The difference in intensity of the emitted light is very striking. Since this first observation, the literature on fluorescence in living plants has become quite extensive; it is fairly easy to collect a great number of variations on the theme of fluorescence fluctuations once an automatic self-recording machine has been installed (67, 90, 114, 164, 188, 189,

232, 312, 332a, 580, 582, 587). Much more difficult is the task of interpreting them uniformly and usefully (171, 181, 182, 298).

Among the phenomena which offer a chance to observe events connected with the primary process, the course of fluorescence was the first to be studied thoroughly. The other two—absorption and production of light—came later because they require much more sensitive instruments utilizing electronic amplifiers.

As a rule only those dyes are considered capable of some photochemical activity which can be shown to be fluorescent. Chlorophyll *in vitro* has of course been long known to be one of them. What gave studies of fluorescence in plants their importance was the convincing demonstration of how closely metabolic transients induced by illuminating or

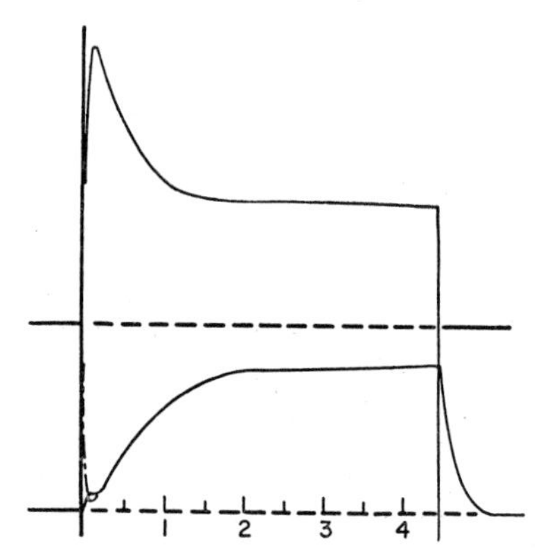

FIG. 53. Induction behavior of wheat (*Triticum* sp.) in 0.03% CO_2 in N_2. Ordinates: rate of CO_2-uptake [lower] and intensity of fluorescence [upper] in relative units; abscissas: time of illumination in minutes. From McAlister and Myers (361a).

darkening the plants are paralleled by fluctuations in the intensity of the fluorescence emitted (188, 361). Fluorescence yield under steady-state conditions is constant at all light intensities when the metabolism is at a minimum, i.e., in pure nitrogen. It shows the greatest changes as a function of light intensity when the plants are photosynthesizing in air containing carbon dioxide.

Plant physiologists and biochemists are, however, generally unaware that this method has given definite and fundamental insights into the mechanism of energy conversion. The basic discoveries may be summarized as follows:

1. Fluctuations of the intensity of fluorescence in plants or chloroplasts disclosed that the essential chemical reactions occur inside or near the chlorophyll complex. The fluorescence yield was seen to depend on the type of chemical transformations proceeding at that mo-

ment. This is true even for a reaction as far removed from the primary process as the fixation of carbon dioxide (see Figs. 51–54).

2. These same observations prove that most of the photochemistry in living chloroplasts starts with the triplet metastable state. In these cases an internal conversion from the singlet state to the latter thus precedes the first chemical step (see Section IV).

3. The spectral analysis of fluorescence in photosynthesizing cells revealed that the energy of light which is effectively absorbed by other chloroplast pigments is not utilized directly but is transferred to chlorophyll a and that this kind of cooperation between photoactive pigments prevails in all species studied, including anaerobic purple bacteria whose fluorescence lies in the infrared.

The technique employed to prove this last point was the following: The algae were illuminated with light which was primarily absorbed by some pigment other than chlorophyll (compare Figs. 41–44). The resulting fluorescent light was analyzed spectroscopically. It was seen that light not absorbed by chlorophyll itself nevertheless caused a typical red chlorophyll fluorescence instead of that of the light absorbing pigment (115). A transfer of energy from other classes of pigments to the chlorophyll is the only possible explanation. This can happen *in vitro*, for instance, between chlorophylls a and b, and it has been seen in pure solutions. It is now generally assumed, therefore, that chlorophyll a acts as the final acceptor for light energy absorbed in a mixture of photoactive pigments. By the same token, the transfer of the excitation energy from one pigment to the other occurs always in the direction of the pigment absorbing smaller quanta—that is, more in the red region of the spectrum (see Table III, Section III). The presence of just a small quantity of a pigment capable of taking away excitation energy from chlorophyll a may interfere harmfully with the efficiency of photosynthesis by draining useful energy into channels where it can be lost simply as heat. At this moment, this is, however, only an assumption which may serve to explain, for instance, the occurrence of "inactive" chlorophyll in certain red algae mentioned above (188a).

One of the earliest among the striking observations concerning fluorescence in algae has been the influence of anaerobic conditions. As Fig. 116 in Section XV shows, the decay of fluorescence after the initial rise at the start of illumination is much slower in the absence of air. This correlates with the delay of photosynthesis after anaerobiosis in the dark seen in those plants which, like *Chlorella*, are particularly sensitive to a lack of oxygen. Because similar effects on the time course of fluorescence can be obtained by adding inhibitors of the narcotic type (meaning inhibitors which block certain reactions by adsorption on catalytic protein surfaces), it seemed plausible that an anaerobic metabolism might give rise to such unspecific inhibitors. This matter, however, is not yet settled because all inhibitors which interfere specifically with the evolution of oxygen act as if they blocked the transfer of energy at the chlorophyll, though it is known that in the presence of these inhibitors the carbon dioxide reduction may continue by way of photoreduction (Fig. 58).

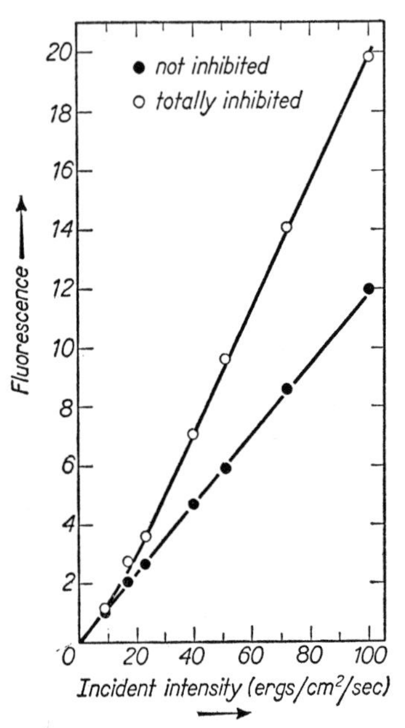

FIG. 54. Steady-state fluorescence in normal, photosynthesizing *Chlorella* sp. and in those completely poisoned by cyanide. From Wassink *et al.* (580).

One great difficulty in trying to use fluorescence measurements for the interpretation of the photochemical process is the fact that there is only a qualitative parallelism (or the inverse relation) between the intensity of light emission and the rate of any other cellular activity chosen as reference. The rate of photosynthesis may be inhibited nearly 100% by the addition of large amounts of cyanide, for instance. The corresponding increase in the intensity of fluorescence amounts at best to twice the value measured in the unpoisoned cells (compare Fig. 54).

The changes in fluorescence are small while the changes in the rate of photosynthesis are big. This must mean that the energy used in photosynthesis cannot be derived entirely from the excited singlet state and that an extensive internal conversion from the singlet to the triplet state happens prior to any specific chemical action. If on the other hand the chemical transformations resulted entirely from the triplet state, there should be no change of fluorescence at all. The fluorescence should be not only small but constant. In fact, however, the small yield of fluorescence doubles when normal photosynthesis becomes completely inhibited. The yield of fluorescence is a measure of the lifetime of the singlet state. If during photosynthesis the fluorescence yield is cut in half, it means that about 50% of the excited molecules must be quenched by direct photochemical action in competition with both fluorescence and transition to the metastable state (compare Fig. 21, Section IV).

According to Franck this proves that in photosynthesis the singlet state is used to about the same extent as the triplet state. We should, therefore, consider the primary act as a cooperation between singlet excited and triplet excited state energies (180–183).

A disturbing note is, however, the fact that all attempts to demonstrate the existence of the triplet state in the living cell by direct observation of spectral changes have so far failed (446).

Besides the two chlorophylls, there are at least three other classes of substances present in the cell or even in the chloroplast which are capable of a strong fluorescence: the pyridine nucleotides, the flavins, and the pteridines (237). Shifts in the absolute concentration of their reduced or of their oxidized forms should, theoretically, be reflected in the yields of the re-emitted specific fluorescence. In order to link these changes firmly to the photochemical activity by direct observation it is necessary to operate with two light sources simultaneously—one that excites the fluorescence of the substance studied but causes no photosynthetic response in the plant, and another which is not absorbed by any other pigment than chlorophyll and which serves to induce photosynthesis. The photocell, finally, should register only the intensities of the radiation emitted specifically by one type of molecule. No wonder that the first attempts to translate this ingenious scheme into practice did not give unequivocal answers.

3. *Light Production by Green Plants*

10^{-8} seconds after irradiation ceases, the chlorophyll molecules stop sending out fluorescent light. In other words, fluorescence can be observed practically only while the plastids are in the light. In 1951 Strehler and Arnold discovered that green plants continue to emit the same kind of red radiation—with an emission spectrum identical to that of the first excited singlet state of chlorophyll—for many minutes or even hours in the dark after the end of a light period (Fig. 55). Therefore, it is permissible to speak of a production of light (491, 492). This luminescence escaped earlier detection because the intensity of the emitted light is at best one-thousandth of the intensity of fluorescence and decays in the course of time.

The discovery that, if we had eyes as sensitive as electronic photomultipliers, we would see the plant world glow in deep red light after sundown is more than an amusing oddity. It is important for two reasons. First: Evidently the chlorophyll in the chloroplast is so arranged as to retain (or be close to some source of) energy for a very long time after energy has been received by light absorption. Second:

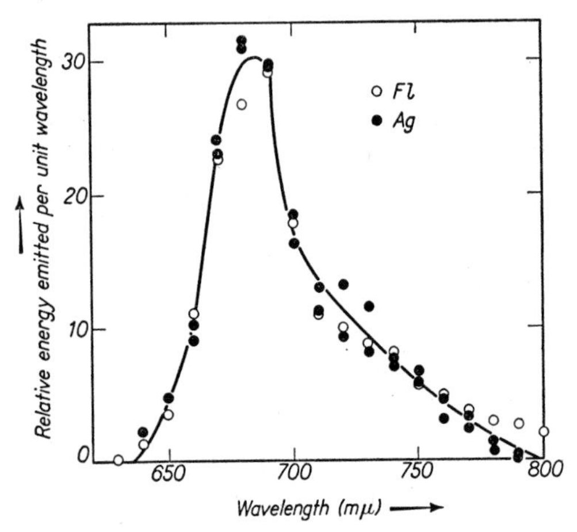

FIG. 55. Identical spectral distribution of fluorescence (*Fl*) and of afterglow (*Ag*) (= delayed light emission, chemiluminescence). According to Arnold *et al.* (7).

The intensity of the light emission which is so much lower than fluorescence reflects nevertheless, just like the latter, the photochemical events in the course of photosynthesis. Both facts together mean that whatever condition of the chlorophyll in the plastid is responsible for the delayed light emission must also be the cause of the efficient role of chlorophyll in photosynthesis. Therefore we are not permitted to dismiss the light emission on account of its faintness as a side reaction of some small otherwise inactive fraction of the pigment not connected with photosynthesis (10, 21, 83, 182, 277, 312, 497, 498).

It is impossible to study the luminescence while the plants are illuminated, since the much stronger fluorescence has exactly the same spectral characteristics (Fig. 55). The nearest approach to measuring the luminescence in a steady state in the light instead of following its decay afterward in the dark is a phosphoroscopic device. The plant material is exposed continuously to light flashes with interposed dark periods so short (milliseconds) that the integrated effect is that of steady illumination. The light emission is recorded during the dark periods between the flashes, after a dark pause of 10^{-8} seconds. The fluorescence has thus time to disappear completely (68, 182, 520).

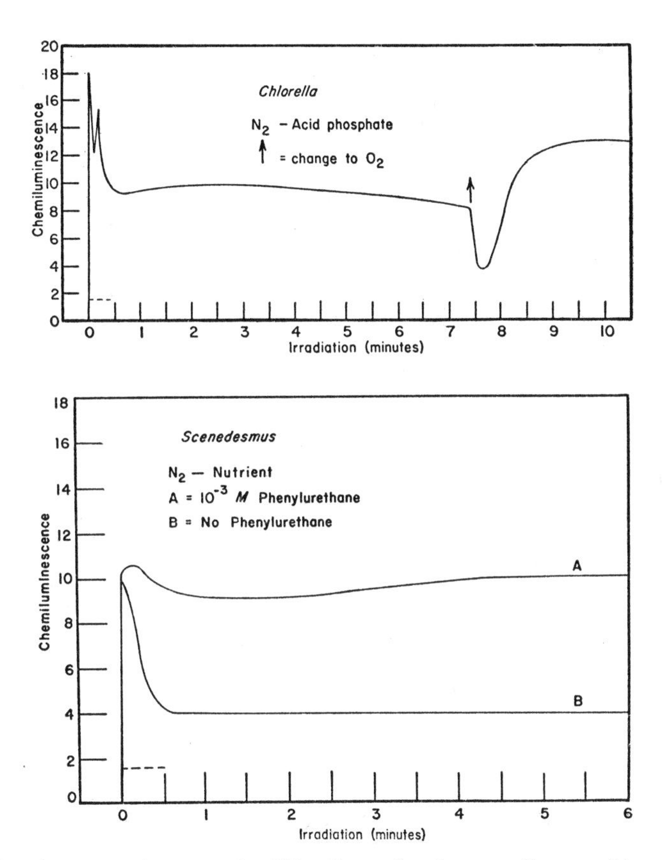

FIG. 56. (Top) Luminescence in *Chlorella* sp. in nitrogen. Change of intensity due to adding oxygen (68, 69).

FIG. 57. (Bottom) Luminescence in *Scenedesmus* sp. in absence and presence of phenylurethane (68, 69).

Figures 56 and 57 are examples of how oxygen or phenylurethane influence the intensity of luminescence emitted by a suspension of algae.

Experiments with *Synechococcus cedrorum, Anacystis nidulans* (blue-green alga), *Porphyridium cruentum* (red alga), and *Rhodospirillum rubrum* (purple bacterium) proved the universality of the phenomenon of delayed light emission. These studies confirmed the fact of energy transfer from accessory light-absorbing pigments to chlorophyll, as well as the discrepancy in some blue-green and red algae between chlorophyll absorption and chlorophyll activity (67, 115, 247, 446).

4. Chloroplast Luminescence

The discovery of light emission by living plants was initiated by studies with isolated chloroplasts which exhibited this characteristic (491)—a fact not too surprising, since chloroplasts perform so many of the reactions which formerly could be seen only in intact cells. The explanation for the luminescence was first sought in certain back reactions among those early photochemical intermediates which could, with the aid of some additional thermal energy, excite the chlorophyll and cause it to re-emit light in its typical red fluorescence band. The difficulty with this explanation was the long lifetime which had to be assigned to the energy-rich intermediates. Later, however, it was found that chloroplasts may be dried and denatured in such a way that they lose any kind of activity resembling their reactions in the plant and yet retain the capacity to re-emit light in the dark for a long time after the period of illumination.

The experiment consists of painting a metal disk green with a chloroplast paste, letting the chloroplasts dry at normal temperatures, and then observing their ability to emit light or to conduct electric current after illumination or during heating (9). The results have been taken as a sign that the purely physical conditions of the solid state of chlorophyll embedded in proteinaceous material are responsible for the effect, and that it should be explained as an excitation of electrons of the kind seen in several types of semiconductors. These observations have given new impetus to research on electron spin resonance in illuminated chloroplast preparations with the idea that they would bring forth a clue to the action of chlorophyll in the living chloroplast. The connection, however, of this phenomenon with photosynthesis still seems tenuous (84, 477; see also *Rev. Modern Phys.* **31**, 1959).

The leading fact remains that luminescence in the plants somehow mirrors the photosynthetic events just as fluorescence does. Figure 58 is a very clear example of such data. The simple device of making algae more and more deficient in manganese leads to a progressive decline in their capacity to evolve oxygen, to an increase in the yield of fluorescence, and to a decrease in the intensity of delayed light emission. All the while, the photochemical reduction of carbon dioxide continues unimpaired (see Section XI).

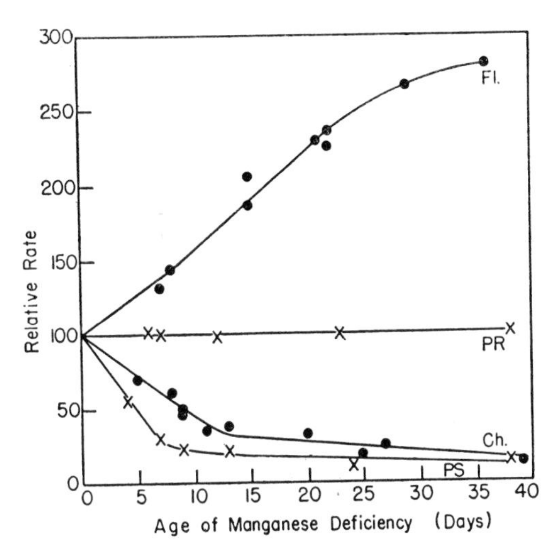

FIG. 58. Influence of increasing manganese deficiency on photosynthesis (*PS*), photoreduction (*PR*), delayed light emission (*Ch*), and fluorescence (*Fl*) under steady-state conditions in *Ankistrodesmus* sp. Experimental conditions: *PS*, Warburg No. 9 buffer, air, 4200 lux; *PR*, phosphate buffer, H_2 + 4% CO_2, 620 lux; *Ch*, air, 13,000 lux; *Fl*, air, 1000 lux. After Kessler *et al.* (312).

VII. Photosynthesis in Flashing Light and the Photosynthetic Unit

A. FLASHING LIGHT

In the section on light saturation, it was stated that the maximum rate of photosynthesis is determined by the rate of turnover of the enzymes in the complete system. In 1932, Emerson and Arnold tested this hypothesis by illuminating algae not continuously, but with light given in pulses or flashes of 10^{-4} seconds' duration (128, 129).

Illumination with light flashes has to be distinguished from intermittent illumination. Both experimental arrangements entail a succession of light and dark periods. A light flash is here defined as a period of illumination so short as to leave the over-all metabolic equilibrium in the cell practically unchanged. Intermittent illumination operates with light periods long enough to start each time a readjustment of the chemical equilibria among pools of intermediate reactants while the light is on (see Section XV). In other words, during a light flash the result or products of absorbed quanta remain uniform. During the light period in intermittent illumination the type of reaction following the primary act begins to shift—let us say from the dark steady-state to the light steady-state condition (220a, Fig. 115).

There is no sharp division between the two types of intermittent light effects, though the ideal flash should be shorter than 10^{-4} seconds. The characteristics of intermittent illumination become dominant at periods lasting longer than 10^{-2} seconds. The dark periods are usually made sufficiently long for the light effects to be reversed completely. With dark intervals which are too short, intermittent illumination soon becomes indistinguishable in its effects from that of continuous illumination having the same integrated light intensity (Fig. 60).

The idea that enzymatic reactions are slow while the primary photochemical process is very fast was beautifully confirmed by measuring the yield of photosynthesis per single light flash while lengthening the dark time interposed between flashes. When flashes of 10^{-4} seconds' duration follow each other too quickly, the light is not fully utilized; the yield per flash is low. By extending the dark period, the yield per flash increases until it levels off and becomes constant when the dark periods last about 0.02 second at normal temperatures (Figs. 59 and 60). At lower temperatures the flashes have to be spaced farther apart in order to reach the same maximum yield per flash; at high temperatures, the dark intervals can be shortened. The maximum yield per flash is itself comparatively insensitive to temperature. The conclusion drawn earlier from the properties exhibited by the light-intensity rate curves in Fig. 24 were thus independently confirmed. Because of their fundamental importance, experiments with light flashes have been repeated often, and the results of Emerson and Arnold have been confirmed and amplified (93, 165, 209, 502).

Complete photosynthesis encompasses several kinds of enzymatic reactions. The saturation rate is determined according to circumstances, by one or another or a combination of rate-limiting processes. One of the first experimental supports of this picture was provided by experiments with flashing light. If one of the enzymatic reactions is slowed down by the effect of a poison, the yield per flash under standard conditions declines, but the dark period between flashes need only be lengthened in order for the yield to go up again. An example is provided by the following experiment.

In the presence of cyanide, the carboxylation becomes the rate-limiting reaction, but given enough time between flashes, the maximum yield per flash stays constant. We know that this is not the only enzymatic system involved in photosynthesis. There is also the complex mechanism for evolving oxygen from water, which is much less susceptible to cyanide poisoning (see Fig. 112). The next question is: To which of these partial systems does the dark period of $\sim 1/100$ of a second, that Emerson and Arnold were measuring, belong? By bundling several flashes together in quick succession and separating these groups

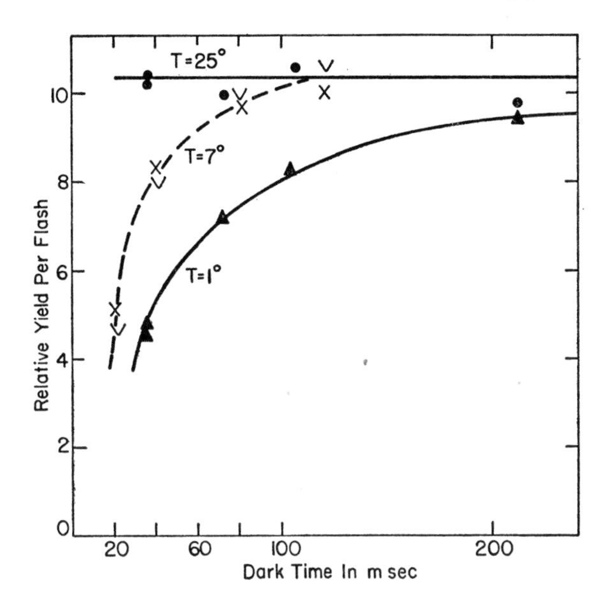

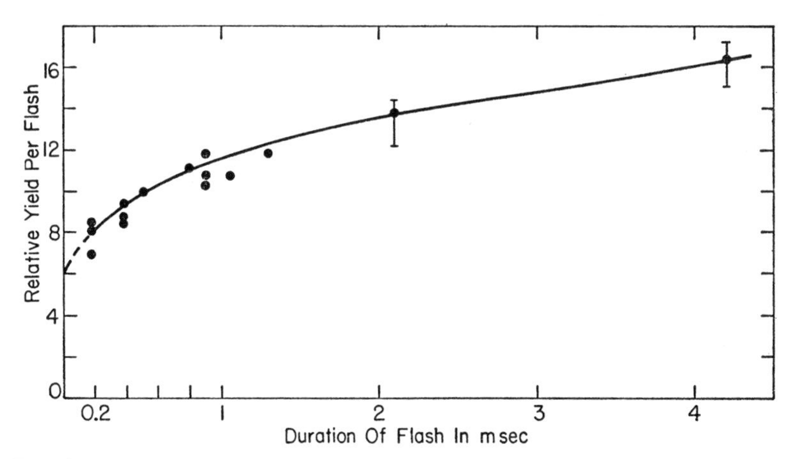

FIG. 59. (Top) Increase of carbon dioxide reduced per flash with increasing length of dark period between flashes. The time required to obtain maximum yield becomes longer with lower temperature. At 25° (●) the "dark reaction" is less than 20 msec; at 7° (×; V) it takes 100 msec; at 1° (▲), over 200 msec. Replotted after Emerson and Arnold (128).

FIG. 60. (Bottom) Relation between maximum yield per saturating flash in *Chlorella* sp. and duration of flashes. Length of dark intervals: 40 msec. Variation of flash time: 0.2–4.0 msec. The curve extrapolates to a finite yield at extremely short flashes which is temperature independent. With longer flashes the yield not only rises, but becomes temperature dependent. From Kok (316a).

of flashes by comparatively long dark pauses, Gaffron and Rieke (209) could show that in cyanide-inhibited cells there is, besides the cyanide-sensitive step, still another dark reaction which requires just $1/100$ of a second to run to completion. This could be seen by varying the length of the dark spaces between flashes inside the small groups. The long pauses between groups allow enough carboxylation products to accumulate, despite the presence of cyanide, to serve as substrate for the photochemistry in a short run of four or six flashes. Since, within each group of flashes, the same rules seem to prevail as in the original flash

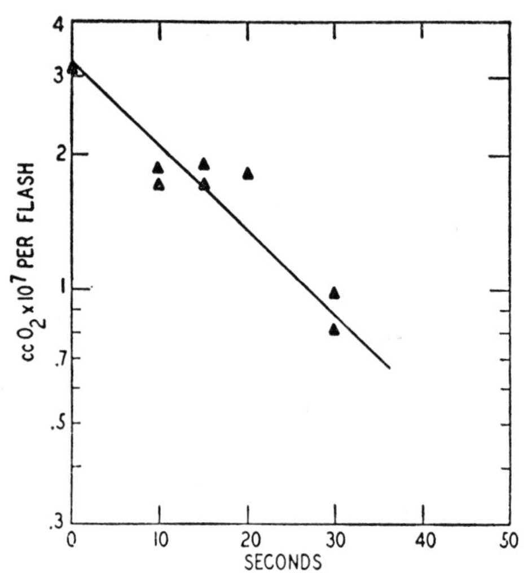

FIG. 61. Decay of the effect of background illumination on oxygen evolution by a single light flash under anaerobic conditions in *Scenedesmus* sp. after the low background light is turned off. No oxygen is evolved by a single flash in complete darkness. A background illumination weaker than is needed for ordinary "compensation" evokes the ability to produce oxygen as the result of a light flash.

experiments with unpoisoned algae, this result means that under optimal conditions the carboxylation cycle does not limit the over-all rate of photosynthesis and that the dark reaction which sets the over-all rate is, therefore, a part of the mechanism concerned with the photolysis of water and the evolution of oxygen. This has been fully confirmed by experiments with chloroplasts in certain Hill reactions. Such chloroplast reactions are insensitive to cyanide, yet in flashing light they still reveal the characteristics of the Emerson-Arnold effect (cf. 436).

A great deal of effort has been applied to the kinetic analysis of flashing light experiments. In view of the now known complexity of the enzymatic system, the rather independent variability of its individual components, and the probability that two types of photoproducts—reduced organic intermediates and energy-rich polyphosphates—are the result of the primary process, it is not too surprising that variations have been found which are difficult to describe exactly with just one set of assumptions.

Methods for detecting very small quantities of oxygen (under anaerobic conditions) have made it possible to study the effects of single, isolated flashes. Thus the anaerobic dark intervals can be made indefinitely long while the integrated light intensity during the time of the experiment approaches zero. This led to the discovery that in some algae, e.g., *Scenedesmus obliquus*, complete darkness and very weak background illumination (much lower than would be necessary to compensate respiration) make a great difference in the result obtained from a single flash of light (179). It is not a very weak oxygen evolution which is the essence of the effect of background light. The background light removes an inhibition which exists for the evolution of oxygen coupled with carbon dioxide reduction. No weak light is necessary for the instantaneous reduction of quinone. The influence of background light upon the ability of one light flash to evolve oxygen persists over dark periods far longer than the 0.02 second of the Emerson-Arnold reaction (see Fig. 61). The solution to this problem may be found in the need for energy-rich phosphate, which the cells under anaerobic conditions produce photochemically at the very lowest light intensities (293) (see Section XIII).

A general difficulty in the study of the effects of single flashes lies in the fact that they are subject to the same determinants which manifest themselves in the induction periods (see Section XVI).

B. THE PHOTOSYNTHETIC UNIT

Describing the experimental separation of enzymatic and photochemical processes by means of flashing light, it was said above that a constant, reproducible, temperature independent yield per light flash is obtained provided the flash is shorter than 10^{-4} second, and the dark pause between flashes is at least 0.02 second long at 20°C. The question of the intensity of the flash was left open. Obviously, since the flash produces only the photochemical effect and the dark period takes care of all chemical transformations, the maximal yield per flash should continue to rise in proportion to the intensity of the flash. If each excited chlorophyll molecule caused the reduction of one carbon dioxide molecule—or, as we should say at the present time, the decomposition of one molecule of water—the yield per flash should increase until the number of molecules photochemically changed became equal to, or at least a simple fraction of, the number of chlorophyll molecules present in the cell. That is, the flash saturation should occur only at extremely high light intensities.

Emerson and Arnold, in performing these experiments, arrived at the paradoxical result that no more carbon dioxide molecules could be reduced (and oxygen evolved) by the action of one intense flash than correspond to about $1/2500$ of the number of chlorophyll molecules present. This ratio remained constant, regardless of variations in the chlorophyll content of the cells. On the other hand, these were the same algae which showed the highest efficiency at low light intensities, under conditions where all the chlorophyll (not only $1/2500$ of it) had necessarily to be active in order to register a more than marginal rate of photosynthesis. The authors pointed out that several thousand chlorophyll molecules might be so arranged as to be able to cause the reduction of one carbon dioxide molecule.

Gaffron and Wohl (202) calculated in 1936 that in dense suspensions of *Chlorella* (where evolution of oxygen begins immediately upon illumination by weak light even after hours of darkness and the quantum yield is good), each chlorophyll molecule should have to wait on the average for an hour or longer to receive the number of quanta necessary to complete the reduction of one molecule of carbon dioxide; always assuming that chlorophyll and carbon dioxide were bound in some stoichiometric ratio to the same mechanism. This, too, was a paradoxical result. But both unexpected results—the low flash saturation and the form of the light-intensity-photosynthesis curve in very weak light—are understandable if an optical unit of 2500 chlorophyll molecules, as indicated by the Emerson-Arnold experiments, collected light energy from different quanta and let it migrate to the "reduction centers." Such a device reduces the necessary survival time for the first intermediate photoproduct—the result of the absorption of one quantum—so drastically as to bring it into line with the plausible lifetimes of chemical intermediates. On the other hand, the entire photosynthetic unit would then be insensitive to further light-absorption acts for the next 0.02 seconds, because it would be occupied with the chemical cycles already set in motion at the reduction center. Inevitably this temporary inactivity should depress the saturation rate of photosynthesis per flash to the level found by Emerson and Arnold. Repetition of their classical experiment with quinone as oxidant gave the same result. At flash saturation, no more oxygen than the equivalent of $1/2000$ of the chlorophyll content was released per flash.

Two decades of discussions concerning the photosynthetic unit have intervened: whether it was physically possible or whether it should be replaced by a model conceived on a more chemical basis. Now the physical unit with its internal energy able to migrate among closely associated pigment molecules is once again the preferred model. The stoichiometry of the photolysis of water molecules and the theoretical quantum yield indicate that the unit so conceived need not contain over two thousand, but only a few hundred, chlorophyll molecules (cf. 115, 318, 342, 436, 446, 512).

The following facts are now usually quoted in favor of an exciton or resonance transfer unit which comprises a crystalline association of 200–400 chlorophyll molecules: (a) the delayed light emission that occurs even in enzymatically inactive chloroplasts (9); (b) the demonstrated occurrence of energy transfer between pigment molecules in the plastid (see page 83); (c) the structures seen in grana and even smaller particles obtained from photosynthetic bacteria (structures much larger than the units themselves, but which guarantee a certain orderly arrangement); (d) the constancy of the amount of pigment found per unit of lamellar surface (see Table II); (e) birefringence and polarization; (f) the disappearance of a specific photoactivity when chloroplast fragments are so small as to contain less than 200 chlorophyll molecules; (g) the fact that one molecule of the herbicide DCMU is sufficient to inactivate up to 200 chlorophyll molecules (see Section XIV).

The question now is whether the creation of electrons and "holes" in an illuminated crystalline layer of chlorophyll molecules—the favored explanation for the delayed light emission—is the very first step of the useful energy conversion in photosynthesis or merely an incidental, nonspecific property of such structures. To some (Franck *et al.*) the essential principle would be the migration, not of the electrons, but of the excitation energy itself. It is well known that this happens under the following conditions: Whenever the spectral characteristics of two pigment molecules are such that the main absorption bands of each overlap, the excitation energy has a high probability of being transferred to that pigment molecule whose absorption band lies farther to the red, that is, the longer wavelengths of the spectrum. The distance between the molecules and the degree of spectral overlapping determine how efficient such a transfer will be. Very slight differences among originally identical molecules, their association with either fats or proteins, the degree of hydration, etc., may cause enough difference to direct the excitation energy from one molecule to the other.

Similar to the detectable layers in the grana, the photosynthetic unit may be a layer of chlorophyll and other pigments between layers of fats and proteins. At the edge of such a molecular "sandwich," the aqueous solution of enzymes and intermediates touches the inner layer of pigments. Only a fraction of the chlorophyll is, therefore, in contact with all the agents necessary to accomplish the chemistry of photosynthesis. The greater part of the pigments form an isolated, semisolid sheet. Light energy absorbed by the pigments inside this structure will migrate to the rim where it can produce the necessary chemical effect. The ratio of "inside" to "outside" chlorophyll is between 150 and 400. Theoretically, all other active pigments should be included in such a structure, but there is, so far, no direct evidence to prove that the phycobilins, for instance, are also located insode the grana. In reality they are easily separated from the fat-soluble chlorophylls and carotenoids by extraction with distilled water. The discovery of active and "inactive" chlorophyll in algae, which also have these water-soluble pigments, seems to support such a distinction between "inside" and "outside" chlorophyll. Regardless of the structure which further research will reveal, the fact remains that a "photosynthetic unit" now seems indispensable to any picture of photosynthesis (8, 162, 181, 233, 318, 332, 345, 347, 512).

VIII. The Storage of Energy and the Efficiency of Photosynthesis

The question: "How efficient is the assimilation of carbon by the green plants?" has two answers, because it may be approached in two ways. Society needs the products of agriculture, and from this point of view the question may mean how much food can be grown on an acre of land—or how much organic material is produced per acre per year. The student of the mechanism of photosynthesis, on the other hand, wants to know how efficiently the light energy is converted within the chlorophyll complex into chemical energy. The menace of overpopulation—so painfully evident in some Asian countries—poses problems which become more acute with the development of what is usually called technological progress. This issue, together with the modern one concerning the food requirement of man on his way into outer space, has engendered a lively discussion as to what extent knowledge of the mechanism of photosynthesis could help solve these problems. Nearly all one needs to know from the scientific point of view are the data in Table V.

On a small scale it is certainly possible to produce with the aid of sunlight fifteen to twenty times more organic matter per unit area than contemporary agriculture achieves. What still remains to be done need not concern us here, for it is a problem in engineering, i.e., how to expand laboratory experiments into large-scale production; or a problem in economics, i.e., whether the cost of such an undertaking is prohibitive; or a problem in psychology, i.e., to make people adjust to a revolutionary change in their eating habits.

TABLE V

SOLAR ENERGY AND THE PRACTICAL YIELD OF PHOTOSYNTHESIS[a]

	Cal/min/cm² (for vertical incidence)
1. Solar energy reaching the earth	1·9
2. Average energy penetrating to surface	0·76
3. Fraction useful for photosynthetic conversion	0·38
	Kcal/acre/year
4. Average illumination of an average acre of the earth's surface on the basis of a 6-hour day and 360 days: $0 \cdot 38 \times 60 \times 6 \times 360 \times 4 \cdot 05 \times 10^7$ cal =	2×10^9
	Metric ton/acre/year
5. 100% conversion of 2×10^9 kcal into chemical energy on the basis of 120 kcal for 30 gm organic matter would yield	500
6. Maximum efficiency of photosynthesis (=30% in continuous illumination) would yield	150
7. An average efficiency of 10% would give	50
8. Extrapolation from laboratory experiments	50
9. Highest crop of sugar cane harvested	40
10. Average yield of intensive agriculture	2

[a] From Gaffron (216).

The upper limit of the efficient production of more food from sunlight, carbon dioxide, and water is set by one figure, namely, the maximum quantum yield of photosynthesis. The determination of this number, signifying the theoretical efficiency of photosynthesis, is discussed in this section.

The number of moles of carbon dioxide reduced (or of oxygen released) per mole of quanta absorbed expresses the quantum *yield*, $1/\phi = CO_2/N_0h\nu$. The number of moles of quanta necessary to reduce one mole of carbon dioxide expresses the quantum requirement or the quantum *number*, $\phi = N_0h\nu/CO_2$. It is this latter number which is given in Table VI.

TABLE VI

MEASUREMENTS OF NUMBERS OF QUANTA NECESSARY TO REDUCE ONE CARBON DIOXIDE MOLECULE TO THE LEVEL OF CARBOHYDRATE, OR TO RELEASE ONE MOLECULE OF OXYGEN FROM WATER

Grouped according to laboratories. If no specific reference is noted, see Chapters 29 and 37 D.4 in Volume II of Rabinowitch's "Photosynthesis and Related Processes" (436) or Emerson's review (141).

A. PHOTOSYNTHESIS

Author	Year	Reference	Plant material	Method	Remarks	Quantum number[a]
Warburg and Negelein	1923	564	*Chlorella*	Manometry	—	4
Warburg and Kubowitz	1946	569	*Chlorella*	Manometry	—	4
Warburg, Burk *et al.*	1949	72	*Chlorella*	Manometry	—	2.7–5
Warburg, Burk *et al.*	1950	570	*Chlorella*	Manometry	—	2.8
Warburg and Burk	1950	571	*Chlorella*	Manometry	pH 9.2	10
Warburg and Burk	1950	571	*Chlorella*	Manometry	—	3–5
Warburg and Geleick	1951	572 (73)	*Chlorella*	Manometry	—	3.5–5
Warburg, Geleick, and Briese	1951	573, 574	*Chlorella*	Manometry	—	2.8
Warburg, Geleick, and Briese	1952		*Chlorella*	Manometry	Bicarbonate buffer	4–12
Warburg *et al.*	1952		*Chlorella*	Manometry	High light intensity	3
Warburg *et al.*	1954		*Chlorella*	Manometry	Pure red light alone	12–∞
			Chlorella	Manometry	With catalytic blue light	3.2
Warburg and Schröder	1957	578, 579	*Chlorella*	Manometry	Average: 4 High: 7.5	2.72
Burk, Hobby, and Hunter	1955	73, 74	*Chlorella*	Manometry	—	3–4
Daniels, Stauffer and Manning	1934	112				
et al.	1938	355	*Chlorella*	Chemistry	—	10
Daniels *et al.*	1939	354	*Chlorella*	Calorimetry	—	13
Petering *et al.*	1939	412	*Chlorella*	Polarography	—	10
Dutton and Manning (Daniels)	1941	113	Diatom: *Nitzschia closterium*	Manometry	—	10

Moore and Duggar (Daniels)	1949	370	*Chlorella*	Calorimetry, polarography	Red light or red plus blue light, no difference	9–10
Emerson and Lewis	1939	134	*Chlorella*	Manometry	10-min periods; results explained by induction phenomena	3
			Chlorella pyrenoidosa	Manometry	—	9.9
			Chlorococcus	Manometry	—	9.6
Emerson and Lewis	1941	135	*Sticchococcus bacillaris*	Manometry	—	9.3
	1943	137	*Scenedesmus* D3	Manometry	—	10.0
			Chroococcus	Manometry	—	12
			Wolffiella lingulata	Manometry	—	17
Tanada (Emerson)	1951	505	Diatom: *Navicula minima*	Manometry	—	9
Nishimura *et al.*	1949	397				
	1951	398	*Chlorella*	Manometry	—	9
Whittingham and Emerson	1953		*Chlorella*	Manometry	—	9
Wassink, Vermuelen, Reman, and Katz	1938		*Chlorella*	Manometry	—	5–9
Wassink and Kersten	1944		Diatom: *Nitzschia dissipata*	Manometry	—	11
Wassink *et al.*	1946		Leaves of various higher plants	Manometry	—	11–13
Kok	1948–49	314	*Chlorella*	Manometry	—	7
					Below compensation	4
Rieke	1939	442	*Chlorella*	Manometry	Results explained by induction phenomena	4–5
Rieke	1949	443	*Chlorella*	Manometry	—	12
			Scenedesmus	Manometry	—	9
Briggs	1929	56	Elm leaves, *Sambucus nigra*	Gas analysis	—	10–12
Gabrielson	1935		*Sinapis alba*	Gas analysis	—	10

TABLE VI (*Continued*)

Author	Year	Reference	Plant material	Method	Remarks	Quantum number[a]
A. PHOTOSYNTHESIS (*con't.*)						
Arnold	1936 (publ. 1949)	5	*Scenedesmus*	Calorimetric	—	10
			Chlorella pyrenoidosa	Calorimetric	—	9
Brackett, Olson, and Crickard	1953	53	*Chlorella pyrenoidosa*	Polarographic, platinum electrode	Depends on chlorophyll concentration	6–13
Tonnelat	1944–46	524	*Chlorella*	Calorimetric	—	7
French and Rabideau	1945	185	*Chlorella pyrenoidosa*	Manometry	—	9
Gabrielson	1947		*Sinapis alba*	Gas analysis	—	12
Yocum	1951		*Ilea fascia* (Brown)	Manometry	—	10
			Porphyra (Red)	Manometry	—	14
Blinks	1954	46, 624	*Ulva* (Green)	Manometry	—	12
Bassham, Shibata, and Calvin	1955	29	*Chlorella*	Paramagnetic O_2	—	7
				Infrared CO_2	Below compensation	5
B. CHLOROPLAST (HILL) REACTIONS						
French and Rabideau	1945	185	Spinach and *Tradescantia*	Manometry	Ferricyanide	12
Ehrmantraut and Rabinowitch	1951	436	*Chlorella and Phytolacca americana*	Manometry	Quinone	10
Warburg	1952		*Chlorella*	Manometry	Quinone	70
Wayrynen *et al.*	1952		Spinach and Swiss chard	Potentiometry	Quinone	8
Schwartz	1955		*Chlorella*	Manometry	Ferricyanide	20
Lumry and Spikes	1957	351	Swiss chard	Potentiometry	Ferricyanide	8

			C. PHOTOREDUCTION			
French	1937		*Streptococcus varians*	Manometry	—	5
			Rhodospirillum (Spirillum) rubrum	Manometry	—	14
Eymers and Wassink	1938		*Chromatium*	Manometry	—	9
Wassink *et al.*	1942		*Chromatium*	Manometry	—	9–14
Rieke	1949	443	*Scendesmus* (adapted)	Manometry	—	8
Larsen *et al.*	1952	326	*Chlorobium thiosulfatophilum*	Manometry	—	9
Larsen	1954	326, 328	*Chromatium*	Manometry	No difference between H_2 and $S_2O_3^{--}$ as reductant	9
			Chromatium	Manometry		9

[a] Noted are the lowest average numbers of a series. Alkaline buffers consistently give values considerably lower than do acid media.

The problem of determining this number can be stated very simply. The difference in free energy between a mole of carbon dioxide and one-sixth mole of hexose (the form in which the reduced carbon appears after the photosynthetic process) is about 118 kcal. (Calculations vary between 115 and 120 kcal according to which states of the reactants are considered.) How many kilocalories of light must be absorbed by the cell pigment in order to cause such a gain in energy? An answer can be found by measuring the light absorbed by the plant, together with the amount either of sugar formed or of oxygen released during the period of illumination. This sounds so simple that one wonders why it took thirty years to come to an agreement about the correct values—and even yet this agreement is not universal. Applying the proper corrections for losses due to light not absorbed by the pigments, or for losses of photosynthetic products by other metabolic processes, poses the same problem regardless of the method used. The task is to choose methods in which the errors are as small as possible so that the corrections become unimportant, or even negligible.

If the first reasonably reliable measurements had shown photosynthesis to be a relatively inefficient process in which only a small fraction of the light is actually caught as chemical energy, the problem would have been of little interest. But the contrary occurred. After eliminating, or minimizing, all avoidable chance losses by providing the cells with optimal conditions in terms of temperature, carbon dioxide concentration, and light intensity, and inventing a good method to determine the amount of light absorbed by the living chloroplast, Warburg and Negelein in 1922 found that no less than three-quarters of the light energy absorbed was stored as chemical energy (563, 564).

The corresponding quantum number was 4. Four primary absorption acts seemed sufficient to transform a molecule of carbon dioxide. Only a relatively simple mechanism with very little internal friction could possibly be as efficient as these measurements indicated. Thus these data were considered to have high theoretical significance, and when, after 1930, the principle of oxidoreduction (538) showed that a transfer of four hydrogen atoms from water was the basic mechanism, the 4-quanta theory of photosynthesis seemed to be definitely established. Granted a few confirmatory measurements by others and the question of the quantum efficiency could have been considered solved. However, a glance at Table VI will tell the reader what in fact happened. During the last twenty years, despite an incredible amount of work by numerous investigators a quantum number of four could not be found again except by Warburg himself and his co-workers.

A. AVOIDABLE AND UNAVOIDABLE ENERGY LOSSES

Obviously the maximum theoretical yield of the photosynthetic mechanism, whatever its value, can never be obtained exactly by experimental methods. It can only be approached asymptotically by using better experimentation or the more skillful evaluation of a great number of varying results. The approach to the optimal value, the maximum efficiency, is from one side only—from that of high quantum numbers signifying "bad" yields, to the lowest number ever to be determined by reproducible, scientifically acceptable methods. It cannot be expected that 100% of the light is absorbed by chlorophyll, that all of the chlorophyll is fully active, that every single cell is at the same high level of efficiency and that all the products of photosynthesis can be accounted for without loss. Even assuming that the technical problem of measuring the light intensity has been perfectly solved, there remains the question of whether some of the losses in light energy are essentially avoidable or unavoidable. Those losses are avoidable which are due to chance variation of the experimental material, etc. Here proper corrections are permissible. Losses of light energy and of end products which are due to the friction in the mechanism of photosynthesis itself, to its way of working, are unavoidable and therefore pertinent to the answer we want to obtain from the efficiency measurements.

The discrepancies in the tabulated results (Table VI) between the lowest quantum numbers reported by Warburg and associates, which range from 2.7 to 5, and those of all other workers which range from 6 to 12, has been the source of a controversy, which has become widely known even beyond the fields of plant physiology and biochemistry.

The main argument advanced in favor of the lowest quantum numbers, 3 and 4, is that certainly only the lowest attainable number is theoretically meaningful. Once such numbers can be obtained again and again, is it not obvious that investigators who are unable to confirm them have not as yet mastered the problem of minimizing the avoidable energy losses?

The argument of those who find quantum numbers at least twice as high runs as follows: We accept naturally the premise that only the lowest number can be used as a basis for theoretical discussion. Looking over the available data outside the Warburg school this seems to be the number 6. On the other hand, accurate efficiency measurements are difficult in many respects; the complex mechanism of photosynthesis may show temporary fluctuation, not only toward the side of lesser efficiency, but also toward that of better efficiencies than what should be called the theoretical quantum number. Therefore, the *average of the lowest numbers found* is as likely to be the correct value as is the *absolute lowest number* obtained. As to the practical problem of eliminating avoidable losses, it is reasonable that with the greater number of independent investigators, the larger variety of methods used, and the avowed wish of the experimenter to push his measurements to the alleged limit of 3 or 4 quanta, it should have been possible, here and there, to confirm the results of the Warburg school. Instead there is an impressive agreement among all other investigators, that further lowering of the quantum numbers below an average of 8 encountered obstacles.

Confronted with the data of Table VI and the arguments just mentioned, the scientists not actually engaged in this kind of work have, during the past twenty years, been at a loss. Should they accept a quantum number of 4, or even 3, which, if correct, would mean that photosynthesis stores light energy with an efficiency which approaches 100%? Fortunately it is, in reality, not difficult to come to a scientifically satisfying conclusion about this issue, because all other aspects of the problem of photosynthesis have not meanwhile remained stationary. The methods of culturing plants and of measuring metabolism and absorption spectra, the biochemistry and the theory of photosynthesis have advanced considerably. Some knowledge about these points is sufficient to put the quantum controversy in the right perspective.

B. Difficulties Encountered in Determining Quantum Numbers

1. The Plant Material

Anyone who has made a series of measurements of photosynthesis at low light intensities will agree that the steadiness of the reaction under controlled conditions is impressive. Algae grown in the proper way can be used as photometers. The plants are indeed cooperative enough to give us easily reproducible photosynthetic rates, and the fluctuations in the values obtained in single experiments are not more than 10%, often much less. Once the possibility of making accurate measurements had been recognized, it was, of course, imperative to go ahead and make them as precisely as possible.

One prerequisite of measuring the optimal quantum yield is that the light-absorbing pigments be fully active. Incomplete energy transfer from accessory pigments and the occurrence of inactive chlorophyll has been dealt with on page 88. Many plants can grow through generations even if the photochemical system is partially damaged (e.g., yellow varieties)—be it on account of inactive or missing pigments or of a deficiency in one or another of the necessary enzymes. The next requirement is that the metabolic activity being measured should be truly photosynthesis as defined by equation (a) in Fig. 2. The light-activated chlorophyll complex has a choice of several reactions, which may proceed in competition with each other. We have phosphorylations, internal Hill reactions, and the reduction of various carboxylated compounds belonging to metabolic systems other than those of the carbohydrate metabolism. We must be sure that the measurements are made when all transient reactions following dark periods have subsided, and that there is no long-lasting interference from other metabolic reactions in the cell. In other words, the simple, over-all equation of photosynthesis expressed by an assimilatory quotient of unity must be closely fulfilled. Small deviations from this ideal condition are inevitable and normal. Particularly with microorganisms, some proteins and fats are synthesized simultaneously with the main carbohydrate products. Thus, it is understandable that the actual figures of maximum quantum yields or the corresponding smallest quantum numbers fluctuate within a certain range which we have to accept as physiological.

However, when there are persistent and large deviations from a quotient of unity, indicating the formation of compounds less reduced than carbohydrates, it is important to explain the anomaly. The unusually low quantum numbers (high efficiencies) published by the Warburg school show a definite correlation with an assimilatory quotient around 1.2. This they have acknowledged, but have not offered a satisfactory explanation. If we write the assimilatory quotient, for the purpose of the discussion, as Warburg does:

$$\gamma = \frac{-CO_2}{+O_2}$$

its average value is 0.94. All quantum yields referring to undisturbed photosynthesis in the steady state should give values between 0.84 and 1.04. If values of γ between 1.2 and 1.3 are found consistently whenever the quantum numbers are very low, it should be obvious that this fact must be thoroughly investigated before valid conclusions can be drawn from such experiments.

Part of the data published in support of the existence of particularly high efficiencies are the result of experiments with intermittent illumination, where the periods used were of the order of 1 minute light and 1 minute dark. In the section on transient effects we will discuss the role of short and long dark periods on the incipient photosynthesis. Figure 62 is an example of the curves obtained manometrically by Warburg *et al.*, during illumination of *Chlorella* in 1-minute intervals. After longer dark times, the transients preceding the new steady state in the light are known to last from 1 minute to several minutes. Until it has been ruled out that neither the physical lag in the gas exchange nor the transient reactions carefully recorded by polarimetric methods (see Sections II and XV) can explain the observations of Warburg, Burk, and others, manometric measurements

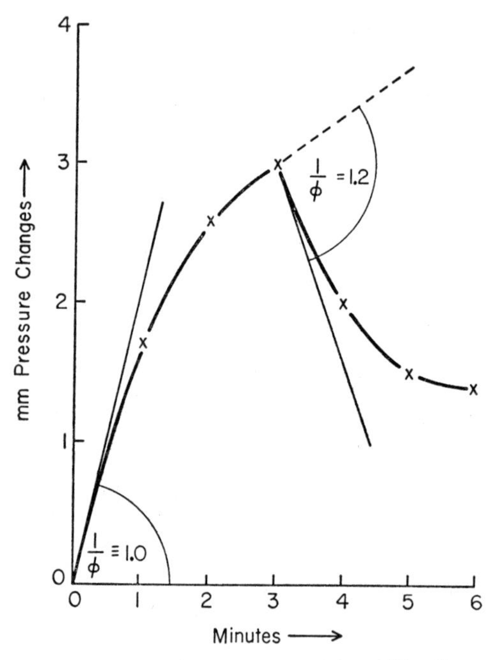

FIG. 62. Manometric pressure changes produced by *Chlorella* sp. in a sequence of light and dark periods of 3 minutes each. One double period as used by Warburg (572) to demonstrate the existence of the "1-quantum process" and the subsequent "back reaction" in the dark. Compare Figs. 32–35 and 122.

with 1-minute periods serve only to demonstrate the existence of these phenomena.

There are *a priori* reasons why algae (see Table VII, page 131) which regularly show an efficiency of 35% cannot be trained to double their output. Thus, if a better yield could be sustained for only a limited time, it would be a discovery of great importance. Unfortunately, however, the detailed directions given by the Warburg school for training or growing experimental plants to give the high yields have changed with embarrassing frequency.

One of the few things not repeated to the point of exhaustion is to test algae whose growth has been synchronized by the proper adjustment of the length of day and night, and to compare the efficiency of photosynthesis before and after cell division. As Tamiya and Pirson (415, 503) have shown, the morphology and chlorophyll content of *Chlorella* before and after division into eight daughter cells is clearly different (see Section II). Mass cultures can be obtained in which nearly all cells are in the same state. Emerson (unpublished) has compared yields of such synchronized cultures and says that the yield in the steady state is the same in the morning and in the evening, while the behavior during induction periods (transients) is different.

2. *Measuring the Absorbed Light*

The light intensity emitted by any light source in the visible region can be measured with greater accuracy than the metabolic reactions in living cells. To say how much of the emitted light has been absorbed by a colored substance already requires two measurements and certain corrections for reflected or scattered light. If the colored substance is enclosed in a richly structured, nonhomogeneous tiny body, like a living cell which contains several different pigments, the problem becomes truly complicated. (Compare Fig. 40 for the effect of scattering on absorption spectra.) Seeing this difficulty, Warburg and Negelein introduced the use of very dense suspensions of assimilating cells. Under these conditions, practically all of the light passing into the vessel is absorbed by the plants. It is only necessary to know the amount of light going into the suspension and how much escapes by scattering backward in the direction of the incident light—not what portion of it passes through. The drawback of this method is that there must be a great excess of living material, ten to twenty times more cells than those which do appreciable photosynthesis at any one moment.

What has been gained in simplifying the problem of measuring light absorption is partially lost by increasing the difficulties of knowing the conditions in the living cells. The stirring of the suspension produces intermittent illumination. While the cells are in front, the light is sufficient for a good deal of net photosynthesis, but when the cells move again into the darker recesses of the vessel their photoreactions fade away after a period of mere compensation of respiration. The greater part of the cells are always in the dark, and the correction for respiration is an order of magnitude larger than the one which would apply for the light-absorbing cells above. It is remarkable, under the circumstances, that this method, if cautiously used, can give results which agree with those of other arrangements.

Working with thin suspensions and with light intensities high above the compensation point offers the great advantage that corrections for respiration may become negligibly small. On the other hand, measurements of the absorbed fraction of light become less accurate. Assuming that the total light entering the measuring sphere can be determined within ±2%, the error in terms of the important absorbed fraction of, let us say, 10% unavoidably becomes two in ten—that is, ±20%. Even this is not so serious provided many measurements are made. But as Emerson has pointed out, systematic errors, which are not canceled out by repetition, arise if two vessels of unequal shape or unequal filling have to be compared, since the pattern of the scattered light inside the sphere shifts appreciably. Such a comparison of two unequal vessels is part of the manometric two-vessel method which Warburg and associates have insisted upon using for thirty years. For a more detailed discussion of methodological points see the recent review (141, 389).

3. *Measuring the Effects of Light*

Quantum numbers are given by the ratio of the light energy absorbed to the effects elicited by the light. For the latter one can choose between the gas exchange, or the quantity of organic matter, or the heat produced. Efficiencies determined on the basis of new organic matter formed exist but are few and inaccurate. Some calorimetric measurements have been made to find the difference between the heat produced by radiation absorbed in live and in dead algae. For the rest, all measurements have relied upon analysis either of carbon dioxide or of oxygen gas specifically (chemically, by infrared absorption, by polarographic or magnetometric methods), or simply of pressure changes in manometers. Because only the manometric method has ever rendered seemingly reliable data in support of quantum numbers of 4 or less, this method, particularly the so-called two-vessel arrangement, has been analyzed independently by Emerson *et al.* (141) and Myers *et al.* (389). There is unanimity among these authors that the two-vessel method tends to magnify small errors (or small corrections applied to direct readings) out of all proportion unless the pressure changes observed on the instrument are truly large. The time necessary to smooth out a physical lag of gas exchanges after each shift from one level of steady-state conditions to the next (e.g., light to dark and the reverse) is between 1 and 2 minutes.

Summing up, one can say that the physiology of the plants as well as the methods for measuring light absorption and light effect present enough difficulties to make untrustworthy any set of data that has been obtained with only one method and one strain of organisms. The reader who prefers to form his own opinion on efficiency measurements without recourse to any thermodynamical or biochemical considerations finds ample material in the data of Table VI. It might be useful to note that all data on low quantum numbers published earlier than 1945 have definitely been shown to be based on one or another methodological error.

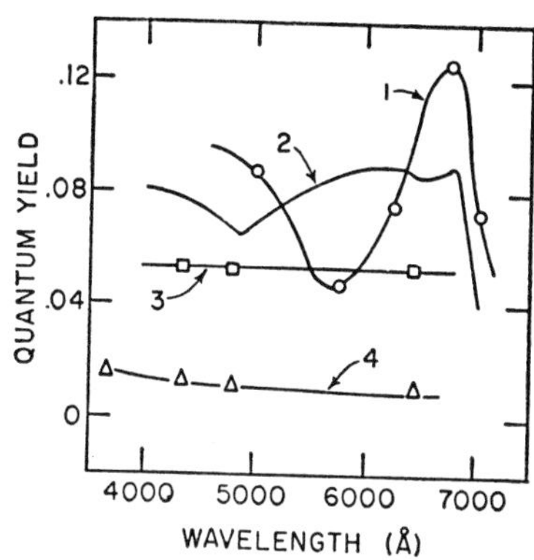

FIG. 63. Curves showing quantum yields for the Hill reaction and photosynthesis as found by different workers. Curve *1* shows the results obtained in the work on the ferricyanide Hill reaction of sugar beet (*Beta vulgaris*) chloroplast fragments as extrapolated to zero light intensity. Curve *2* represents the average values for *Chlorella* sp. photosynthesis as measured by Emerson and Lewis. Curve *3* depicts the average results for the quinone and ferricyanide Hill reactions of lyophilized *Chlorella* sp. cells and the quinone Hill reaction for both whole and lyophilized *Chlorella* sp. cells as reported by Schwartz. The data in curve *4* were obtained by Warburg with the quinone Hill reaction of spinach (*Spinacia oleracea*) chloroplast preparations. From Lumry *et al.* (351).

The oxygen evolution with artificial oxidants in illuminated chloroplasts has given quantum yields which fall into the range characteristic of the intact plant (see Table VI and Fig. 63).

C. OXYGEN EVOLUTION

The photolysis of water in living cells promotes the reduction of carbon dioxide and the synthesis or transformation of many organic substances in various ways. As long as this set of reactions remains coupled with a re-formation of water, there is no appreciable over-all storage of free energy (see Section X and Table VI). The energy gain achieved by photosynthesis is due entirely to the slow rate of back reactions inside the cell and to the fact that sugars do not burn spontaneously in air at temperatures below the boiling point of water.

The high activation energy standing between free oxygen and most organic substances is responsible for the low rate of autoxidation as compared with the rate of photosynthesis. As pointed out in Section I, Fig. 6, the light energy is used not only for storing energy in combustible chemicals, but also to overcome the activation-energy barrier. Next to the primary process leading to the photolysis of water, the evolution of oxygen is the most specific feature of photosynthesis. How efficiently the plants accomplish this is an important point in the debate about quantum yields.

1. *The Alleged Role of Catalase*

The evolution of oxygen during photosynthesis has been compared to the action of catalase upon hydrogen peroxide. The similarity seen in the action of such specific inhibitors as hydroxylamine or cyanide upon both processes has for many years supported the idea that hydrogen peroxide is indeed a precursor of photosynthetic oxygen. The following experiments, however, oppose this idea.

First, it is possible to inhibit the action of catalase by cyanide in living algae (*Scenedesmus*) without interfering much with the photochemical liberation of oxygen. Second, it is possible to inhibit specifically the oxygen liberation but not the photoreduction, by a poison (DCMU, an herbicide) which does not interfere with the activity of catalase (41). Third, an accumulation of hydrogen peroxide in poisoned algae has never been seen, nor is the photochemical mechanism destroyed or damaged by light in the presence of inhibitors; yet, in the presence of cyanide the addition of very small amounts of hydrogen peroxide (10^{-4} M) suffices to depress rather irreversibly the rate of photosynthesis at high light intensities (203). All this supports the view that stepwise dismutation of the YOH hydroxyls and the release of oxygen do not proceed via the intermediate formation of free hydrogen peroxide, but that the reaction is accomplished by a succession of steps probably catalyzed by one or more iron porphyrins of the cytochrome type. Nevertheless it is convenient to retain the expression "photoperoxide" to characterize one of the intermediates in the path leading to free oxygen.

2. *The Role of Manganese*

While we should remember that at this writing the part assigned to the cytochromes is extremely plausible but not yet certain, it has been definitely shown that manganese ion is essential for the progress of this reaction. When algae are cultivated in manganese-deficient media the chlorophyll content hardly suffers, yet photosynthesis declines progressively to very low values while respiratory reactions are enhanced (413, 417). Addition of manganous sulfate restores photosynthesis within a short time (30 minutes to an hour), a period that seems too short to be connected with any growth reaction or synthesis of an enzyme.

The place in the mechanism where manganese plays its essential role was discovered by comparing photoreduction with photosynthesis in such manganese-deficient algae. It turned out that the more developed the manganese deficiency, the lower the rate of oxygen liberation but the higher the ability of the algae to reduce carbon dioxide with molecular hydrogen (305, 309, 312) (Fig. 58). This means that we have to place the action of manganese in the path leading to oxygen beyond the spot where the hydrogenase-hydrogen system branches off (Figs. 92, 96, Section XI). Certain effects in chloroplast preparations brought about either by adding manganese or by removing it are in agreement with this interpretation. Very likely there are more enzymatic reactions requiring manganous ions as a cofactor, but the one here described is the easiest to recognize (147).

3. The Role of Quinones: Vitamin K and Coenzyme Q

The endogenous carotenes protect purple bacteria and algae against photooxidation by oxygen (see Sections III and VI). The quenching of the metastable excited state of chlorophyll in pure solutions may be a clue to the mechanism involved. On the other hand, a direct interaction of the carotenes with the oxygen of photosynthesis is also a way to explain the need for carotenes in aerobic photosynthesizing cells.

Such a view was, at first, apparently supported by experiments of Lynch and French (353), who extracted dried chloroplast preparations with petroleum ether, thus removing most of the β-carotene together with a number of fatty substances soluble in petroleum ether. Preparations so treated gave definitely lower rates of dye reduction in the light. If the extracted substances were added back to the dried preparations the rate of reduction increased again. These experiments were confirmed by Bishop, who measured oxygen evolution by normal, extracted, and reconstituted chloroplast preparations (Fig. 64) (43). The active ingredient in these petroleum ether extracts, however, turned out not to be β-carotene but a quinone, vitamin K or a similar chemical, which accompanied the lipids and carotenoids. The proof is simple: Purified commercial carotene and carotene from carrots are inactive, while small amounts of menadione (2-methyl-1,4-naphthoquinone) dissolved in petroleum ether can substitute for the original extract (Fig. 65).

In Section XIII we shall see that vitamin K is one among several rather dissimilar compounds capable of serving as electron transfer agents in the photophosphorylation promoted by chloroplast preparations. But this ability is shared with a number of non-natural pigments. There is, therefore, no compelling need at present to connect the activation of oxygen evolution in extracted chloroplasts with the effect on photophosphorylation. Particularly since—contrary to expectation

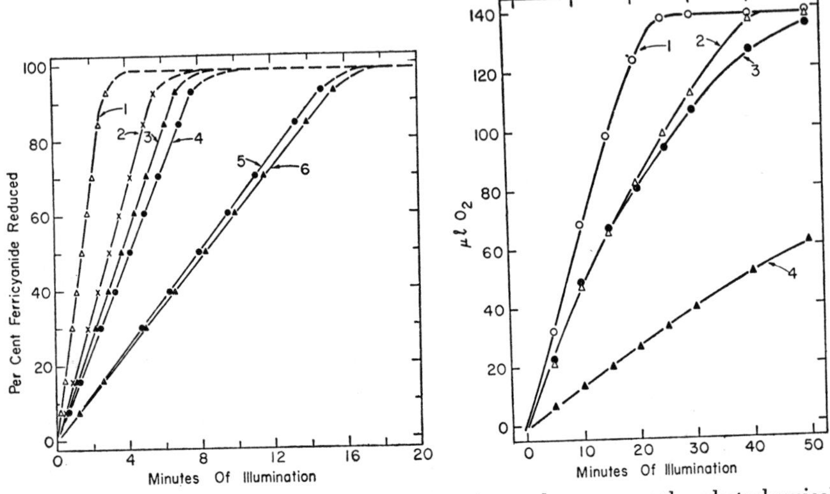

FIG. 64. (Left) The effect of addition of various substances on the photochemical activity of petroleum ether-extracted chloroplasts. Curve *1*, control, no extraction; curve *2*, 0.1 mg menadione; curve *3*, petroleum ether extract; curve *4*, "partially purified" β-carotene; curve *5*, 0.1 mg purified β-carotene; curve *6*, extracted chloroplasts. Temperature, 15°C. Gas phase, prepurified nitrogen. From Bishop (43).

FIG. 65. (Right) The capacity of menadione and of the petroleum ether extract to restore the oxygen-producing power of illuminated chloroplasts. Curve *1*, control; curve *2*, petroleum ether extract; curve *3*, 1 mg menadione; curve *4*, extracted chloroplasts. Temperature, 10°C. Gas phase, prepurified nitrogen (43).

based on the literature about vitamin K—the latter is not the original natural quinone present in the living material and removed from the chloroplasts by the petrolether treatment. The true substance was found by Bishop to be the same substituted *p*-benzoquinone which Crane had just recently extracted from higher plants (103a). In a slightly different form this benzoquinone seems to be present in most living cells. It has been described under the name "ubiquinone" or "coenzyme Q."

D. THE ENERGETICS OF PHOTOSYNTHESIS

The theoretical inquiry concerning the quantum requirement became important when Wohl in 1935 first recognized how astonishingly high the efficiency of photosynthesis would be if the process really proceeded with only 4 light quanta (or photons) per carbon atom reduced (202, 615). Four einsteins (1 einstein = 1 mole quantum = $N_0 h\nu$), he argued, must cover not only the 118 kcal actually stored in the end products but also all activation energies required to have fairly stable intermediates. Otherwise a high rate of back reaction among the intermediates would make photosynthesis very inefficient, particularly at low light intensities; and we know that the reverse is true. If, for simplicity's sake, hydrogen peroxide (H_2O_2) is assumed to be a precursor to oxygen, the 23 kcal of heat released when it dismutates to oxygen and water must be added to the energy stored in the reduced products. Thus Wohl arrived at an estimate of 180 kcal necessary to achieve photosynthesis, while 4 einsteins provided only 164 kcal.

TABLE VII
FRANCK'S ENERGY BUDGET OF PHOTOSYNTHESIS

Budget entries	4 quanta (kcal)	2.7 quanta[a] (kcal)
Energy income for process with:		
(a) Singlet-singlet transition at 41 kcal	164	111
(b) Singlet-triplet transition at about 26 kcal	104	71
Energy expenditure:		
Free energy stored per CH_2O	117	117
Losses in photochemical steps at 7 kcal	28	19
Losses for evolution of one O_2	20	20
Losses for radical transmutation at 1.5 kcal	6	4
Losses for carboxylation with one CO_2 + phosphorylation	13	13
Total energy demand:	184	173

[a] Highest efficiency (= smallest quantum number) reported. See Table VI.

Later, similar estimates by other authors went as high as 210 kcal. The whole matter has been carefully reviewed again by Franck (173, 176). He arrives, by conservative estimates, at a total energy demand of 184 kcal for a 4-quanta process and 173 kcal for a 3-quanta process, while the energy available in the singlet transition amounts to 164 and 123 kcal, respectively (see Table VII). The more steps photosynthesis is composed of, the higher the losses, since each intermediate step has its own specific activation energy (cf. 217, 436).

The reader not familiar with the physical laws governing photochemical reactions is referred to Section III and Fig. 21. Here we repeat only that in using white sunlight the plant suffers an immediat loss of energy in the very act of light absorption. At one end of th absorption spectrum of chlorophyll, in blue light, where a photo contains 70 kcal per einstein, the loss amounts to 30 kcal, or 40% If there had been a tendency or a need in nature to develop plant which had to use light with the highest efficiency, not one essentia pigment, but an entire series of coordinated pigments would hav evolved. As we have said in Section VI,A, there are indeed other pig ments which take part in photosynthesis, but they are of an accessor nature, not independently able to produce photosynthesis, and th energy absorbed is subject to the same or even larger losses.

Any discussion of a miraculous efficiency in photosynthesis is, *priori*, restricted to the set of reactions which follow the absorptio process in the chlorophyll molecule. Photosynthesis is wasteful unles considered in relation to monochromatic light at $\lambda = 680$ mμ. Al efficiency calculations begin with the energy-rich, "excited" conditio of the first singlet state (see Fig. 21), into which the chlorophyl molecule is brought by any quantum that it has absorbed, regardles of the latter's energy content. The energy available per photon i chlorophyll is thus well defined, and amounts to 41 kcal (or 164 kca for 4 hours).

One particular type of energy loss, which was not taken int account in earlier calculations, is that of the transition from the single into the triplet metastable state. This must happen as the studies o fluorescence have shown. The loss involved is at least 10 kcal pe einstein. This is why a 4-quanta process starting from the metastabl triplet state has an energy income of at best 124 kcal, against a deman of 184. The conclusion from these calculations is that photosynthesi with 3 quanta is quite impossible, and with 4 quanta only under th unwarranted assumption that the chemistry originates from the single state and all losses are utilized by the cell to produce additional energy rich phosphate bonds. Considering that no other metabolic mechanisn has been shown to work with such an overall efficiency, and considerin that light is available in excess, it is hard to understand why photo synthesis alone should have evolved as a practically "frictionless ma chine."

One fact that should have brought the controversy about quantun numbers to an early end was the repeated appearance of values belov 3 [2.6, 2.7, 2.8 (see Table VI)] in the papers of Warburg *et al.* (571 573, 579). Any method capable of producing results so obviously i contradiction to fundamental tenets of modern physics is thereby show to be untrustworthy. With the now generally accepted values betwee

6 and 10 quanta, there is energy to spare and the need for further discussion of this matter is indeed eliminated.

E. QUANTUM NUMBERS AND BIOCHEMICAL MECHANISM

To the biologist, to whom activation energies and excitation levels in light-absorbing pigments mean little, the data in Table VI dealing with photoreductions and chloroplast reactions may appear as the strongest support which can be put forward in favor of a lower limit of 6 to 10 in quantum requirements. The reduction of carbon dioxide by means of hydrogen gas as it happens in purple bacteria and adapted algae involves a negligible change in free energy—less than 2 kcal, as compared with 118 kcal in photosynthesis. Yet the quantum requirement in photoreduction is about 9, the same as it is in photosynthesis with the evolution of oxygen from water. As Larsen (326,

TABLE VIII
THEORETICAL AND OBSERVED QUANTUM REQUIREMENTS FOR CARBON DIOXIDE ASSIMILATION IN SULFUR BACTERIA[a]

Organism	Electron donor		ΔF°_{298}/mole CO_2 (kcal)	Quantum number		Efficiency (%)
	Reduced	Oxidized		Theoretical minimum	Observed	
Chromatium	H_2	H_2O	1.7	<1	9	0.6
at λ 870 mμ	$S_2O_3^{--}$	$S_4O_6^{--}$	98.5	3	9	33.0
Chlorobium	H_2	H_2O	1.7	<1	9	0.5
at λ 730 mμ	$S_2O_3^{--}$	SO_4^{--}	29.2	1	9	8.3
	$S_4O_6^{--}$	SO_4^{--}	30.2	1	9	8.5

[a] From Larsen (326, 328).

328) points out, this means that the extra chemical energy, the difference between 118 and 2 kcal, is lost and is not available for the formation of cell material. It is available, however, for the purpose of using other hydrogen (or electron) donors in reactions which would hardly ever proceed in the dark without the aid of a special energy source (see Table VIII). This observation is one of the strongest arguments in favor of the proposition that the photochemistry is the same in all cases, regardless of the enzymatic reactions which follow. It is also pertinent to the discussion whether the living cell could minimize the energy losses in photosynthesis by coupling the decomposition of the precursor to free oxygen with the formation of energy-rich phosphate. The purple bacteria would have ample and better opportunities to do this, but they apparently do not.

The biochemical approach to the question of over-all energetics is possible only if we have a model for the reducing process and for the mechanism of oxygen evolution. It should provide for an independent check on the conclusions derived from physical and chemical principles. At present we have a complete model only for the Calvin-Benson cycle. Bassham *et al.* (29) have carefully calculated the minimum energy needed to permit the reduction cycle to proceed in the desired direction at the necessary speed. The energy is provided by two molecules of reduced coenzyme II (TPN) and three molecules of ATP. The result of their calculation is that at least 136 kcal per gram mole of carbon dioxide have to be delivered photochemically to make the cycle turn. If there are no other points of "friction," the cycle might run with 85% efficiency. But this does not tell us anything yet about the efficiency with which TPN and ATP are formed by the illuminated chlorophyll complex. Considering the losses involved in the elimination of free oxygen, the stabilization of radicals, the internal conversion into triplet states, etc., an efficiency of 75% would be extremely good—surpassing that of any better-known synthetic process. Consequently, the total energy demand would be $(136 \times 100)/75 = 180$ kcal. Again, a quantum number of 4 seems to lie outside any probable limit for the theoretical efficiency.

Parallel to the controversy about likely and unlikely quantum numbers and the proper way to determine them, there has developed a related one about the mechanism of photosynthesis. This present chapter is replete with data supporting a view of the photosynthetic process as an oxidoreduction process composed of several semi-independent enzymatic systems. Ignoring the mass of biochemical, physical, and kinetic evidence almost completely, Warburg and Burk have proposed a new and wholly independent theory of photosynthesis (72–74, 571, 578). It is based solely on the assumption that 3 light quanta fulfill the theoretical energy requirement and on the observation of transient manometric pressure changes of the kind shown in Fig. 62.

According to these authors, photosynthesis consists of two main parts: a photochemical forward reaction and an enzymatic back reaction. In this back reaction most of the reduced products and most of the oxygen formed by the photochemical steps react, causing an extra respiration at a rate twice that of the over-all process. The energy released in this light respiration is funneled (presumably via energy-rich phosphate bonds) into a chlorophyll-water complex (or, in some versions, into a chlorophyll-carbon dioxide-water complex). Upon absorption of one photon, this energy-rich pigment complex releases one molecule of oxygen gas and thereby becomes a strong reducing agent which converts carbon dioxide into that organic substance which immediately reacts back, not completely but only to the point where the energy developed suffices to make the next 1-quantum step possible. The facts that this back reaction with oxygen in the light has not been seen in any other laboratory, though certain elaborate experiments were set up to find it (see Section V,E), and that the energy-charged chlorophyll complex (symbolized by Warburg as RH_4O_2 in the equations below) has no biochemically ascertainable identity, did not prevent Warburg from summing up his views as follows (we quote in translation from Warburg and Krippahl, 1954):

"The following equations sum up our measurements of the light reaction and of the recovery reaction. Under our experimental conditions (a) and (b) proceed in the light, (c) and (d) in the dark. In steady-state photosynthesis the four reactions proceed simultaneously; only reaction (e) can be measured. In red light, with $N_0h\nu = 40{,}000$ cal, its yield in chemical energy is at least $(\frac{1}{3} \times 112{,}000)/40{,}000 = 93\%$.

$$\begin{aligned}
&\text{(a)}\ 1\,N_0h\nu + RH_4O_2 = RH_4 + 1\,O_2\\
&\text{(b)}\ RH_4 + 1\,CO_2 = R + 2\,H_2O + 1\,C\\
&\text{(c)}\ \tfrac{2}{3}\,(C) + \tfrac{2}{3}\,(O_2) = \tfrac{2}{3}\,(CO_2) + 70{,}000\ \text{cal}\\
&\text{(d)}\ 70{,}000\ \text{cal} + R + 2\,H_2O = RH_4O_2\\
\hline
&\text{(e)}\ N_0h\nu + \tfrac{1}{3}\,(CO_2) = \tfrac{1}{3}\,(C) + \tfrac{1}{3}\,(O_2)
\end{aligned}$$

The equations (a) to (d) contain no theory. They constitute the complete solution of the quantum problem of photosynthesis."

Since the over-all process (e) runs with "at least 93%" efficiency, the partial reactions (a) to (d)—which in their turn are only the symbols for very complicated processes—should proceed with (at least) 100% efficiency. In other words, we are asked to believe that photosynthesis is a frictionless machine! We are left with the fact that the results of Warburg and associates have remained either irreproducible whatever the method tried, or, when occasionally confirmed, have been found to be based on observations which obviously required additional and special explanations (141, 176, 218, 314, 436, 441).

Biochemical analysis will decide, in the near future, which of the measured values between 6 and 10 comes nearest to the theoretical requirements of the mechanism of photosynthesis. With an excess of energy available—for instance, 8 quanta with over 320 kcal—many different mechanisms can be devised without coming into conflict with thermodynamics.

Warburg *et al.* have of course not remained unaware of the disbelief their publications have met among other workers in the field. Therefore they have taken pains to specify in nearly every publication how to obtain cells giving the highest efficiency. The list of the essential pretreatments is long but quite inconsistent. One of their more recent discoveries—substantiated by them with numerous experimental protocols—is the need for catalytic amounts of blue light. In pure red light of λ 644 mμ there is very little photosynthesis or even none at all (578). Adding blue light of λ 480 mμ not only restores the photosynthetic activity but brings it to maximum efficiency. If this were true it means that all workers—including Warburg himself, who in earlier years reported good photosynthesis with 8 or 4 quanta in red light—must have had accidentally a considerable amount of blue light as an impurity in their supposedly monochromatic light source. Bassham *et al.* (29) as well as Emerson (137, 138) have tried to see this effect of blue light but could not find it. Also the claim that chlorophyll and carbon dioxide form a complex in the ratio 1:1 which decomposes under the influence of fluoride was easily disproved (42, 576, 577).

IX. The Fixation and Reduction of Carbon Dioxide

A. ENZYMATIC CARBOXYLATIONS IN LIVING CELLS

Enzymatic carboxylations were discovered in 1936 (617), and this discovery changed the approach to the problems of carbon dioxide fixation in green plants. Subsequently it was established that chemosynthetic carboxylations occur in all living cells, though their significance was not always clear. It soon became possible to distinguish four major types of carbon dioxide reductions. Table IX summarizes the typical, over-all reactions in which carbon dioxide is involved.

We have, first, the purely heterotrophic organisms where carbon dioxide is added to an organic compound and subsequently reduced by pyridine nucleotide-linked enzymes at the expense of respiratory processes. Since the latter consume an organic nutrient, this kind of chemosynthesis does not increase the total energy content of the cell (26, 143–146, 540, 545–547, 617–621).

There are, second, the chemoautotrophic organisms: bacteria that obtain their available energy from the oxidation of molecular hydrogen, inorganic nitrogen compounds, sulfur compounds, iron salts, etc. With these, the assimilation of carbon dioxide leads, of course, to a gain in organic material (cf. 37, 410, 411, 499, 532, 622).

The third class is composed of those organisms which utilize organic substances yet are dependent upon light energy for their growth. These photoheterotrophs are closely related to, and sometimes identical with, the photoautotrophic organisms in the fourth class, but the over-all action of light consists mainly in the transformation of one organic compound into another. This quasi-catalytic action can, but need not, be coupled with an uptake of free carbon dioxide. The photoheterotrophs are discussed in more detail in the section on purple bacteria.

TABLE IX

TYPICAL WAYS OF METABOLIC CARBON DIOXIDE FIXATION

Chemoheterotroph

a. $CO_2 + CH_3.CO.COOH \rightleftarrows COOH.CH_2.CO.COOH$

$COOH.CH_2.CO.COOH + DPN(H_2) \rightleftarrows COOH.CH_2.CHOH.COOH + DPN$

b. $CO_2 + 2\ CH_3.CH_2OH \rightarrow 2\ CH_3.COOH + CH_4$

c. $C_5H_9O_5\textcircled{P} + ATP \rightarrow C_5H_8O_5\textcircled{P}_2 + H_2O + ADP$

$CO_2 + C_5H_8O_5\textcircled{P}_2 + H_2O \rightarrow 2\ C_3H_5O_3\textcircled{P}$

Chemoautotroph

d. $2\ H_2S + O_2 \rightarrow 2\ H_2O + 2\ S$

$2\ S + 3\ O_2 + 2\ H_2O \rightarrow 2\ H_2SO_4$

$CO_2 + 2\ H_2S \rightarrow 2\ H_2O + 2\ S + (CH_2O)$

e. $4\ H_2 + 2\ O_2 \rightarrow 4\ H_2O$

$CO_2 + 4\ H_2 \rightarrow 2\ H_2O + (CH_2O)$

f. $4\ H_2 + 2\ CO_2 \rightarrow CH_2.COOH + 2\ H_2O$

Photoheterotroph

g. $CO_2 + 2\ CH_3.CHOH.CH_3 \xrightarrow{\text{light}} 2\ CH_3.CO.CH_3 + (CH_2O) + H_2O$

h. $4\ CH_3.COOH \rightarrow CO_2 + \text{bacteria}$

Photoautotroph

i. $CO_2 + 2\ H_2S \xrightarrow{\text{light}} (CH_2O) + 2\ S + H_2O$

j. $CO_2 + 2\ H_2 \xrightarrow{\text{light}} CH_2O + 2\ H_2O$

k. $CO_2 + 4\ HOH \xrightarrow{\text{light}} CH_2O + 3\ H_2O + O_2$

The fourth class are the photoautotrophs, cells which use only carbon dioxide and inorganic substances to form all the compounds they need. The necessary energy is delivered by pigment systems which absorb light between λ 360 mμ and λ 900 mμ. Whether the use of light leads to an over-all gain in energy depends on the free energy available in the substances other than carbon dioxide which enter into the over-all reaction. A bacterium using hydrogen or hydrogen sulfide does not contribute to a storage of solar energy; but green plants store about 30 kcal per hydrogen atom transferred because they take the hydrogen from water. The energy harnessed by plants can be roughly measured by the heat generated when carbohydrates are burned. In the last analysis, the achievement of solar energy storage rests on the ability of the plants to release free molecular oxygen as a waste product.

The reactions shown in Table IX made it seem plausible that the carboxylation in the green plants would reveal itself as similar to one or another of the many being discovered in other kinds of living cells. No sooner would a new carboxylation reaction be described which could introduce carbon dioxide into organic compounds, than a scheme of photosynthesis was drawn which fitted this new reaction. The trouble was that hardly any of these carboxylations could lead directly to the formation of carbohydrate. The most reasonable proposal was that of K. Thimann, who pointed out as early as 1938 that the reversal of the decarboxylation of pyruvate would do the trick. It was ignored because pyruvate undergoes an anaerobic decarboxylation to acetaldehyde and carbon dioxide, with a large decrease in free energy ($\Delta F =$ 15,000 calmole) indicating a practically irreversible reaction, a view which was later altered when the mechanism of oxidative carboxylation of pyruvate was elucidated (338, 339).

Even though the aerobic decarboxylation of pyruvate to acetyl coenzyme A and carbon dioxide is strongly exergonic, this system may be reversible, since the over-all reaction occurs in many steps. The intermediates (acetaldehyde-diphosphothiamine, 5-acetyl lipoate) bridge the large energy gap between pyruvate and acetyl-coenzyme-A by dividing it up into smaller steps. In this way it may be possible to reverse the system in the same manner as the steps in glycolysis. Evidence of reversal of this system has been negative in heterotrophic cells, but there is a report that the photoassimilation of acetate occurs via a carboxylation of acetyl coenzyme A (see Chapter 5, this volume).

Speculations on the nature of the carboxylation involved in photosynthesis and on the interaction between photosynthesis and respiration convinced most investigators that ordinary chemical analysis of the cell constituents would not decide which intermediates might belong to respiration and which to photosynthesis; this awaited the opportunity to use some isotopes of carbon.

B. The Use of Carbon Isotopes and the Discovery of Labeled Phosphoglyceric Acid

The production of several carbon isotopes (C^{11}, C^{13}, C^{14}) finally provided the tools with which to distinguish experimentally between the intermediates of photosynthesis and those of respiration. Now it could be expected that "tagging" plants in the light would identify the intermediates of one metabolic line only. Some early attempts with radioactive C^{11} by Kamen and co-workers did not proceed very far because of the short half-life (20 minutes) of this particular isotope (cf. 436, 540). C^{13}, which is not radioactive, requires a mass spectrograph for its analysis, but it has been used, and continues to be useful, in biological research. Most experiments in photosynthesis which were done with these two isotopes have been superseded by work with the radioactive isotope, C^{14} (half-life, 5000 years).

After several years of intense search for the carboxylation reaction in photosynthesis, it now seems definitely established that a reaction between a C_5 compound (ribulose diphosphate) and carbon dioxide is the first step, resulting in the formation of two molecules of 3-phosphoglyceric acid (hereafter written as phosphoglyceric acid).

$$HCO_3^- + \begin{array}{c} H_2\text{—}C\text{—}O\text{—}PO_3^{--} \\ | \\ C{=}O \\ | \\ H\text{—}C\text{—}OH \\ | \\ H\text{—}C\text{—}OH \\ | \\ H_2\text{—}C\text{—}OPO_3^{--} \end{array} \rightarrow 2 \begin{array}{c} COO^- \\ | \\ HCOH \\ | \\ H_2\text{—}C\text{—}O\text{—}PO_3^{--} \end{array} + H^+ \qquad \text{(h)}$$

The reaction is strongly exergonic ($\Delta F = -8000$ calories per mole). It has been reported to be irreversible (34–36, 77–82, 150–154).

This reaction does not need light energy to proceed. Discovered first in photoautotrophic cells, it was later found to occur in the chemosynthetic bacteria as well as in the heterotrophic *Escherichia coli* (433, 434, 557).

The all-important energy-storing step in the light is, then, the reduction of an acid group to an aldehyde group:

$$R.C\begin{array}{l} {/\!\!/}O \\ \diagdown OH \end{array} + 2\,[H] \rightarrow R.C\begin{array}{l} {/\!\!/}O \\ \diagdown H \end{array} + H_2O \qquad \text{(i)}$$

and the simplest scheme for the assimilation of carbon can be written [equation (j)]:

$$C_5 + C_1 \rightleftarrows C_6 \nearrow 2C_3 \xrightarrow{\text{light}} 2C_3 \text{ triose} \qquad \text{(j,i)}$$

$$C_6 \overset{\text{light}}{\dashrightarrow} C_6 \text{ hexose} \qquad \text{(j,ii)}$$

(2C₃ triose → C₆ hexose)

Simple as the principle underlying studies of photosynthesis with radioactive carbon dioxide may seem, there are inherent possibilities for errors, and hardly any of these have been missed. The reactions promoted by light and those that follow are so fast that longer periods of photosynthesis with tracer carbon render the plant radioactive

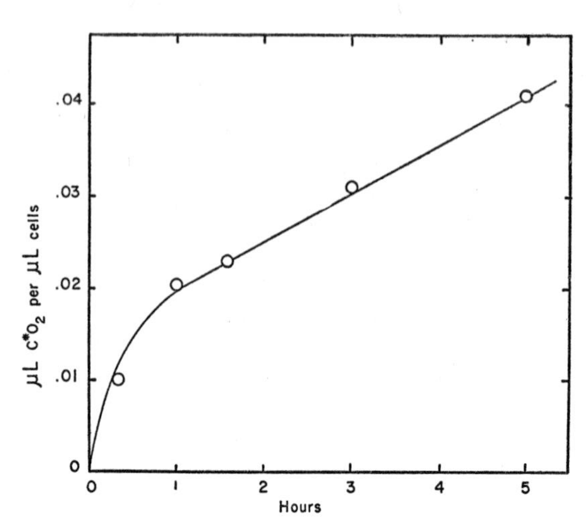

FIG. 66. Time course of the aerobic fixation of labeled carbon dioxide at 25°C in the dark by *Scenedesmus* sp. (60).

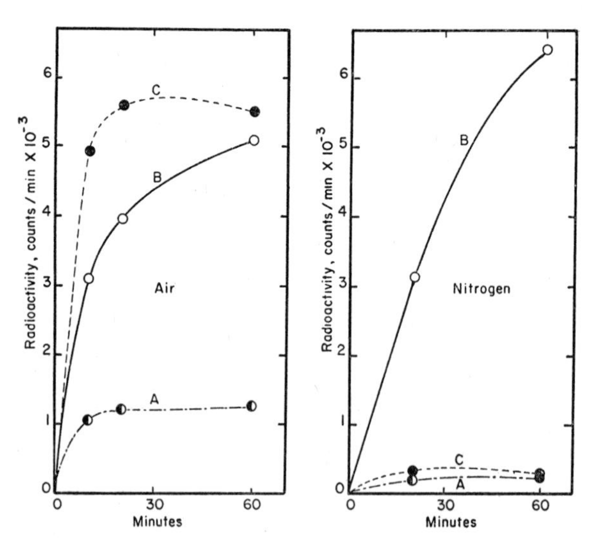

FIG. 67. Importance of respiration for the transport of carbon fixed in the dark into various cell constituents. *Scenedesmus* sp. at 25°C takes up labeled carbon dioxide under aerobic and anaerobic conditions. It enters by exchange into water-extractable substances (curve *B*), which only by respiration are transformed into fats (curve *A*) and water-insoluble cell constituents (curve *C*) (60).

throughout. Though useful for the manufacture of labeled plant constituents, prolonged experiments with $C^{14}O_2$ have little value for the kinetic analysis of a metabolic mechanism (59, 75).

Nevertheless, it is necessary to work under steady-state conditions (unless one is deliberately engaged in studying transient effects). If

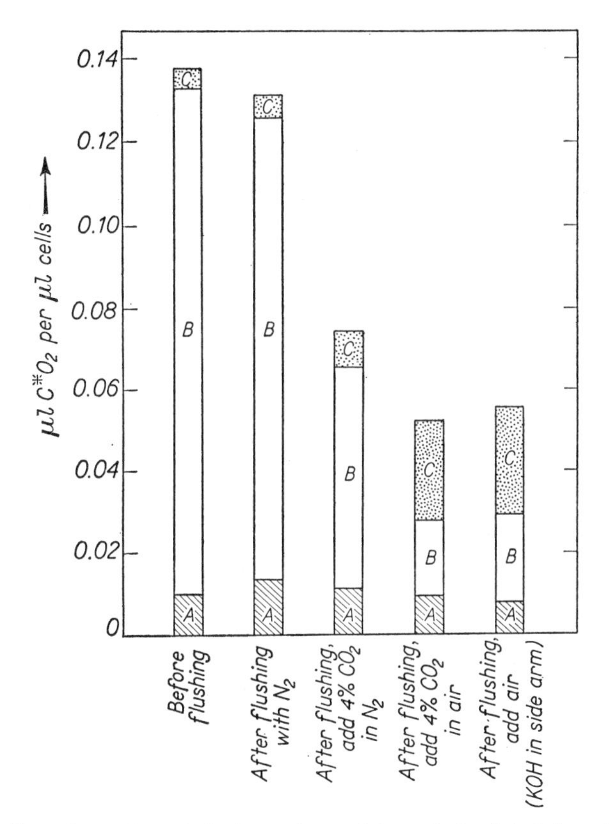

FIG. 68. Transformation of dark products. Most of the labeled carbon dioxide ($C^{14}O_2$) picked up in the dark under nitrogen by *Scenedesmus* sp. at 25°C is rapidly lost again through exchange with $C^{12}O_2$, partly transformed in air by respiration into stable cell constituents. *A*, Benzine extractable; *B*, hot water extractable; *C*, hot water insoluble (60).

the tracer carbon is supplied just prior to illumination, respiratory reactions will exchange it through various reversible decarboxylation steps (see Figs. 66, 67, 68). Some of the substances—or even preferentially such substances—will become reduced during short exposures. The labeled carbon dioxide is thus channeled into paths different from the prominent one of photosynthesis in its steady state. At high light intensities the transformation of the first intermediates into secondary compounds is very fast, and at low light intensities the rate of photosynthesis may be comparable to that of respiration. The concentration of photoproducts may not be much different from that of the exchange products, not to mention the possibility that freshly reduced compounds can immediately enter the respiratory system. Brown *et al.* (60) found that a few minutes of photosynthesis were sufficient to distribute the radioactive carbon throughout the cell. The times during which labeling experiments could be useful in trapping the immediate fixation products had, therefore, to be shortened. The distribution of the newly assimilated carbon via secondary reactions into fats and insoluble materials is surprisingly fast. In aerobic organisms respiration is important. This was shown by Brown and associates in comparing aerobic with anaerobic conditions in algae (see Fig. 67). In anaerobic organisms, like some purple bacteria, whose growth phase is closely linked with the photochemical reactions, we may expect no such demonstrable separation between photosynthetic and chemosynthetic fixation.

It was clear then, that illumination periods of a minute or less had to be used. The amounts of fixation products formed in seconds rather than minutes could be calculated to be rather small. Thus, the first identification of some truly photosynthetic intermediate products was done successfully not by isolation and chemical analysis, but by way of sensitive radiochromatography. Paper chromatograms of extracts of the early products were laid on the surface of photographic films. After an appropriate period of exposure, the radiation would make spots on the film. The darkness of these spots was roughly proportional to the amount of radiocarbon present in the substances separated on the chromatogram. Figure 69 gives examples of the work of Calvin *et al.* (30–34, 77–82). At normal temperatures, the number of compounds labeled by radiocarbon in very short times turned out to be unexpectedly high.

The experiments of the type which led to the discovery of the first recognizable carboxylated compound are now usually done as follows: A suspension of algae (*Chlorella* or *Scenedesmus* spp.) is illuminated strongly in a cooled narrow vessel while carbon dioxide in air bubbles through the suspension. After steady-state conditions have presumably been reached, some radioactive carbon dioxide is quickly introduced and dispersed in the suspension. After a certain time, measured in seconds, the suspension is dropped through a wide stopper or a trap door into an excess of boiling alcohol. This supposedly stops instantly all further metabolic activity. The alcohol is evaporated to dryness and

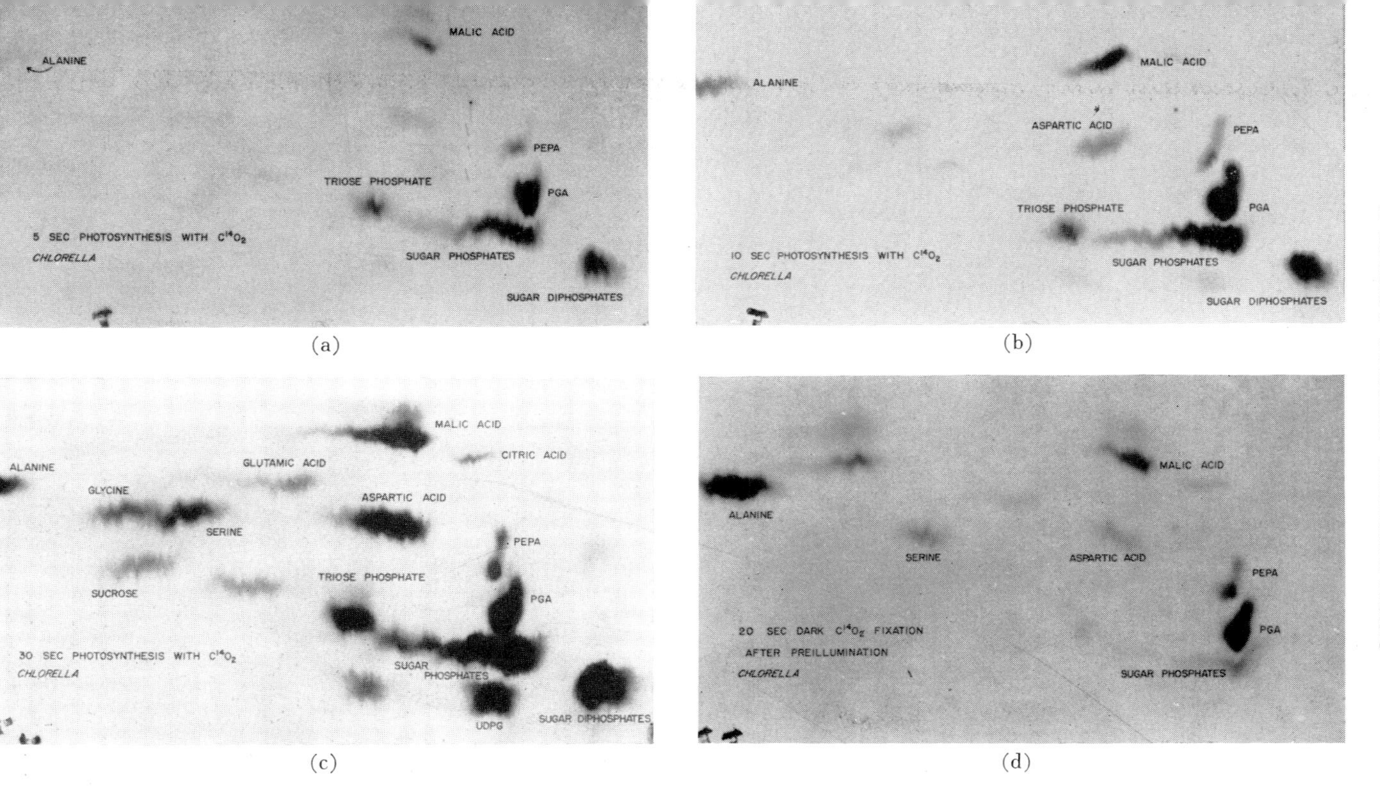

FIG. 69. Radiochromatograms showing the incorporation of radioactive tracer carbon into various organic compounds under the influence of light in unicellular algae. a, Five seconds; b, 10 seconds; c, 30-seconds photosynthesis in *Chlorella* sp. In (a), only PGA and its reduction products are found. d, The incorporation of tracer carbon into several compounds after "preillumination." Besides PGA, there are several derivatives of pyruvic acid present. (After Benson and Calvin.)

the remaining sediment of algae and (extracted) pigments are extracted again with hot water or buffer. The material present in the aqueous solution is subjected to chromatography and radioautography as described above. If the time the illuminated algae were in contact with radioactive carbon was very short and the temperature of the suspension very low, the chromatogram will look like the one shown in Fig. 69a, where all the radioactivity seems to be concentrated in three spots. The assimilated labeled carbon spreads into more and more compounds the longer the time of exposure and the higher the temperature (see Figs. 69,a–c). Calvin and Benson found that the short exposures left radioactivity mainly in a spot which occupied the same position as phosphoglyceric acid in the controls.

When the phosphoglyceric acid formed in such experiments was chemically broken down to ascertain which of the three carbons in the molecule contained the radioactivity, it was found essentially in the carboxyl group. The fact that the two remaining carbon atoms nearly always showed some appreciable radioactivity at first seemed to be a puzzling complication. With somewhat longer exposures, more and more radioactive phosphorylated sugars appeared on the chromatograms. The distribution of radioactivity in the hexose molecules indicated a reductive condensation from two molecules of three carbons each (Fig. 81). Thus Benson and Calvin obtained evidence which pointed to phosphoglyceric acid as the carboxylation product of an enzymatic reaction which preceded the effect of light and was followed by a photochemical reduction of the acid to the aldehyde in the light and a subsequent condensation of triose to glucose (32). That the addition of radioactive carbon dioxide to photosynthesizing algae and quick killing in boiling alcohol really leads to carboxyl-labeled phosphoglyceric acid was confirmed by Fager and Rosenberg who gave the first chemical analysis of derivatives of the isolated phosphoglyceric acid (150, 151). With somewhat longer exposures not only more and more sugar phosphates appear on the chromatograms, but also some pyruvate, malate, and amino acids (486, 487) (see Fig. 69c).

For a time it seemed as if the sequence of phosphoglyceric acid formation, reduction to triose phosphate, and condensation to hexose phosphate—that is, a simple reversal of the glycolytic pathway—was all but proved. It remained only to explain the way radioactive carbon entered so rapidly into that part of the phosphoglyceric acid molecule which serves as acceptor for free carbon dioxide. At the time of this writing, the hypothesis of a simple reversal of glycolysis by the action of light is again doubtful, even from the biochemical point of view. Physicists approaching photosynthesis in terms of its mechanism and kinetics had never regarded this alluringly simple proposition as adequate. The complexities involved in this problem—the choice to be made between (i) and (ii) in equation (j) above—are discussed in the rest of this section.

C. THE CARBOXYLATION CYCLE

Phosphoglyceric acid, with the labeled carbon in the carboxyl group, can arise only by the addition of the tracer carbon dioxide to a 2-carbon compound or to a larger molecule from which the 3-carbon acid splits off after the carboxylation. The chemical degradation necessary to establish the important role of the carboxyl group revealed that after 2 minutes of photosynthesis nearly as much radioactivity could be found in the remaining two carbons of the phosphoglyceric acid as in its carboxyl group (32, 149–151). Thus, this 2-carbon acceptor must be rapidly regenerated from the very products of photosynthesis.

It is known that phosphoglyceric acid is an important metabolite in the glycolytic pathway. It can be dehydrated to phosphoenolpyruvic acid or reduced to glyceraldehyde-3-phosphate. Since the new results seemed to indicate a reversal of the glycolytic breakdown of carbohydrates, it seemed appropriate to think of other biochemical analogies. Calvin *et al.* first conceived the regeneration of the 2-carbon acceptor as a cycle via a second carboxylation of the Wood-Werkman type. They proposed numerous schemes based on known metabolic reactions in plants (80, 436). The general idea, upheld till 1953, is shown in Fig. 70. Fager *et al.* (149, 214), however, pointed out that the kinetics of the distribution of the labeled carbon among the compounds appearing in these hypothetical cycles left no room for a second carboxylation and did not support any one of these hypotheses. They said that the acceptor formation would very likely proceed in a cycle working mainly on the reduction level of carbohydrate, and suggested that in some way the 2-carbon acceptor would have its origin in the freshly formed hexose (Fig. 71). The accumulation of more experimental evidence confirmed this idea. First came the surprising discovery by Benson (36) that two of the earliest compounds to receive labeled carbon among the sugar phosphates were sedoheptulose and ribulose. Thus a C_7 and a C_5 sugar phosphate were somehow involved in a cycle starting with PGA and leading back to it. The existence of such a cycle is now firmly established (Fig. 72).

The analysis of the rise and fall of the relative concentration of the tracer carbon in the individual carbon atoms of a hexose, a heptulose, a pentulose, etc., opened an entirely new chapter of carbohydrate transformations in green cells—and not only in green cells. An enormous amount of work went into the separation of a series of new enzymes (see the reviews cited in references 548 and 577). The carbon reduction cycle as of 1958 according to Bassham and Calvin is shown in Fig. 73. The most important point is that the plant, in order to regain the

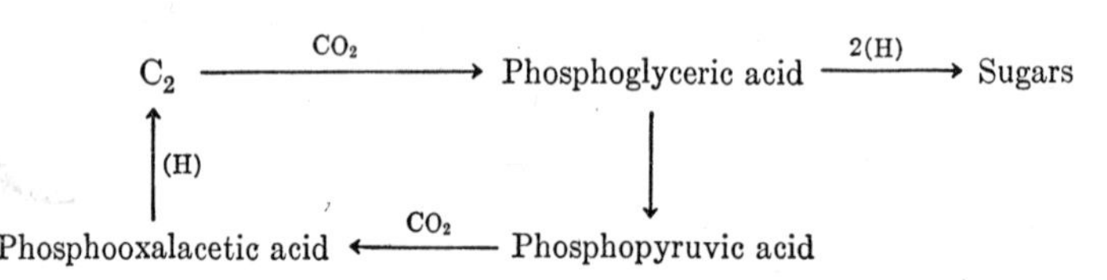

FIGS. 70–72. Development of ideas on the photosynthetic carboxylation cycle.
FIG. 70. Two carboxylations, various dicarboxylic acids, and corresponding reduction steps. After Benson and Calvin, 1951 (34, 35, 80).

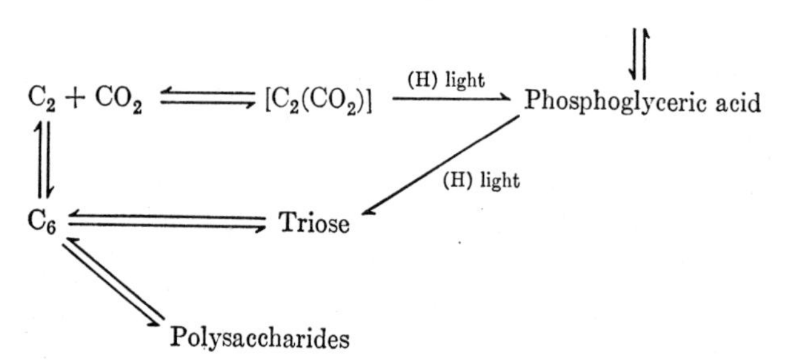

FIG. 71. One carboxylation, two light steps. Cycle proceeding on the level of carbohydrates. After Fager, 1950 (149, 214).

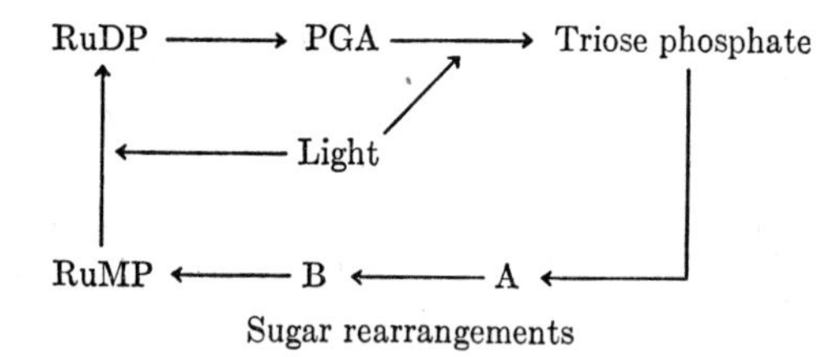

FIG. 72. One carboxylation, two light steps. Ribulose diphosphate as acceptor for CO_2. From Calvin *et al.*, 1956 (82).

acceptor molecule ribulose diphosphate in the over-all fixation of just one new carbon atom

$$C_1 + C_5 \rightarrow C_6 \rightarrow C_5 + \tfrac{1}{6} \text{ hexose} \qquad \text{(k)}$$

must have recourse to a mechanism of unusual complexity.

Because the carboxylation reaction has been found in nonphotosynthetic microorganisms (269, 433, 557), it is probable that the regeneration of the acceptor (ribulose diphosphate) may also proceed by purely

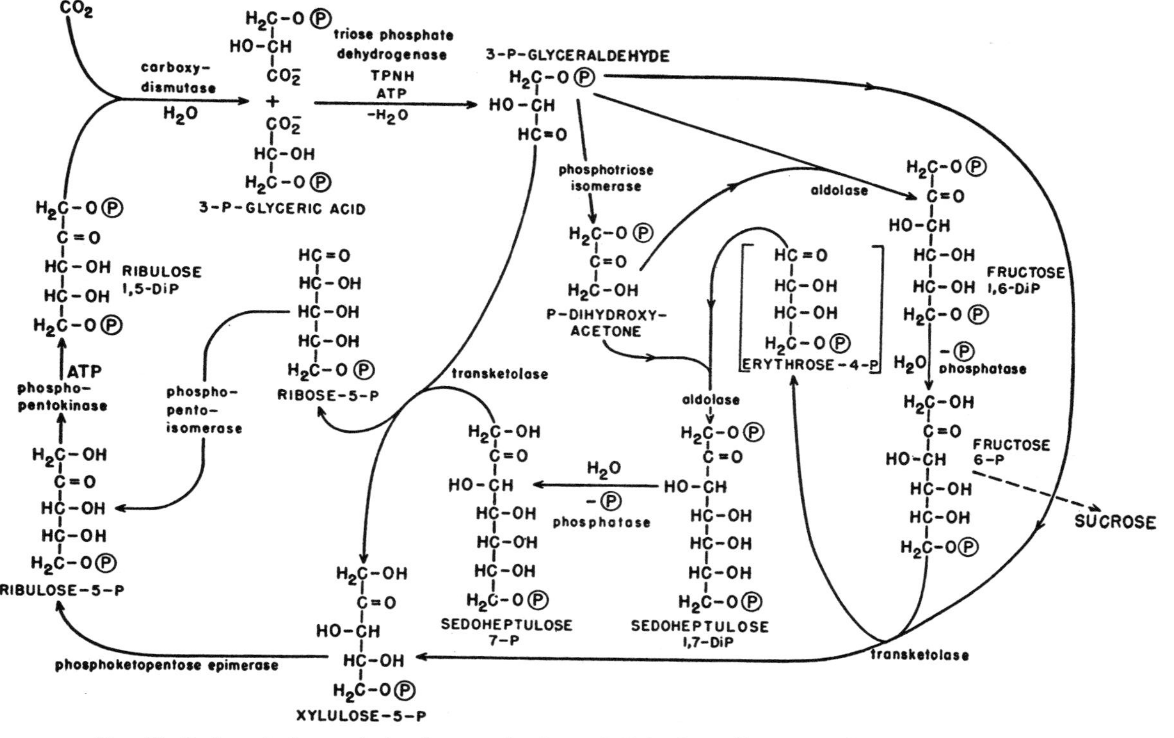

FIG. 73. Carboxylation cycle in photosynthesis as of 1958. According to Bassham and Calvin (32).

chemosynthetic means. It is now a problem of general biochemistry, quite apart from photosynthesis, to see how many variants of this cycle exist. According to the scheme of Fig. 73, all that is needed to keep the cycle going is a source of reducing agents (H) such as TPNH and of energy-rich phosphate, ATP. What has been emphasized in our introductory section—the looseness of the coupling of carbon dioxide fixation with the photochemistry—is quite apparent also in this scheme.

D. THE ROLE OF LIGHT IN THE CARBON CYCLE

We mentioned in the first section that a variety of known metabolic syntheses may be coupled to the photochemical mechanism. In order

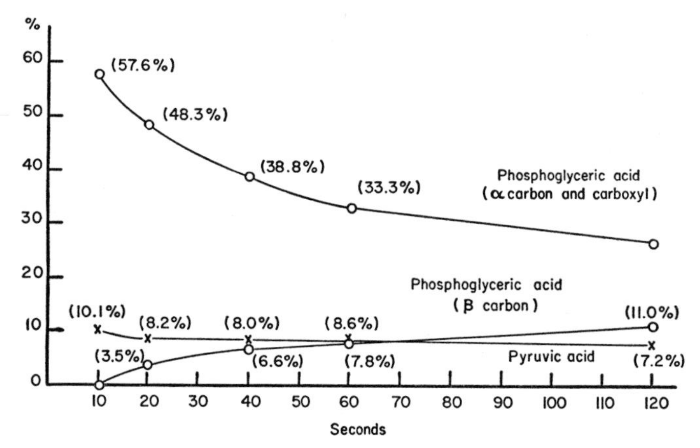

FIG. 74. Decrease of percentage of tracer carbon found in PGA with increasing time of photosynthesis in the presence of tracer. Extrapolation to zero time is unlikely to reach 100% (150).

to establish the pre-eminence of the carboxylation leading to phosphoglyceric acid among other probable carboxylation steps, two points had to be settled. First one had to ask: Is the reaction leading to PGA truly the major way by which carbon dioxide is pulled into the carbon cycle, and, if so, how closely is it connected with the photochemistry of chlorophyll? The proof that it is indeed the major point of entrance was seen in the results of experiments of the kind shown in Fig. 69a. This figure records the distribution in various early assimilation products of the carbon absorbed from carbon dioxide.

Figure 74 gives the curve for the decrease with time in the percentage of the total carbon which is fixed in PGA. The nearer to zero time (the moment of adding the tracer carbon dioxide to the photosynthesizing suspension of algae), the greater the fraction of the total carbon[14] taken up which can be located in the 3-carbon compound. Noteworthy, however, is the fact that the shape of the curve does not seem to point to a 100% fixation in PGA at zero time. The maximum seen here is 60%, and an extrapolation to a value above 80% at zero time is not justified by the shape of the curve. Table X furnishes a recent example where after 5 seconds as much as 74% of all tracer was in PGA. This seems to give better support to the idea of an exclusive

TABLE X
PERCENTAGE OF TOTAL RADIOACTIVITY FOUND IN PGA AFTER SHORT PERIODS OF PHOTOSYNTHESIS WITH LABELED CARBON DIOXIDE IN *Scenedesmus*[a,b]

Time of contact with $C^{14}O_2$ (seconds)	Per cent C^{14} in PGA
5	74
30	53
120	34

[a] From Metzner *et al.* (367).
[b] Cells killed in boiling ethanol.

first fixation in the carboxyl group. Still, there is room for a hypothetical compound, an unstable precursor, between the C_5 acceptor and the PGA, which might be lost during the isolation of the latter [see equation (j, ii) page 139].

There also was some doubt as to the degree of exchange of photosynthetically produced PGA with respiratory PGA already present in the cell. Fager and Rosenberg made a kinetic study and proved that, under steady-state conditions, a little time is required after the plants have come into contact with the tracer carbon before it appears in the first products. Figure 75 demonstrates that the extrapolation backward of the line plotting the increase of fixation with time crosses the abscissa after, and not before, the moment when $C^{14}O_2$ was added. These data disposed of the exchange hypothesis.

The second point, the question whether the carboxylation leading to PGA is one of the photochemical steps or purely enzymatic, was settled by "preillumination" experiments. These consist of illuminating the sample of algae for a while in the absence of carbon dioxide and then adding tracer carbon dioxide at the moment when the light is turned off. In 1937, McAlister and Myers (361) had observed that carbon dioxide continues to be taken up for a short time after illumination ceases. This they called the "pick-up," and its existence was confirmed in the years to follow. Benson, Bassham and Calvin, and associates, in 1950, were the first to demonstrate that a "pick-up" effect could be seen with tracer carbon dioxide after preilluminatio of the algae in absence of carbon dioxide under nitrogen (34). Th chromatogram shown in Fig. 69d is one of the results they obtained Their earlier experiments of this type had given astonishingly larg amounts of succinate. The number of C^{14}-compounds visible on thi chromatogram, and the similarity of the picture to that often obtaine by somewhat longer photosynthesis, supported the idea of a genera "reducing power." It was believed that the plants would fill a reservoi

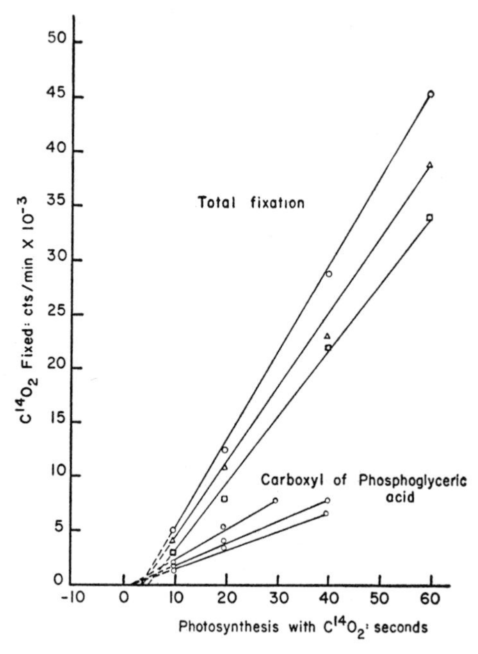

FIG. 75. Time course of entry of tracer carbon during photosynthesis. Extrapola tion of curve cuts abscissa a moment after the time of adding tracer, thus provin the absence of extensive exchange reactions. Contrast Fig. 66 (151).

with such a general reducing agent during anaerobic preillumination Afterward, in the dark, this could promote not only the fixation reac tion (or several fixation reactions) but also other reduction steps.

Fager, however, in a set of similar experiments obtained the result summarized in Fig. 76, which seemed to contradict those expressed b Fig. 69d above (215).

Because of what we know at present about the multiplicity of possi ble reactions, both types of results can now be understood. The decisiv factor is the concentration of the regular carbon dioxide acceptor— ribulose diphosphate. In Fager's experiment it turned out that what

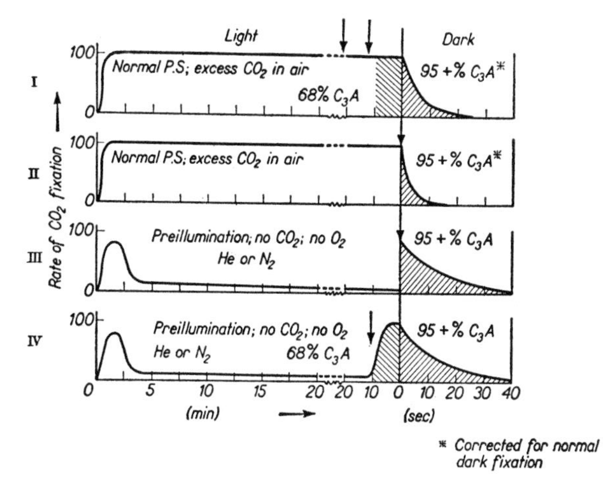

FIG. 76. Rates of carbon dioxide fixation by *Scenedesmus* sp. during, and immediately after, a period of illumination, and nature of products of carbon dioxide "pick-up." ↓ Signifies moment of adding $C^{14}O_2$; shaded area indicates time and course of its fixation. Curve *I*. Normal, aerobic photosynthesis. $C^{14}O_2$ added 10 or 20 seconds before darkening. Curve *II*. Like *I*. $C^{14}O_2$ added at the moment of darkening. Curve *III*. Anaerobic preillumination in absence of carbon dioxide. $C^{14}O_2$ added at darkening. Curve *IV*. Like *III*. $C^{14}O_2$ added 10 seconds before darkening. In all cases the dark-fixation product was PGA and some pyruvate (215).

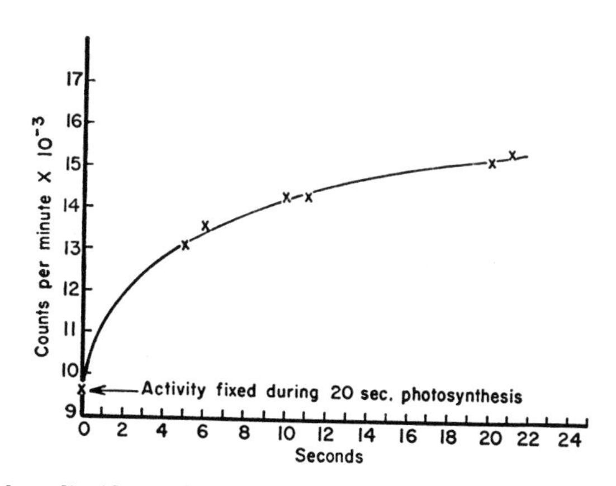

FIG. 77. Carbon dioxide "pick-up" as seen with the aid of tracer carbon. Activity of C^{14} fixed vs time in the dark after photosynthesis. Note that the ordinate is shortened. The curve starts at the point where, after 15 minutes of photosynthesis with excess $C^{12}O_2$ and 20 seconds more with $C^{14}O_2$, fixation of tracer has been under way in the light. The magnitude of the "pick-up" corresponds to about 10 seconds of photosynthesis. See curve *I* in Fig. 76 (214).

ever survived the illumination had to be one single acceptor for carbon dioxide, because the products of the dark fixation could be quantitatively accounted for as phosphoglyceric and pyruvic acids (Fig. 77). He could prove that the pyruvate was not the precursor of the phosphoglyceric acid, but rather a secondary product or, at best, one formed by a divergent path originating directly from a precursor common to both substances. As shown in Table XI, shortening of the illumination

TABLE XI
SEQUENCE OF FIXATION IN PHOSPHOGLYCERIC AND PYRUVIC ACIDS

	Treatment		
Tracer fixed in:	15-Minute illumination	1-Minute illumination	15-Minute illumination $+10^{-3}M$ F^-
Total	4000	5340	2600
Phosphoglyceric acid	2400	2360	1800
Pyruvic acid	760	200	160
Ratio (PGA:Py)	3:1	12:1	11:1

period or the poisoning of enolase with fluoride shifted the ratio between phosphoglycerate and pyruvate still more in favor of the former (152–154). Cyanide inhibited this "pick-up" carboxylation in the same way it does photosynthesis (214).

Calvin and Massini (32, 81) then performed the very telling experiment shown in Fig. 78. They observed not only the appearance of phosphoglyceric acid, but also the concomitant disappearance of diphosphates during the "pick-up" immediately after darkening. Thus the fate of the diphosphates became linked with that of PGA. Sudden withdrawal of carbon dioxide during stationary photosynthesis produces the reverse effect—an accumulation of ribulose while phosphoglyceric acid disappears (Fig. 79). When it was found that during this reaction the rate of the PGA formation was twice that of the carbon dioxide absorption, equation (h) page 139, became the only possible way to formulate the carboxylation (32). Since this carboxylation proceeds after the light has been turned off and at a rate comparable to photosynthesis, it is evident that light is not required for this particular step.

The role of light is therefore restricted to two other steps—photophosphorylation (Section XIII, Fig. 108) and the reduction of phosphoglyceric acid to glyceraldehyde-3-phosphate (compare the schemes of Figs. 3, 81). The first is necessary to produce ribulose diphosphate, the second can be interpreted as the reversal of the corresponding step in

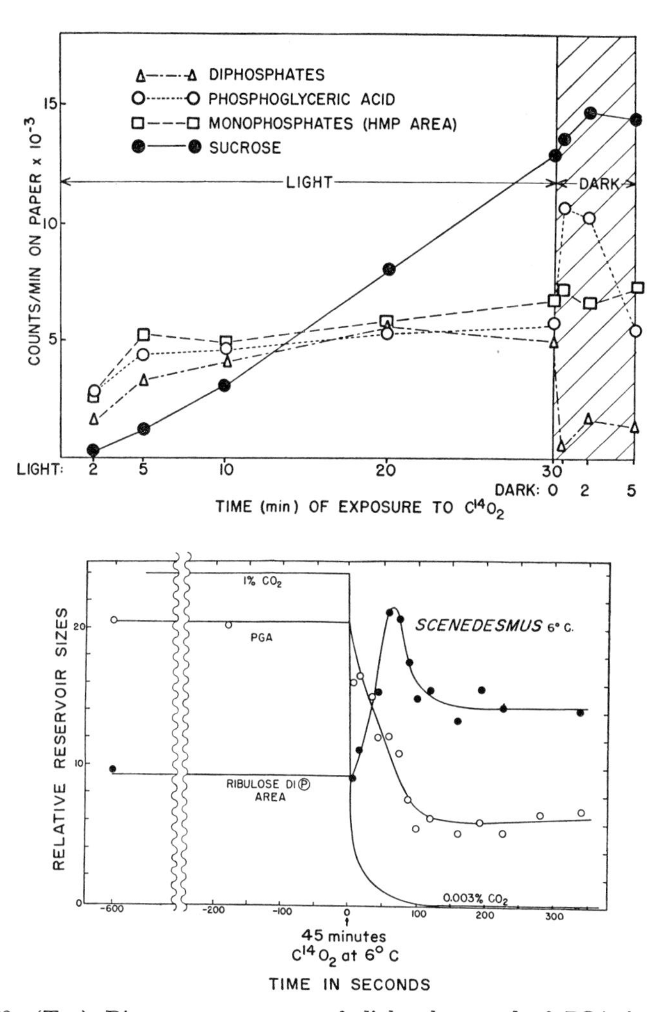

FIG. 78. (Top) Divergent movement of diphosphate and of PGA immediately after darkening. Steady-state photosynthesis with tracer carbon during ½ hour establishes a constant level for both intermediates. During the first 30 seconds in the dark, PGA increases at the expense of diphosphate (32).

FIG. 79. (Bottom) Sudden withdrawal of carbon dioxide from illuminated *Scenedesmus* sp. leads to a decline in the steady-state concentration of PGA and a corresponding increase in that of RuDP (32).

glycolysis. Since both—the photophosphorylation and the implied reduction of TPN or DPN—have indeed been shown to occur with illuminated chloroplasts, this view of photosynthesis seemed definitely established. The distribution of radioactivity among the carbons of the hexose carbon chain found after a few seconds of photosynthesis

TABLE XII
DISTRIBUTION OF TRACER CARBON IN PRODUCTS OF PHOTOSYNTHESIS

15 Seconds' photosynthesis, soybean leaves[a]
 Alanine: CH_3—19%; $CHNH_2$—20%; COOH—60%
15 Seconds' photosynthesis, barley[b]
 Glyceric acid: $HOCH_2$—23%; CHOH—21%; COOH—56%
 Glycolic acid: $HOCH_2$—50%; COOH—50%
 Hexoses: $C_{1,6}$—24%; $C_{2,5}$—25%; $C_{3,4}$—52%
30 Seconds' photosynthesis, *Scenedesmus*
 Glyceric acid: $HOCH_2$—10%; HOCH—7%; COOH—81%
 Hexoses: $C_{1,6}$—6%; $C_{2,5}$—7%; $C_{3,4}$—87%

[a] L. P. Vernon and S. Aronoff.
[b] A. A. Benson and M. Calvin.

(Table XII) also admitted hardly any other explanation (32). To gether with the distribution of C^{14} in other sugars (Fig. 80), it fur nished the basis for the scheme of Fig. 73.

PGA	RuDP	SMP	HMP
CH_2O Ⓟ	CH_2O Ⓟ*	CH_2OH	C
HCOH	C=O*	C=O	C
CO_2H***	HCOH***	HOCH*	C*
	HCOH	HCOH*	C*
	CH_2O Ⓟ	HCOH*	C
		HCOH	C
		CH_2O Ⓟ	

FIG. 80. Distribution of radioactive carbon in certain sugars. PGA = phosphc glyceric acid; RuDP = ribulose diphosphate; SMP = seduheptulose monophosphate HMP = hexose monophosphate. From Bassham and Calvin (32).

Lately, however, it has become increasingly doubtful whether thes conclusions are unequivocable. Kandler (292–294) has measured th turnover of phosphorylation in the light, and found that too littl energy-rich phosphate is delivered to keep the Benson-Calvin cycl going in the manner proposed by the California school (this require three ATP molecules per molecule of carbon dioxide reduced). Kandle insisted that another way should be sought by which the same end, i.e. the carboxylation of RuDP and its regeneration, could be accomplishe with a smaller number of phosphate transfers. Furthermore, a carefu reinvestigation by Gibbs and Kandler of the distribution of C^{14} withi the sugar molecules gave the results shown in Table XIII (295). They

TABLE XIIIa
DISTRIBUTION OF TOTAL ACTIVITY AMONG THE CARBON ATOMS OF GLUCOSE

Plant	Intensity (foot-candles)	Time	Sugar source	Tracer content of glucose carbon atoms in % of total activity					
				1	2	3	4	5	6
Chlorella[b]	4000	10 sec	Starch	3.7	2.9	39	52	1.1	1.3
			Monophosphate	6.3	6.6	40	53	1.0	1.2
			UDPG	4.8	4.6	42	47	0.7	1.1
Chlorella[c]	4000	60 sec	Starch	7.4	9.5	33	44	2.7	3.0
			Monophosphate	8.8	7.4	32	42	3.3	6.0
			UDPG	7.0	5.7	37	42	3.3	4.7
			Unknown PO_4	8.4	7.7	33	41	4.5	5.5
Sunflower leaves	70	15 min	Sucrose	10	11	22	41	7.8	8.1
Canna leaves	2000	24 hr	Sucrose	17.3	16.6	16.9	16.5	16.5	16.6

[a] Representative data from Gibbs (229).
[b] *Chlorella* was illuminated 5 minutes in N_2 before introduction of $C^{14}O_2$.
[c] *Chlorella* was incubated with $C^{14}O_2$ in the dark for 5 minutes before photosynthesis occurred.

TABLE XIIIb
EFFECT OF GLUCOSE FEEDING ON DISTRIBUTION OF C^{14} IN SUCROSE FORMED DURING PHOTOSYNTHESIS: *Chlorella*[a]

Time (min)	CO_2 (μmoles)	Tracer content of glucose carbon atoms in % of total activity: −Glucose 1	2	3	4	5	6	+Glucose 1	2	3	4	5	6
15	10	17	16	22	29	7	9	16	16	27	28	5	6
45	50	17	15	18	25	8	10	15	14	26	31	6	8
180	200	16	16	16	19	15	17	17	13	25	31	7	8

[a] Light intensity—700 foot-candles, final concentration of glucose 0.55 μmoles/ml. Phosphate buffer ($M/30$), pH 5.6. Glucose respiration and photosynthesis at compensation point. One milliliter of packed chlorella cells per 100 ml buffer. Cells starved 16 hours by shaking in H_2O in dark.

This experiment indicates that exogenous glucose can enter the cycle from the C_2 acceptor and keep the sugar asymetrically labeled by dilution. According to Gibbs and Kandler (229).

found a most marked asymmetry in the distribution of C^{14} among the carbons of the sugar. Such results require the assumption of some exchange reactions between the various carbohydrates of the Benson-Calvin cycle if PGA is to be retained in the role originally assigned to it.

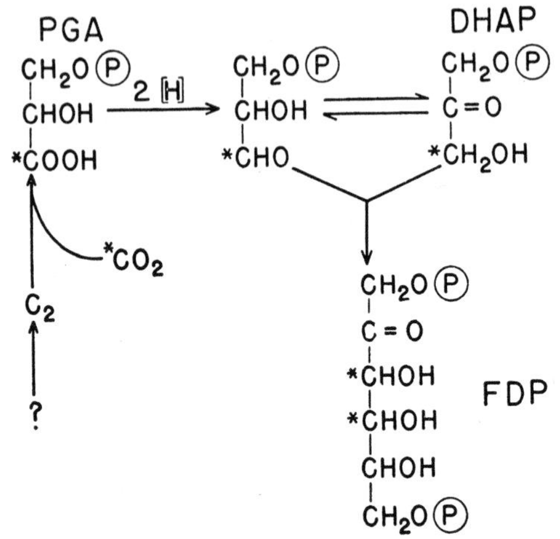

PGA: CH_2OⓅ — CHOH — *COOH $\xrightarrow{2[H]}$ CH_2OⓅ — CHOH — *CHO ⇌ DHAP: CH_2OⓅ — C=O — *CH_2OH

*COOH ← *CO_2 + C_2 ← ?

*CHO + *CH_2OH → FDP: CH_2OⓅ — C=O — *CHOH — *CHOH — CHOH — CH_2OⓅ

FIG. 81. Path of carbon from CO_2 to hexose.

Breakdown of Glucose by *Lactobacillus casei*

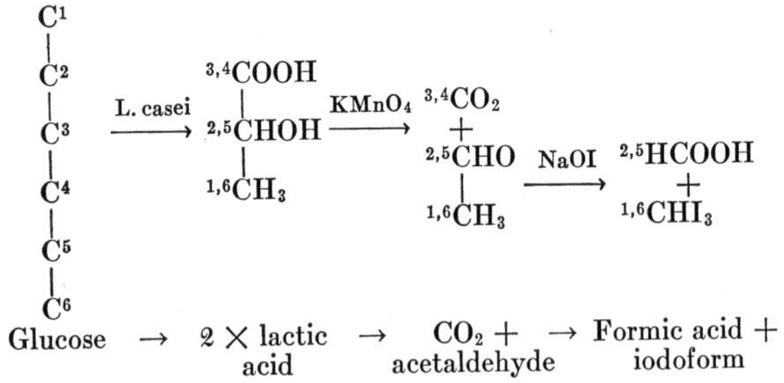

C^1—C^2—C^3—C^4—C^5—C^6 $\xrightarrow{L.\ casei}$ $^{3,4}COOH$—$^{2,5}CHOH$—$^{1,6}CH_3$ $\xrightarrow{KMnO_4}$ $^{3,4}CO_2$ + $^{2,5}CHO$—$^{1,6}CH_3$ $\xrightarrow{NaOI}$ $^{2,5}HCOOH$ + $^{1,6}CHI_3$

Glucose → 2 × lactic acid → CO_2 + acetaldehyde → Formic acid + iodoform

FIG. 82. Method by which the results shown in Figs. 80 and 81 have been established.

There is, however, a simpler explanation which takes account of both difficulties—the insufficient phosphorylation rate and the asymmetric distribution of the tracer carbon in hexoses. If a precursor to PGA, and not PGA itself, were reduced in the light, the latter would be bypassed as long as the light exerts its power. Only in the dark would phosphoglyceric acid be an end product of the carboxylation reaction. The assumption of a dual pathway is not in contradiction to the actual observations (compare Fig. 124).

The experimental discrepancy between the results obtained may find its explanation in the methods used to isolate the carbon atoms in the hexose molecule. Figure 82 is a scheme showing how the data of Figs.

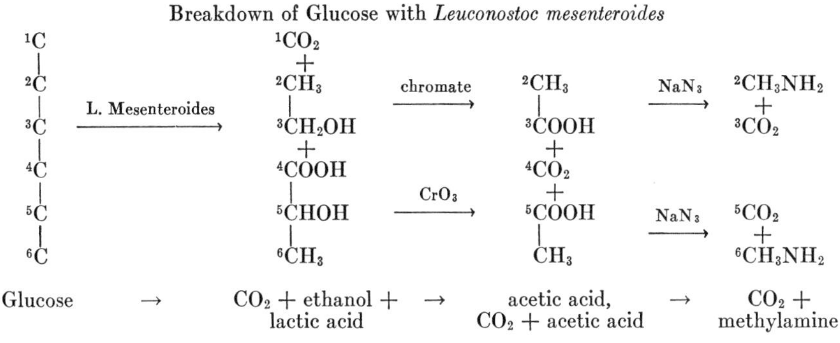

Fig. 83. Method of Gibbs and Kandler (229) for the isolation of single carbon atoms in hexose.

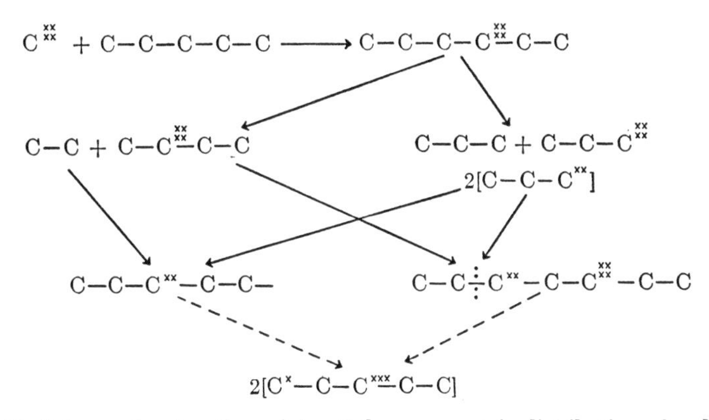

Fig. 84. Scheme showing the origin of the asymmetric distribution of radioactive carbon in certain sugars. Adapted from Gibbs and Kandler (229).

80 and 81 have been obtained. Figure 83 shows the same for the newer method. The asymmetric distribution of the radioactivity in the sugar molecules can be accounted for by the scheme shown in Fig. 84.

Whether the carboxylation proceeds in the dark with stable PGA as its product or in the light with a different result, in both cases the initial step is most probably the formation of an addition product of ribulose diphosphate and carbon dioxide on the surface of an enzyme.

In current discussions this is depicted as a branched 6-carbon acid which in reality need not exist. Its reduction in the light and subsequent rearrangement into a straight-chain molecule prevents the dismutation into two equal parts that otherwise appear as PGA.

E. The Carboxylation Enzyme

The carboxylation enzyme has been called carboxydismutase and "ribulose diphosphate carboxylase." The first name implies a mechanism; it might be preferable to speak of the enzyme simply as a carboxylase.

Fager showed that what survives in green cells after a preillumination in the absence of carbon dioxide is not a general "reducing power," but a specific acceptor for carbon dioxide. When carbon dioxide was given in the dark, over 90% of the product was PGA; cell-free macerates of spinach (*Spinacia oleracea*) leaves were found to contain the enzyme responsible for this carboxylation. The crude enzyme extract was sensitive toward Cu^{2+} ions, toward *p*-chloromercuribenzoate, and to air. Treatment with cysteine restored the activity after inhibition by oxygen. This suggested the presence of essential sulfhydryl groups in the enzymes. Cyanide inhibited the activity of the extract about as much as that of the intact cell.

The acceptor extractable from preilluminated spinach leaves had the properties of a moderately stable phosphate sugar ester (152–154). Later studies by Horecker and Weisbach, Jacoby *et al.*, and Quayl *et al.*, showed that this phosphate ester, which could combine with carbon dioxide in the presence of the enzyme, was ribulose diphosphate. In the crude chloroplast preparation, the greatest influence of light was not upon the fixation and formation of PGA, but on a fraction which presumably contained the sugars (269, 276, 359, 433, 434, 557).

Such chloroplast extracts contain an enzyme which promotes the phosphorylation of ribulose diphosphate from ATP. This explains why Fager found a slow fixation of $C^{14}O_2$ which sometimes continued for more than 10 minutes. Further purification of the enzyme revealed a molecular weight of 300,000, a pH optimum at 7.7, and the need of magnesium ion as cofactor. *In vitro,* the enzyme, as presently prepared, is much less active than *in vivo* and requires relatively high concentrations of CO_2. Nevertheless, it is quite specific for ribulose diphosphate, and the conversion of the latter into two molecules of phosphoglyceric acid. The sluggishness might be explained by a two-step mechanism of which only the first—the combining of ribulose diphosphate with carbon dioxide—proceeds rapidly *in vitro,* the subsequent splitting going on slowly, outside the living cell. In spinach the enzyme appears to represent a large fraction of the soluble proteins in the chloroplasts.

It came as a surprise that this enzyme is not the exclusive property of the chlorophyll-containing plants, though in the plants themselves it remains associated with the chloroplast and has a tendency to disappear when conditions are unfavorable for the development of green plastids (194). *Thiobacillus* sp., as well as pentose-grown *Escherichia* (*Bacterium*) *coli*, contain an enzyme which carboxylates RuDP to give PGA. In *E. coli* the carboxylase seems to be an adaptive enzyme. Considering this, we need not postulate a fixed connection between the photochemical apparatus and the carbon dioxide fixation system. The disappearance of the enzyme in algae "bleached" by heterotrophic growth in the dark could be the consequence of the loss of substrate. On this assumption, normal glycolytic metabolism of the cell, which survives the "bleaching" in the dark, must not supply sufficient ribulose or ribulose derivatives to preserve the adaptive carboxylation enzyme. If true, this would point to a rather clear-cut separation between the respiratory and the photosynthetic mechanisms, despite occasional cross-linkages between them (such as a transfer or exchange of PGA).

It is now evident that, in cells having this enzyme, diphosphoribulose is not stable and accumulates only in the absence of carbon dioxide —a condition which can occur only in the light under nitrogen. After a dark period, the acceptor for the carboxylation reaction is present in rather small concentrations or not at all, since it has been removed by the reaction with respiratory carbon dioxide. This circumstance alone is sufficient to cause some of the induction phenomena which we shall describe below (Section XV).

F. OTHER CARBOXYLATIONS, OTHER PRODUCTS

After a very short period of photosynthesis with tracer carbon dioxide, the majority of chromatograms (as well as chemical analyses) of the soluble products indicate that some labeled carbon enters quickly into the dicarboxylic acids, amino acids, and fats. The rates of formation and the total amounts of these substances are greater than can be accounted for by normal unstimulated respiratory exchange reactions. Therefore, light must have an accelerating effect on the synthesis of dicarboxylic acids, amino acids, and fats. Very likely PGA is partially diverted into these side reactions before it is photochemically reduced to triose phosphate. This would seem even more plausible if it were confirmed that the photochemical steps in the Calvin-Benson cycle bypass some PGA molecules which then would not go to triose phosphate (229–231, 294, 367, 371, 433, 438, 525). Stable PGA, once formed by the carboxylation of RuDP, would lead in the direction of phosphopyruvate or pyruvate and after a second carboxylation to oxalacetate and malate.

How the assimilated carbon is distributed among the various compounds depends on the experimental circumstances, the age of the cells, and, particularly, the length and intensity of illumination (the presence of reduced nitrogen compounds diverts potential fat builders into amino acids) (92, 158–160, 369, 473, 591). Transient periods between light and darkness are characterized by the appearance of compounds which are not accumulated further in steady-state photosynthesis. A low partial pressure of carbon dioxide which does not saturate the normal carboxylation reaction with RuDP still gives a good rate in the

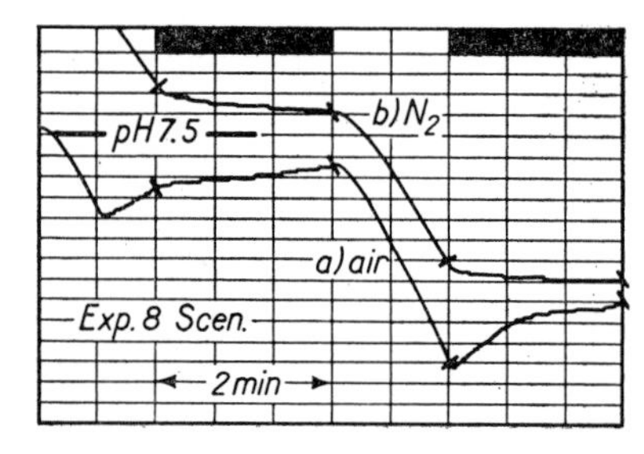

FIG. 85. Light-induced CO_2 fixation in labile compounds during 40 seconds of illumination after 2 minutes of darkness. Recorded pH changes with *Scenedesmus* sp. in *M*/500 bicarbonate. CO_2 concentration limiting. No special effect under anaerobic conditions (curve *b*). Additional, but unstable, CO_2 fixation in air (curve *a*) (cf. 217). The pH increases from 7.5 to 7.6. Dark periods are indicated by solid blocks. Compare Fig. 122, page 233.

reductive carboxylation of pyruvate (24, 557, 559). This may produce a shift toward oxalacetate, particularly under aerobic conditions when glycolysis provides more pyruvate (360, 545, 548). At least this is a plausible explanation of the effect shown in Fig. 85, where the uptake of carbon dioxide under low, rate-limiting carbon dioxide partial pressure evidently consists of two separate reactions. Under anaerobic conditions (curve *b*) there is only the usual permanent fixation of carbon dioxide (compare Fig. 38, Section V). In air (curve *a*) we see superimposed a second fixation, which is temporary. The extra carbon dioxide fixed aerobically is lost again in the dark.

It is as yet unknown whether it is the intermediates or the finished products of photosynthesis which are used preferentially to synthesize lipids in fat-storing plants like diatoms. But since we know that several coenzymes may be reduced directly, the normal pathways of fat synthesis could be set in motion by photochemical reactions. The experiments of Fogg point to an immediate synthesis of fats in the light from constituents of the ribulose cycle rather than from stored carbohydrates. At low partial pressures of carbon dioxide, much of the ribulose diphosphate (or perhaps an earlier intermediate) in the carboxylation cycle gives rise to a 2-carbon fragment, which appears as glycolic acid outside the cell (80). Tolbert *et al.* (518–520) observed that phosphoglycolic acid or glycolic acid can appear very quickly as excretion products in photosynthesis. Both carbon atoms of this acid are equally labeled when the experiment is run with $C^{14}O_2$ as a tracer. These authors consider glycolic acid to be the source of glycine and serine, for these compounds showed a labeling which fitted better with that found in glycolic acid than in PGA. The ease with which a 2-carbon fragment can be made available for metabolic synthesis in the plant during illumination is one point in favor of the idea that ribulose diphosphate is cleaved prior to the addition of carbon dioxide in the normal carboxylation reaction. Further experimentation with cell-free enzymes will decide this point (230, 433).

The most complex picture of the interplay between photochemistry and synthesis of organic compounds in green plants is found in the succulents. [There may be other examples in the plant kingdom which exhibit still greater deviations from what we now accept as "normal," but they have not yet been described (507).] Many thick-leaved succulents have an excess of tissue that contributes little or nothing to the photochemistry proper. What is generally observed is the over-all result of the gas exchange produced by at least two types of cells (54, 323).

To a much greater degree than in algae, the lengths of light and dark periods (day and night) influence the type of gas exchange which is found under seemingly steady-state conditions. At first it sounds puzzling if we are told that light sometimes causes an evolution of carbon dioxide which may continue for hours and that this trend is reversed in the dark. More will be said about this in relation to organic acid metabolism in Volume 4. Here it must suffice to refer to the introductory section and the scheme of Fig. 4 to show that the problem is more concerned with the specific biochemistry of succulent plants than with their photosynthesis, for the photolysis of water can be coupled with numerous quite dissimilar enzymatic processes (compare the metabolism of purple bacteria, Section X).

X. Carbon Assimilation in Purple and Green Bacteria

The purple sulfur bacteria, the green sulfur bacteria, and several related forms (which use, instead of sulfur compounds, various organic substances as well as molecular hydrogen), provided the first experimental evidence that photosynthesis is not the unique, inflexible reaction it seemed to be until 1930. These bacteria contain several carotenoids and one main active pigment—bacteriochlorophyll—which differs only slightly in composition from the chlorophyll of green plants (see Section III). The most conspicuous difference is the absorption spectrum of bacteriochlorophyll; it extends far into the invisible infrared, and absorption ends, instead of at λ 700 mμ (as does chlorophyll), at about λ 900 mμ (cf. 234, 329). Thus all the light between these two wavelengths, though useless for the green plants, can be utilized by purple bacteria.

Purple bacteria were first observed in 1882 by Engelmann, and in 1888 by Winogradsky (606). Engelmann recognized that light was essential for the activity of these organisms and therefore concluded that they were photosynthetic organisms like the green plants. During the next fifty years several studies were made, mainly about the way these bacteria could be cultivated; but nothing definite was discovered about their way of utilizing light energy. Why such photosynthetic organisms, for instance, should grow preferentially in organic media was one of the unsolved questions.

A few years before the discovery of chemosynthetic carbon dioxide fixation, new investigations on the metabolism of the purple bacteria proved that a photochemical carbon dioxide reduction could occur in a way which differed profoundly from that of green plants (198, 199, 374). Furthermore, in contrast to the supposed uniformity of photosynthesis in higher plants, the bacterial photosynthesis revealed a great variability (541). Not every species of purple bacteria can perform all varieties of the photosynthetic reactions so far discovered. Some can be grown autotrophically with nothing but hydrogen gas, carbon dioxide, and minerals (cf. 249). Others get along in a mineral medium containing sodium acetate as the sole carbon source. Most are obligate anaerobes, and this is particularly true of the organisms classified as Thiorhodaceae (typical member: *Chromatium*). Thiorhodaceae are commonly found in sulfur springs or by the shores of lakes or seas, where a rich supply of decaying organic matter guarantees a continuous production of hydrogen sulfide through the activity of sulfate-reducing bacteria (537, 538).

Athiorhodaceae (nonsulfur purple bacteria) specialize in the photochemical utilization of fatty acids, 4-carbon dicarboxylic acids, and, to a lesser degree, aliphatic alcohols. Different species and strains have their predilections not only for selected organic compounds, but also for a more or less alkaline medium. In contrast to some of the green unicellular algae, which photosynthesize (or even grow) in a pH range from 3.8 to 9.5, genera of purple bacteria can often be separated in enrichment cultures by proper adjustment of the pH of the culture medium.

Chlorella has become a favorite object for laboratory work because it is so easy to cultivate. At the present time *Rhodospirillum rubrum*, a nonsulfur (Athiorhodaceae) purple bacterium, is taking a similar preferred place among the photosynthetic bacteria (273). It can be grown aerobically on organic media in the dark, a condition which facilitates handling. On the other hand, the presence of a functional respiratory system complicates the analysis of its photosynthetic metabolism, just as respiration does in the green plant (123, 124).

As mentioned in the introductory section, studies on purple bacteria opened the way to a new theoretical understanding of the mechanism of photosynthesis, particularly through van Niel's (at that time radically new) interpretation of the photochemistry as a light-induced oxidoreduction process. To establish the present view that all the photochemical effects mediated by chlorophylls in living cells are fundamentally the same required years of painstaking analytical comparison between the metabolism of green plants and that of the photosynthetic bacteria.

Among the differences between angiosperms and purple bacteria, the inability of the latter to liberate oxygen is the most fundamental. Van Niel (538) in his studies with sulfur-reducing bacteria, and Gaffron (198) and Muller (374) with bacteria which use aliphatic acids, found no trace of oxygen evolution in the light, though the carbon of carbon dioxide was rapidly converted into cell material. The assimilation of carbon dioxide does not continue, as in green plants, as long as the illumination lasts, but it ceases whenever the sulfur compounds or aliphatic acids become exhausted, despite continued illumination. Figure 86 shows this for the uptake of carbon dioxide coupled to the disappearance of butyric acid.

In 1931, van Niel found a relationship between carbon dioxide and hydrogen sulfide metabolized by green bacteria which fitted nicely the over-all equation:

$$CO_2 + 2\,H_2S \xrightarrow{\text{light}} (CH_2O) + 2\,S + H_2O \qquad (1)$$

The analogy with the equation used for describing photosynthesis was, of course, striking, and this led to the view that carbon dioxide could not have been decomposed directly by light, but must have been reduced by sulfide.

The hypothesis of a photoreduction replaced the earlier view of a photodecomposition of carbon dioxide. Van Niel and Muller pointed out that this would also fit best such reactions as the simultaneous utilization of organic compounds and carbon dioxide in the light. Later Foster (cf. 541) found a strain of purple bacteria which used isopropyl alcohol only partially as a hydrogen donor—leaving acetone as an

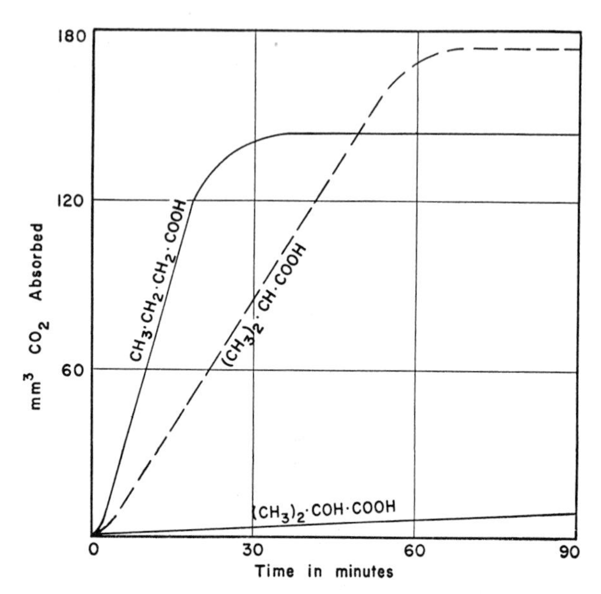

FIG. 86. Carbon dioxide absorption by a suspension of purple bacteria, *Rhodopseudomonas parva* (*Rhodovibrio parvus*), in the presence of: 0.1 ml $M/20$ *n*-butyric acid; 0.1 ml $M/20$ isobutyric acid, and 0.1 ml $M/20$ α-oxyisobutyric acid (166, 199).

excretion product while assimilating carbon dioxide according to the equation:

$$2 \cdot CH_3 \cdot CHOH \cdot CH_3 + CO_{2x} \xrightarrow{\text{light}} 2 \cdot CH_3 \cdot CO \cdot CH_3 + H_2O + (CH_2O) \qquad (m)$$

This seemed to prove that organic compounds are used only as hydrogen donors, being, perhaps, completely broken down in the process, while free carbon dioxide was the carbon source for the synthetic processes in the bacterial cell.

Meanwhile, we have learned that this is not quite the case. Experiments with C^{14}-labeled organic acids show that parts of the latter are incorporated directly into the bacteria. But what matters here is the principle of oxidoreduction. Making use of Wieland's and Kluyver's concepts of metabolic dehydrogenations and oxidoreductions in living cells, van Niel conceived of photosynthesis as an analogous process—a reduction of carbon dioxide by hydrogen which originates from water. If this hypothesis was correct it also implied that the oxygen of photosynthesis was derived from water and not from the carbon dioxide molecules. Hill's discovery in 1937 of other photochemical reactions coupled with oxygen evolution in green chloroplasts, and finally the results obtained with the oxygen isotope O^{18}, have definitely established this as the mechanism of photosynthesis (see Section XII).

A. LIGHT UTILIZATION AND EMISSION

1. The Light-Intensity Curve

In Fig. 24, Section V, the light-intensity versus rate curve for photosynthesis in plants is strictly linear at the lower light intensities. This means that the light quanta are used efficiently throughout this range of intensity. The light-intensity curve for the gas exchange in purple bacteria is often sigmoid in the beginning (like the curve in Fig. 25) (184, 501). This is due either to a reservoir of internal hydrogen donors which are reduced in preference to the substrates given externally, or to the light-induced evolution of some hydrogen gas (see Section XI). From a theoretical point of view these causes are trivial. There is no need to assume a special kind of photochemistry in these bacteria.

2. Saturation Rate

The saturation rate of photosynthesis in green plants can vary considerably. The corresponding maximum rate of photoreduction in purple bacteria is still more variable, because, in addition to such

TABLE XIV
RELATIVE RATES OF PHOTOREDUCTION WITH FATTY ACIDS IN ATHIORHODACEAE

a. Depression of rate in *Rhodopseudomonas* (*Rhodovibrio*) with changes at the α carbon atom (ref. 199)

Normal :—CH_2·COOH	Relative rates for normal acid set at:100		
iso : >CH·COOH	Butyric :40	Valeric :70	Caproic:10
(iso)-oxy: >COH·COOH	Acetic : 0	Butyric : 3	
tertiary : $\geqslant$C·COOH	Trimethylacetic	(Valeric): 0	

b. Increase in rate in presence of two acids (*Rhodospirillum*) (refs. 123, 124)

Acetic	: 59	Acetic	: 33
Propionic	: 37	Succinic	: 33
Acetic + propionic	:100	Acetic + succinic	:100

factors as temperature, carbon dioxide tension, and pH, the specificity and reactivity of enzymes which attack the various organic and inorganic hydrogen donors may determine the speed of the over-all reaction. An example of comparative rates for some aliphatic acids is shown in Table XIV. As van Niel pointed out (539, 541), the rate of carbon fixation in a mixture of substrates often surpasses the rate which obtains with any one of the substrates alone. And there are cases known (123, 199) where one organic substrate catalyzes the utilization of another.

3. *Action Spectra*

The action spectra definitely follow the absorption spectra of bacteriochlorophyll. Engelmann, in 1882, illuminated a suspension of purple bacteria with light dispersed into a spectrum and noted the accumulation of the bacteria in the infrared region around λ 860 mμ. The carotenoids, particularly those absorbing strongly in the blue, are either ineffective or of varying efficiency, according to what reaction is being tested: phototaxis, photoreduction, or photophosphorylation. Some energy transfer from carotene to bacteriochlorophyll has been described by Duysens (see Section VI). It is certain, however, that photoreduction and growth proceed normally in the absence of carotenes (98, 99, 245).

In green sulfur bacteria (*Chlorobium* spp.), the active pigment is a special chlorophyll whose first excited singlet state has only a little less energy than that of chlorophyll a. The corresponding absorption band lies around λ 740 mμ. Yet, like *Chromatium,* the green *Chlorobium* is an obligate anaerobe and is incapable of evolving oxygen in the light (327).

4. *Light Emission*

Emission of light as either fluorescence or long-lasting luminescence occurs in purple bacteria just as in the green plant. The main emission band lies in the infrared, around λ 900 mμ. The effect of normal and artificially induced variations in the rate of photoreduction upon the yield and intensity of fluorescence was carefully studied by Wassink *et al.* (582). Their results have been reinterpreted by Franck (171). He has pointed out that in green plants reactions of the oxidized photoproduct (YOH) coming from the photolysis of water has a much stronger influence on the fluorescence than the reactions concerned with the fixation of carbon dioxide.

In the absence of the proper reducing substrate, such as hydrogen, hydrogen sulfide, or organic substances, purple bacteria give about twice as much fluorescent light as during steady-state photoreduction. This is the same kind of effect which is seen in green plants whenever oxygen liberation is inhibited either by poisons or by lack of manganese (see Fig. 117, Section XIV). If we accept the view that photoreduction and photosynthesis begin with the same primary process, the circumstances determining their relationship to fluorescence should also be the same. Absence of reducing agents in purple bacteria leads to the same basic disturbance as poisoning of oxygen evolution in green plants—namely, an excess of oxidized photoproducts.

The same methods which revealed *spectral changes* in illuminated plants have been used successfully with purple bacteria. In addition to shifts in the infrared bands of bacteriochlorophyll, certain changes around λ 500 mμ have been recorded. The latter are being interpreted as changes in the oxidation-reduction state of cytochromes (115, 122). The discovery and isolation of cytochromes in purple bacteria, especially in the obligate anaerobe *Chromatium* sp. by Kamen *et al.* (550) has again drawn attention to this class of compounds as likely catalysts in photosynthetic processes (see Section III). The *Chromatium* cytochrome appears to combine properties of the "b" type as far as potentials are concerned with those of the "c" type, though it is autooxidizable (287–289). Similar cytochromes have been extracted from a green sulfur bacterium, *Chlorobium* sp.

5. *The Efficiency of Photoreduction*

The efficiency of photoreduction—the smallest quantum number per carbon dioxide molecule reduced—is the same as that found in green plants (see Table VI, Section VIII). This holds true for any type of external hydrogen donor given—that is, it bears no relation to the actual over-all free energy change of the process. Larsen has again determined quantum numbers for *Chromatium* sp. and for *Chlorobium* sp., in the presence of thiosulfate, hydrogen, or hydrogen sulfide (326, 328). The lowest average quantum number found was 9. The free energy change in the over-all reaction:

$$CO_2 + 2\,H_2 \rightarrow (CH_2O) + H_2O \tag{n}$$

is negligible: 2 kcal, as compared with 118 kcal in photosynthesis (Table VIII).

A quantum number of unity—even a chain reaction involving the assimilation of several carbon dioxide molecules—would be thermodynamically feasible. But nothing even approaching such efficiencies has been found. Hence, a theoretical picture of a simple, light-sensitized electron transfer chain between carboxylic acid and the ultimate hydrogen donor does not do justice to the experimental fact. An intermediate step requiring the energy of several absorbed photons must be part of the mechanism. In other words, the assumption is unavoidable that the photochemistry involved is of the same kind that operates in green plants, i.e., the photolysis of water. And, as already mentioned in Section VIII, the chemical energy resulting from the oxidation of free hydrogen is not available for the formation of cell material.

B. Products and Intermediates of Photoreduction

The products and intermediates of photoreduction in red and green sulfur and red nonsulfur bacteria have long been studied, but the results are still confusing.

The over-all reaction with hydrogen or hydrogen sulfide fits the observations of various investigators conveniently when written as if the reduction product were a carbohydrate (542, 581). The observed ratio of hydrogen to carbon dioxide was 1.85 to 2.25 in *Rhodopseudomonas parva* (*Rhodovibrio parvus*); 2.3 to 2.9 in "*Streptococcus varians*"; 2 in *Rhodopseudomonas* (*Rhodobacillus*) *palustris;* 1.8 to 2.25 in *Chromatium* sp.; and 2.05 to 2.35 in *Chlorobium thiosulfatophilum* (327). However, purple bacteria, as a rule, do not grow on carbohydrates. They are unable to ferment them, and only in rare cases has it been possible to demonstrate in dried cell preparations the enzymes which are typical of glycolysis (453–455).

TABLE XV

	Composition	
	Per cent C	Per cent H
Purple bacteria[a]	55.7	7.4
Carbohydrate (CH_2O)	40.0	6.7
Polycrotonic acid $(C_4H_6O_2)_n$	55.8	7.0

[a] A metabolic ratio of 2.25 H_2 to 1 CO_2—as it has often been measured—corresponds more closely to the over-all composition of the bacteria.

Elementary carbon-hydrogen analyses of the bacterial substance gave values which indicated that it is decidedly more reduced than that which constitutes a green plant. Table XV shows that the bacteria approach the composition of a polymer of crotonic acid, which was once extracted as a chloroform-soluble substance from *Rhodopseudomonas parva.* This significant difference between the photometabolism of the anaerobic bacteria and that of the aerobic plants is seen again in the results obtained with radioactive carbon. Photoreduction of $C^{14}O_2$ with either hydrogen gas or acetate by *Rhodospirillum* (*Spirillum*) *rubrum* yielded considerable amounts of phosphoglyceric acid—as (presumably) the first stable intermediate, just as in the experiments with green plants. But thenceforward the reactions differ. "At no time," write Glover *et al.* (232) "has anaerobic (photo) metabolism or dark metabolism, either in the presence of hydrogen or acetate, resulted in the production of visible amounts of labeled hexose, free or bound (phosphorylated)." Later experiments with another bacterium, *Rhodopseudomonas capsulata*, confirmed the initial formation of phosphoglyceric acid, but not the statement about the absence of sugar phosphates. However, these newer experiments were mainly done with longer exposures. It seems that up to 2 minutes' fixation time in the light the sugar phosphates have been negligible also in this case.

In the preceding sections we discussed at length the fact that the fixation of carbon dioxide in the carboxyl group of phosphoglyceric acid is the result of a exergonic enzymatic reaction with diphosphoribulose. If the pattern in purple bacteria is the same, it follows that their deviation from the green plants is to be found in the photochemical steps or in the fate of the reduction products. Among the latter, succinate, α-ketoglutarate, and malate could be identified. Some as yet unidentified substance behaved as if it were related to α-ketoglutaric acid. It was an early fixation product and contained the bulk of the activity originally present in acetate (232, 280, 325).

Gaffron pointed out in 1935 that the data then available made it necessary to assume the formation of at least two types of compounds. Substances like acetic acid or lactic acid, which have an over-all formula corresponding to that of carbohydrate, can be reduced still further in the presence of molecular hydrogen. Certain purple bacteria grow in the light in mineral media containing acetate as the only hydrogen donor and as the sole carbon source.

If the reaction with acetate is observed manometrically, one finds that one molecule of carbon dioxide is released for about every four molecules of acetate which are converted into bacteria. Experiments with labeled acetate have confirmed that the carboxyl group is the source of the carbon dioxide developed during acetate metabolism. Considering that this process:

$$CH_3{\cdot}COOH \xrightarrow{\text{light}} CO_2 + \text{bacterial substance} \qquad (o)$$

ought to proceed with the decomposition of water in the photochemical reaction as the core of the entire mechanism, the least complex sequence of reactions accomplishing a pure acetate assimilation is that indicated in Fig. 87. A photochemistry dealing exclusively with acetate would lead to the formation of fats and partly to that of carbohydrates.

There are only a few reactions in this scheme which have not, as yet, been explored in other microorganisms. Acetoacetate in combination with coenzyme A is a known intermediate in fat metabolism. The sequence of reactions on the left side of the scheme offers no theoretical problem, since it is well known. A polymerized crotonic acid of the formula $C_4H_6O_2$, found in *Rhodopseudomonas parva* (*Rhodovibrio parvus*), has been mentioned above. The interconversion of acetoacetate and acetone in *Rhodopseudomonas gelatinosa* has been established by Siegel (463–465). What is left to be proved are the steps leading from acetone to carbohydrates.

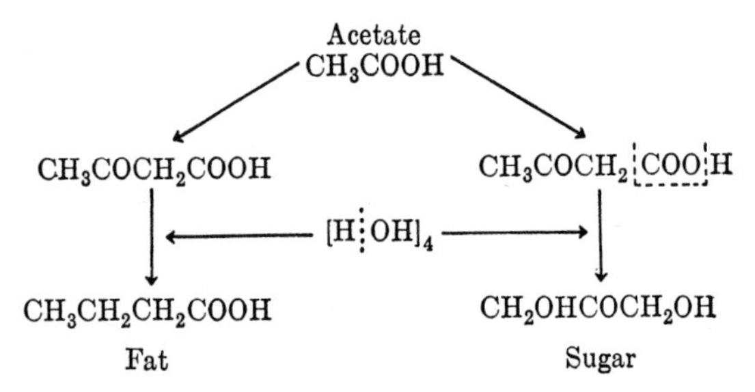

FIG. 87. Simplified hypothetical scheme of fatty acid assimilation in purple bacteria. Photochemical oxidoreduction of acetate leading to fats and carbohydrates (220).

Among the more satisfactory attempts to obtain balanced data are the experiments of Bregoff and Kamen *et al.* on the decomposition of malate (55). They found that malate—one of the best nutrients for all kinds of purple bacteria—yields about one carbon dioxide released per molecule decomposed (223–225, 281).

Applying the scheme of Fig. 87 to this reaction gives the following:

$$\begin{aligned} &2\ \text{malate} \xrightarrow[2\,H_2O]{\text{light}} 1\ \text{succinate} + 1\ \text{pyruvate} + 2\ H_2O + 1\ CO_2 \\ &1\ \text{succinate} + 1\ \text{pyruvate} \xrightarrow[2\,H_2O]{\text{light}} 3\ \text{acetate} + 1\ H_2O + 1\ CO_2 \end{aligned} \qquad \text{(p)}$$

The acetate in turn is utilized as assumed above. Further experiments with tracers are needed to establish this view. It is unlikely that the bacteria will attack acetate exclusively. Carbon dioxide is always present and its assimilation may give rise to 3-carbon acids (phosphoglyceric and pyruvic) or dicarboxylic acids by way of the carboxylation of pyruvate (488). In long-term (growing) experiments with doubly labeled acetate (C^{13} and C^{14}) and labeled bicarbonate, the analysis of the proteins showed 45% incorporation of the methyl carbon, 25% of the carboxyl carbon, and only 10% of the free carbon dioxide (104, 123, 226).

In the presence of fluoroacetate the dark metabolism of all organic substrates becomes inhibited. In the light this inhibition persists for acetate as hydrogen donor but not for propionate (124) (Table XVI).

TABLE XVI
ACETATE AND PROPIONATE ASSIMILATION IN *Rhodospirillum* (*Spirillum*) *rubrum*. INHIBITION BY 10^{-3} *M* FLUOROACETATE (FA)[a]

Substrate:	None (endogenous)		Acetate		Propionate	
Inhibitor:	None	10^{-3} *M* FA	None	10^{-3} *M* FA	None	10^{-3} *M* FA
Dark, air						
O_2 uptake, Q_{O_2}	4.8	1.6	11.2	1.6	10.9	1.6
Light, nitrogen						
CO_2 uptake, Q_{CO_2}	0.9	0.5	18.7	2.7	13.1	10.0

[a] From Elsden and Ormerod, (124).

In *Rhodopseudomonas* (*Rhodobacillus*) *palustris* the oxidation of higher fatty acids in the dark appears to proceed via a mechanism which does not include all the well-known steps of the Krebs cycle (526). Nevertheless, the higher fatty acids can be assumed to be broken down to acetyl or acetoacetyl units while serving as hydrogen donors for the reduction of carbon dioxide.

During photoreduction with higher aliphatic acids, where the amount of carbon dioxide entering into the reaction depends on the number of methylene groups in the molecule and stoichiometric relations are far from simple, we must expect a rapid succession of first products or early intermediates. In all probability, the experience gained in studying the oxidation of fats and of long-chain fatty acids, must be brought to bear on this problem. We may assume that the chains are broken down into 2-carbon or acetyl-CoA groups. These are utilized partly according to the hypothetical scheme in Fig. 87 above, partly as hydrogen donors for the reduction of carbon dioxide, and partly as acceptors for carboxylation reactions. Experience has shown that different strains of bacteria may have striking differences in their ability to deal with certain organic substrates despite the similarity of the over-all pattern.

Assuming the mechanism of fatty acid dissimilation in the purple bacteria to be similar to the pathway recently elucidated in mammalian mitochondria, reduced diphosphopyridine nucleotide is produced when the Δ-hydroxy fatty acid is oxidized to the β-keto acid. If this is the major source of reducing power for the reduction of CO_2, then a departure occurs from the reduction made in the green plant. In the latter, the photosynthetic pyridine nucleotide reducing enzyme discovered recently by San Pietro and Lang (451) in chloroplasts is a triphosphopyridine nucleotide system. The following speculation could be made about the purple bacteria: (a) The oxidation of the β-hydroxy fatty acid is linked to triphosphopyridine nucleotide. (b) The organism possesses a strong pyridine nucleotide transhydrogenase. (c) If not either of these, then the induction of the carboxyl group to the aldehyde level in an early step in photosynthesis is linked to diphosphopyridine nucleotide. It is also possible that the reduction of carbon dioxide to the aldehyde is not pyridine nucleotide linked, and that no relation exists between fatty acid oxidation and carbon dioxide reduction. At present, little is known about the oxidation of fatty acids in this group of bacteria (123).

A very recent and important contribution to this question is due to Stanier *et al.* (480a). By feeding radioactively labeled substances to starved anaerobic *Spirillum rubrum*, they proved that certain organic molecules like acetate and butyrate are assimilated quite directly in the light, i.e., without the interposition of a carbon dioxide reduction cycle. The polycrotonic acid $(C_4H_6O_2)_n$, a condensation product of β-hydroxybutyric acid, was shown to be a major storage product—a means by which the bacteria incorporate large amounts of fatty acids in a neutral and innocuous form. Thus, "the general inferences of Gaffron concerning the role of organic substrates in the photometabolism of purple bacteria have been confirmed and extended" (cf. 199). With mixed substrates and coupled to a variety of enzyme systems, even a basically simple oxidoreduction mechanism, such as the one shown in Fig. 87, can account for a bewildering spread of experimental results. The scheme predicts, however, that in combination with inorganic hydrogen donors, which react with the primary photochemical oxidant, much less of the organic food need to be oxidized to "produce reducing power." Consequently, more organic molecules can be assimilated directly. This has been shown to be the case. In the presence of molecular hydrogen, Stanier's bacteria transformed no less than 85% of the assimilated acetate into the reserve polymer.

Tables XIV–XVI are examples of the complexities encountered in attempts to unravel the mechanism of the utilization of organic compounds in the light. There is not only the question of specificity of enzymes for each one of the different substrates, but also that of a comparatively slow oxidation process transforming compounds unsuitable for direct photoreduction into others which are, and that of enzymatic adaptation. Growth experiments may therefore give quite different results from those of short-term metabolic studies (543).

C. FERMENTATION AND RESPIRATION

1. *Fermentation*

In higher plants, the mature leaf is a carbohydrate factory. Growth occurs elsewhere, continues in the dark, and is supported by means of respiration. This respiration and the growth processes it promotes are a disturbance during photosynthesis experiments with unicellular algae.

In (anaerobic) purple bacteria that grow only in the light (and they can grow very fast) all essential metabolic processes leading to a complete, new cell occur simultaneously and are not easily separable. In other words, *photo*synthetic and *chemo*synthetic mechanisms are welded into one. This is a necessity because, in the dark, no fermentation can be seen that would provide enough energy for continuing the growth process. In certain anaerobic heterotrophs among the purple bacteria, a measurable gas exchange practically comes to a standstill as soon as the light is turned off; only a very low rate of carbon dioxide formation can be observed (198). Yet the synthetic abilities of these organisms are amazingly efficient; in cultures grown in butyrate, the only products which could be recovered were the bacteria themselves. No excretion products in any significant amount were found (374).

The situation is somewhat different in the Thiorhodaceae. Van Niel emphasized that his cultures were not able to sustain a typical fermentation even with added substrates, confirming earlier similar observations. Nevertheless, immediately after a period of fast photoreduction with sulfur compounds, a strain of a *Chromatium* sp. begins to develop H_2S, CO_2, and organic acid. First observed by Gaffron (200), the complexity of this fermentation, which decreases in rate rapidly with time, was a subject of some prolonged polemics concerning the magnitude, significance, and origin of the hydrogen sulfide formed in the dark. It is now established that these purple sulfur bacteria can produce considerable amounts of hydrogen sulfide, carbon dioxide, and acetic acid (249, 538a).

The origin of the hydrogen sulfide is normally the sulfur stored previously in the cells according to equation (1). The process, therefore, resembles respiration when seen as the reversal of photosynthesis.

However, the energy is released in such small amounts that it is not utilized by the bacteria for growth. Colloidal sulfur added externally is reduced even faster than the endogenous product. The rate is about two cell volumes of H_2S per hour. The next step, the photochemical oxidation of endogenous sulfur to sulfate, is not reversible. These bacteria are unable to reduce sulfate in the dark.

2. *Uptake of Oxygen and Respiration*

"Uptake of oxygen" and "respiration" are not synonymous in purple bacteria. As long as the partial pressure of oxygen is very low, and reducing agents, such as hydrogen gas, are in excess, anaerobic conditions are essentially maintained in the cells despite a continuous absorption of oxygen. The situation is similar to that described below for adapted algae and often seen in "Knall gas" bacteria. An oxyhydrogen reaction, or its equivalent with other hydrogen donors, proceeds rapidly enough to prevent an inactivation of oxygen-sensitive enzymes such as hydrogenase. Under truly aerobic conditions, many purple bacteria show a typical respiratory gas exchange, but only certain photoheterotrophic strains are permanently tolerant to air and able to grow aerobically. *Rhodospirillum rubrum*, the best-known example of the last category, is now being cultivated in aerated malate media in many laboratories.

TABLE XVII

ACETATE ASSIMILATION IN *Rhodospirillum (Spirillum) rubrum*. INHIBITION OF OXYGEN UPTAKE BY LIGHT[a,b]

Conditions	CO_2 Produced (μl)	O_2 Consumed (μl)
Dark, air	208	204
Light, air	51	0
Light, nitrogen	51	0

[a] Time required for complete decomposition of 0.1 ml of a 0.10 *M* solution was 70 minutes.
[b] Van Niel (539).

In contrast to green plants, where respiration proceeds fairly independently of the photochemistry in the chloroplasts, respiration in purple bacteria appears to be much more closely linked to the light reactions. One of the surprising observations is that the uptake of oxygen is regulated by the light intensity. At high light intensity the uptake of oxygen ceases and the assimilation of acetate proceeds as if the organism were under anaerobic conditions (see Table XVII). Van

Niel, who first observed this phenomenon, pointed out that it leads to a saving of organic material, since now the light provides the energy which otherwise would have to come from the combustion of some of the acetate (539). The photoinhibition of oxygen consumption by *Rhodospirillum rubrum* has been confirmed by a mass spectrometric method (278). The inhibition was seen to increase with the light intensity until 85% of the respiratory reaction was suppressed.

To explain these results we may assume either a specific inhibitory effect of light upon the uptake of oxygen by the oxidase system or a competition for a common catalyst on the path toward the dehydrogenase. An inhibition of carbon dioxide evolution by light is understandable in terms of reduction of coenzymes, but no similar effect on oxygen uptake can be expected—nor has it been seen in green plants. In fact the experiment of Brown proved the contrary—that the absorption of oxygen by green plants continues in the light. Thus a greater affinity of the oxidized compounds arising from the photolysis of water for some intermediate link seems to fit the case better (cf. 549).

XI. Hydrogenases in Bacteria and Adapted Algae

A. PHOTOREDUCTION IN ALGAE

The over-all equation summarizing photoreduction in purple bacteria does not specify the intermediate steps of the process. *A priori*, there is no need to assume any decomposition of water molecules when CO_2 is reduced by equivalent amounts of H_2S, H_2, thiosulfate, etc. Thermodynamical, as well as biochemical, reasoning would permit a mechanism based upon an oxidoreduction chain leading from the reductant to the oxidant—from hydrogen to carbon dioxide—with a photosensitizer inserted to speed up the process. This would be the easiest way to explain why only the green plants evolve oxygen in the light: for they certainly achieve a photolysis of water. On the other hand, as van Niel pointed out in 1935, the idea of a photolysis of water as an intermediate reaction in the mechanism of purple bacteria would bring the two types of photosyntheses much closer together theoretically.

At the present time we are as certain of the existence in the purple bacteria of such a photoreaction with water as one can be on the basis of circumstantial evidence. Perhaps definitive experiments with deuterium and tritium, which are so difficult because of the ever-present exchange reactions, may one day be performed convincingly.

The present experimental evidence is of two kinds. The one is the fact that photoreduction as an over-all reaction is not *more*, but much *less*, efficient energetically than photosynthesis but that the minimum number of quanta required for the reduction of one carbon dioxide molecule is the same (see Section VIII and Table VIII). The other fact is that several strains of algae belonging to different classes can be induced to switch (reversibly) from normal photosynthesis to a bacterial type of photometabolism.

1. Adaptation

Between 1935 and 1939, Gaffron repeatedly observed that when certain algae had been kept in the dark under nitrogen for several hours, they could reduce carbon dioxide in the light without the corresponding evolution of oxygen. The suspicion that this effect was due to an internal reduction of the expected oxygen prior to its release as gas was confirmed by incubating the algae in an atmosphere of hydrogen. If cells of *Scenedesmus* sp. are so treated, carbon dioxide is reduced as usual upon illumination. The oxygen of photosynthesis fails to appear, however, and, instead, an equivalent amount of hydrogen gas is absorbed. The over-all gas exchange is that of equation (1), first found in purple bacteria (205, 210).

Algae which are capable of adaptation contain an enzyme, hydrogenase, in a latent form, which remains inactive and undetectable until it is activated by a dark period in the complete absence of oxygen. At first this adaptation to a metabolism with hydrogen appeared to be a rather isolated phenomenon. By now it has been established that hydrogenase may occur not only in a few strains of green algae, but also in blue-green, red, and brown algae, and in marine as well as in fresh-water species (190, 191). No higher plant with a facultative hydrogenase has as yet been found.

After an incubation period and adaptation to the anaerobic type of carbon dioxide reduction, the absorption of hydrogen in the light may continue indefinitely provided the light intensity does not surpass a certain low threshold value. Whenever one attempts to speed up the rate of photoreduction in algae by raising the light intensity above this threshold, the rate of hydrogen absorption declines and the usual form of photosynthesis soon reappears (Fig. 88). The reduction of carbon dioxide is once more coupled with the evolution of oxygen.

The ease with which the return to normal conditions, the "deadaptation" (cf. 436), can be brought about makes it likely that the switch from the aerobic type of metabolism to the anaerobic one does not involve a fundamental change in the photochemistry or the assimilation of carbon. Results of experiments with radioactive carbon dioxide agree with this view. The intermediate products of the photometabolism with hydrogen are also not significantly different from those found under aerobic conditions, except for a relative increase in the malic acid fraction. Obviously, two different mechanisms can explain the behavior of the algae. In the first, a precursor of oxygen (the YOH of Fig. 4) is directly reduced by means of the hydrogenase system, which, therefore, interferes with the release of oxygen as free gas. Or the oxygen of photosynthesis is first released as usual and subsequently reduced in a separate reaction with hydrogen.

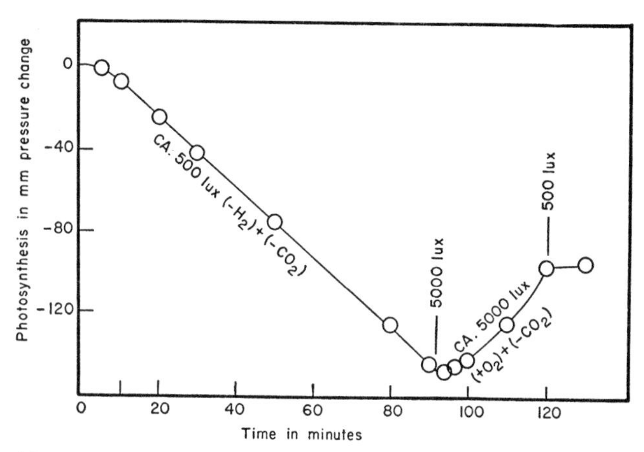

FIG. 88. Absorption of hydrogen and carbon dioxide in the light after an incubation under hydrogen in the dark by *Scenedesmus* sp. Higher light intensity causes return to normal photosynthesis and inactivation of the hydrogenase. From Gaffron (205).

Not only the photosynthetic organisms but numerous bacteria as well possess hydrogenase, and many derive the energy for chemosynthetic growth from the reduction of oxygen by hydrogen via the hydrogenase enzyme system (cf. 37, 227, 228, 313, 410, 411, 456). A combination of normal photosynthesis with the oxyhydrogen reaction in algae would, in the first approximation, be indistinguishable from a true internal photoreduction of the bacterial type. In adapted algae small amounts of oxygen are indeed reduced in the dark. Furthermore, this potential energy source is not wasted. Carbon dioxide is reduced chemosynthetically in the dark while the oxyhydrogen reaction proceeds (208, 210).

The question whether true photoreduction exists at all in algae has arisen several times. The arguments presented in Gaffron's first papers in favor of the photoreductive mechanism (for instance, a test for oxygen with luminous bacteria present in the suspension of algae, and the suppression of the specific reactions leading to oxygen evolution by selective poisons) still left room for doubt. The doubt increased when the most sensitive method for detecting traces of oxygen revealed an evolution of that gas from thoroughly adapted algae (Fig. 89). This, obviously, meant that a small fraction of the cells in a suspension of

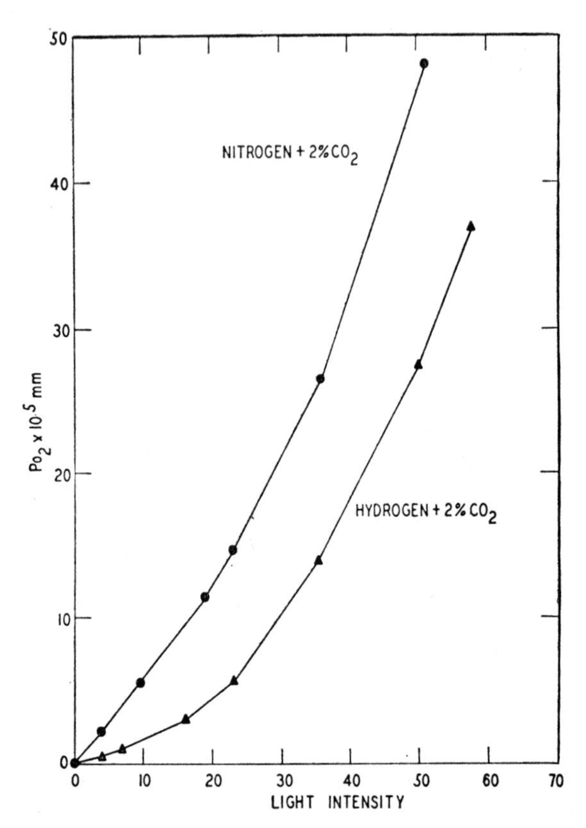

FIG. 89. Evolution of oxygen under anaerobic conditions, under nitrogen, and under hydrogen, as measured in a stream of gas at extremely low oxygen partial pressures. Adaptation of *Scenedesmus* sp. to hydrogen depresses but does not prevent the release of free oxygen (compare Section V) (272).

algae remained permanently unadapted or that the ability to evolve oxygen did not disappear automatically when the hydrogenase became active. Further investigation with a mass spectrometer and isotopes as tracers solved the problem (271, 272).

Adaptation itself is a slow process. The time required varies greatly with the class and strain of alga used for the experiment and it ranges from minutes in *Chlamydomonas* to days in *Chlorella*. The sensitivity of the oxygen-releasing enzyme system toward the effects of anaerobiosis is equally variable (see Figs. 37, 39, Section V), as is the resistance of the hydrogenase to inactivation by oxygen. In *Scenedesmus* it is possible to have complete adaptation to photoreduction with hydrogen without an impairment of the capacity to evolve photosynthetic oxygen (2).

This circumstance leads to a free competition between the hydrogenase and the "photocatalase" (short for "oxygen-evolving enzyme system"). As long as the production of the active hydroxyls (the YOH compounds) is slow at low light intensity, the reduction is the preferred reaction. Yet traces of oxygen are liberated even after many hours of prior adaptation in complete darkness. What makes the switch to photosynthesis with oxygen evolution, the "deadaptation," irreversible, is the autooxidation of the hydrogenase, which renders it inactive. This sensitivity to oxygen is a trait that hydrogenase in algae has in common with other hydrogenases present in nonphotosynthetic microorganisms. The trace of oxygen which appears even at low light intensities remains harmless insofar as the active hydrogenase removes it by reduction. If the experiment is done in a stream of hydrogen (or nitrogen), it is possible to raise the light intensity and thereby cause a rapid evolution of photosynthetic oxygen without inactivating the hydrogenase. The gas stream keeps the oxygen at a very low partial pressure, and, after return to a low light intensity, photoreduction is again the preferred reaction. There are situations when all four reactions—photosynthesis, photoreduction, oxyhydrogen reaction, and chemoreduction of carbon dioxide—are going on simultaneously, as in the scheme of Fig. 96 (271, 272).

The idea of a free competition, as expressed in Fig. 96, rests further on the observation that everything which favors photoreduction diminishes the rate of oxygen evolution and vice versa—e.g., observations of such effects as those of selective poisons or of manganese deficiency (41, 206, 312).

A problem connected with the photometabolism in plants is that of the appearance of hydrogenase—the mechanism of adaptation. Does the activation under anaerobic conditions consist merely in the reduction of trivalent to divalent iron? In the strains of *Chlorella* which must be incubated for days (105, 106) until their pattern of fermentation changes to one including the evolution of hydrogen gas, the phenomenon is evidently of another kind than in *Scenedesmus*, *Chlamydomonas*, *Ulva*, etc. These latter algae, in which adaptation is quick, are, of course, the better subjects for photosynthetic investigations, while *Chlorella* might be of interest to those wanting to learn more about enzyme formation.

2. *Stabilization of Photoreduction in the Presence of Inhibitors of Photosynthesis*

The proof that a true photoreduction exists in adapted algae can be given by a simple experiment. After adaptation in the dark, so much of a specific poison is added to the suspension of algae that not a trace of oxygen would be evolved in the light under normal, aerobic conditions. This treatment interferes little or not at all with the mechanism

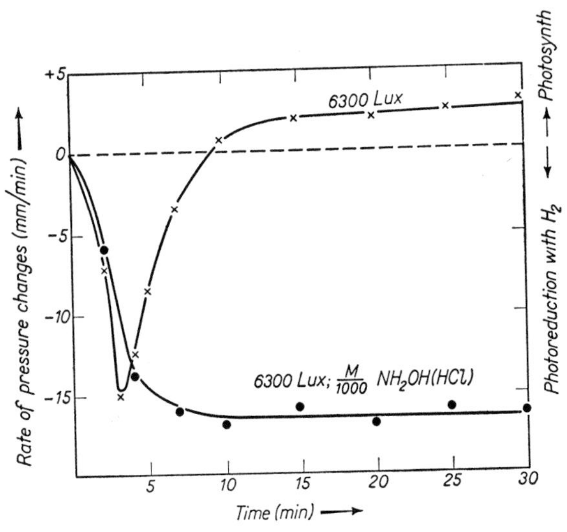

FIG. 90. Deadaptation of hydrogen-adapted *Scenedesmus* sp. by a prolonged illumination of too high a light intensity and prevention of deadaptation by hydroxylamine (206).

of photoreduction. Now the light intensity and, thereby, the rate of hydrogen absorption can be much increased without the risk of deadaptation and inactivation of the hydrogenase. The anaerobic conditions are then stabilized, and it is possible to study the characteristics of the photoreduction in a much wider range of intensities.

Substances which mainly inhibit the evolution of oxygen and not the utilization of hydrogen are: hydroxylamine (see Fig. 90), vitamin K, phthiocol, *o*-phenanthroline, and the herbicide DCMU (3(3,4-dichlorophenyl)-1,1-dimethylurea). The most interesting among these inhibitors is the DCMU (41). It works in concentrations in the cell that are far below that of chlorophyll and does not interfere with any other major metabolic reaction, such as respiration, fermentation, catalase activity, adaptation, the oxyhydrogen reaction, or photophosphorylation (Fig. 91).

The simplest explanation of these observations agrees with the scheme shown in Fig. 96. Any block in the path of oxygen, beyond the point where it branches off from the alternative path leading to the

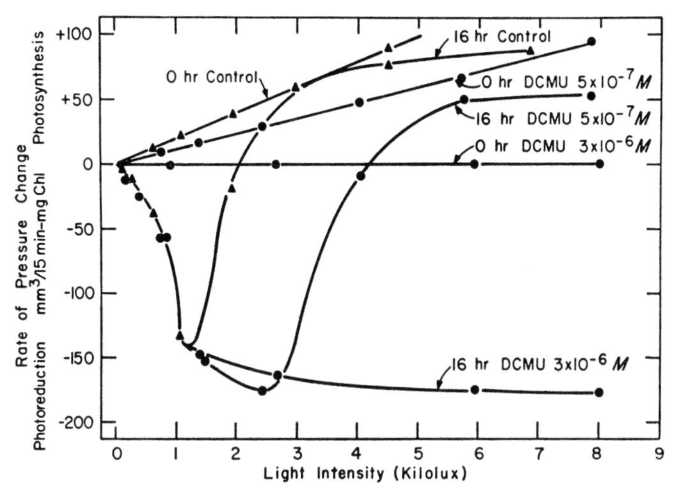

FIG. 91. Complete stabilization of photoreduction of *Scenedesmus* sp. by small concentrations of the herbicide DCMU (see Section XIV). Rates of photosynthesis in air (4% CO_2) (corrected for respiration) and of photoreduction in hydrogen (4% CO_2) at increasing light intensities. Unpoisoned, the algae deadapt at 1 Klux; with 5×10^{-7} *M* DCMU, at 2.5 Klux; with 3×10^{-6} *M* DCMU, not at all. No photosynthesis is possible with 3×10^{-6} *M* DCMU, regardless of the incident intensity. From Bishop (41).

hydrogenase, forces the flow of the reaction into the latter; conversely, in the adapted but unstabilized algae any decrease in the capacity of the hydrogenase results in greater oxygen production and speedier deadaptation.

3. *Photoreduction in Manganese-Deficient Algae*

Photoreduction, as described in the preceding paragraphs, is obviously a good means to distinguish between factors essential and necessary for the Benson-Calvin cycle or for the primary process, and those pertaining to the mechanism of oxygen evolution. By using the adaptation as an analytic tool, it became possible to locate the place where manganese ions exert their influence upon photosynthesis. It has long been known that among the metallic elements manganese is essential for plants and for photosynthesis.

In 1937 Pirson observed that manganese deficiency in algae lowers the rate of photosynthesis and increases that of respiration long before any other damage to the cells becomes apparent. A little manganese sulfate added to the medium relieves the symptoms within half an hour and the algae perform normally again (413). Kessler grew algae (*Ankistrodesmus* sp.) under conditions where they became deficient in manganese, and then compared their capacity to reduce carbon dioxide in air and in hydrogen. Figure 58, Section VI, shows the result obtained. In this drawing the initial metabolic rate of healthy normal

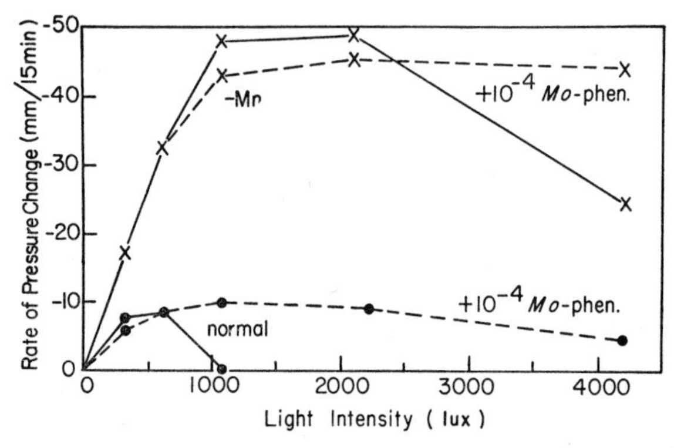

FIG. 92. Maximum rates of photoreduction with hydrogen in normal and manganese-deficient *Ankistrodesmus braunii* at increasing light intensities. *o*-Phenanthroline prevents deadaptation or decline of rates in strong light. From Kessler (307).

cells at a moderate light intensity is set at 100% for photoreduction and for photosynthesis. With decreasing manganese, only normal photosynthesis declines, while the ability to photoreduce carbon dioxide with hydrogen remains undisturbed. It is remarkable that photoreduction is normal even in cultures grown under unhealthy conditions for over a month (305, 307, 312). These and similar experiments have proved that manganese is essential for the complete set of reactions making up normal photosynthesis but is unnecessary when the mechanism of oxygen evolution is not operating. A stabilization of the bacterial type of carbon dioxide reduction in algae is, therefore, not only brought about by the *inhibition* of a catalyst in the path of oxygen, but also by its *removal*.

As expected, the adapted, manganese-deficient algae tolerate much higher light intensities and give very good rates of photoreduction. Yet it is hardly possible to remove all the catalytic manganese from the photochemical mechanism without doing more general damage to the plant. Thus, a partial or complete deadaptation due to some residual evolution of oxygen is found at high light intensities (Fig. 92). True light saturation curves with fast rates of hydrogen absorption can be obtained by a combination of manganese deficiency and poisoning with *o*-phenanthroline or with DCMU. It should not be overlooked, however, that the "photocatalase" is not the only enzyme system where manganese is essential, for its effects extend to other aspects of metabolism. Table XVIII gives a general survey of the effects of manganese deficiency.

TABLE XVIII
CONSEQUENCES OF MANGANESE DEFICIENCY IN GREEN ALGAE

Not inhibited	Inhibited
Photoreduction	Photosynthesis
Oxyhydrogen reaction	Chloroplast (Hill) reaction
Glucose incorporation in the dark	Glucose incorporation in the light
Respiration with added glucose	Hydrogen production in the light
Chlorophyll formation	Hydrogen fermentation in the dark
Catalase activity	Endogenous respiration
	Nitrite reduction (all conditions)

B. THE OXYHYDROGEN REACTION AND CHEMOSYNTHESIS

When adapted algae in an atmosphere of hydrogen come in contact with very small amounts of oxygen, they absorb it in a reaction which is different from normal respiration. Figure 93 shows the time course of the ensuing gas change. Not only does the oxygen disappear together with two equivalents of hydrogen, but some additional hydrogen is taken up, together with carbon dioxide when this gas is also present. The process consists of a coupling of two reactions, as expressed in the following equations:

$$4\ H_2 + 2\ O_2 \rightarrow 4\ H_2O$$
$$2\ H_2 + CO_2 \rightarrow (CH_2O) + H_2O$$

The reduction of two molecules of oxygen promotes the reduction of one molecule of carbon dioxide (208, 456). The average of a number of measurements agrees with a ratio of $\Delta H_2/\Delta CO_2 = 2$–that is, a reduction to the level of carbohydrate.

As in photoreduction, we have here, too, the peculiar situation that a reduction of carbon dioxide with hydrogen, which thermodynamically requires barely 2 kcal, proceeds only in conjunction with another reduction which releases $2 \times 113 = 226$ kcal. The stoichiometry of a complex mechanism is here much more important, obviously, than the over-all changes in free energy. As far as the stoichiometric efficiency is concerned, the ratio 2 O_2 to 1 CO_2 is about the best the oxyhydrogen reaction is capable of delivering (cf. 456). As long as the hydrogenase is fully active, all oxygen is reduced to water by hydrogen gas. No respiratory formation of carbon dioxide could be detected (208, 271).

Of course, removing all carbon dioxide from the cell suspension stops the second reaction. But it does more than that; the oxyhydrogen

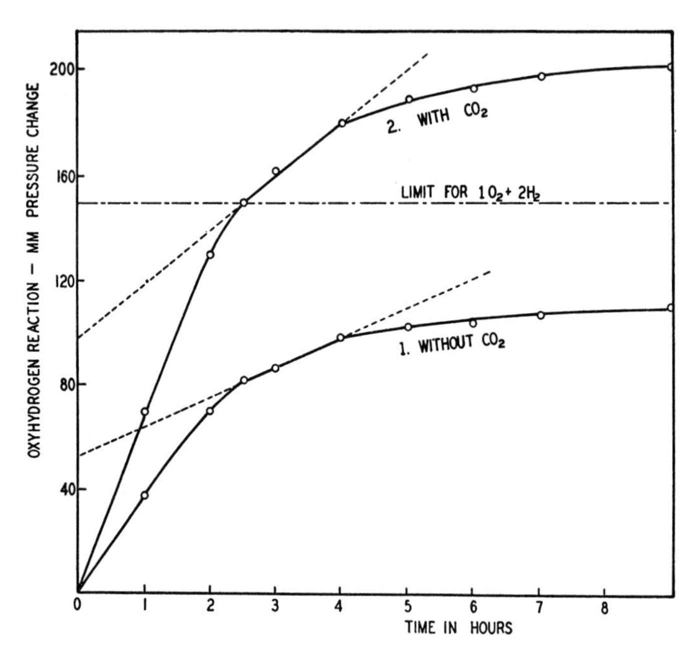

FIG. 93. Reduction of oxygen with hydrogen in the dark by adapted *Scenedesmus* sp. In the presence of carbon dioxide, the hydrogen taken up far exceeds the amount calculated. In the absence of CO_2, less hydrogen is utilized than expected.

reaction itself becomes disturbed and does not run to completion. On the average, now, only one equivalent of hydrogen is taken up, together with oxygen (Fig. 94). The second equivalent is furnished by endogenous hydrogen donors. As further studies showed, the chemosynthetic reduction seems more nearly related to other nonphotochemical processes than to photosynthesis in the same cell (271).

Hydrogenomonas, a (nonphotosynthetic) bacterium which grows in a gas mixture of 75% H_2:20% O_2:5% CO_2, also requires carbon dioxide not only as a carbon source but also as a catalytic agent in its intermediary metabolism. Some carbon dioxide must be present for the formation of energy-rich phosphate, even if other organic compounds are available as supplementary hydrogen donors. Some similar linkage between hydrogen oxidation, phosphorylation, and need for carbon dioxide might be the reason for the behavior of adapted algae.

The adapted algae are unable to make good use of the carbon assimilated under anaerobic conditions. In contrast to some species of purple bacteria which multiply rapidly and often exclusively under anaerobic conditions—e.g., in an atmosphere of hydrogen and carbon dioxide—the algae have so far not been seen to divide or grow while engaged in photoreduction or the oxyhydrogen reaction. They are purely

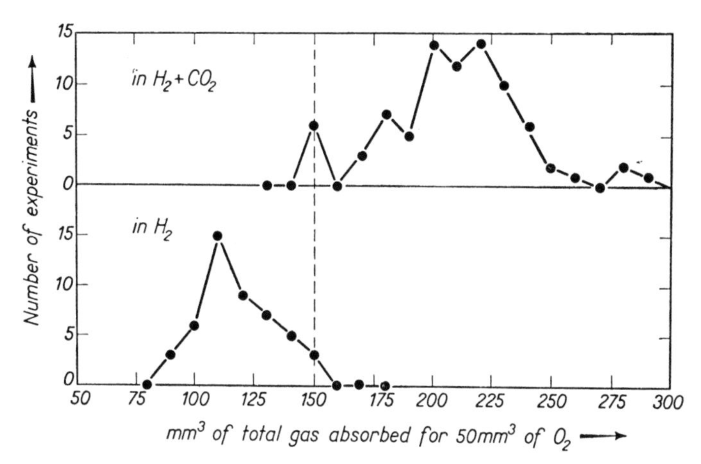

FIG. 94. Oxyhydrogen reaction in *Scenedesmus* sp. in presence and in absence of 4% CO_2. Statistical distribution of final volume of total gas disappeared after the introduction of 50 mm^3 of oxygen into an atmosphere of hydrogen. Straightforward formation of water from 50 mm^3 of oxygen corresponds to dashed line at 150 mm^3 on the abscissa (208).

aerobic organisms. Their anaerobic reactions coupled to hydrogenase are, perhaps, evolutionary relics in the metabolic pattern.

C. THE PHOTOCHEMICAL EVOLUTION OF HYDROGEN BY ALGAE AND PURPLE BACTERIA

When algae capable of adaptation to photoreduction are incubated anaerobically under nitrogen or helium instead of hydrogen, the activation of the hydrogenase takes place just the same. It can now be noticed by an increase of the rate of gas evolution due to the fermentation reactions. At first, only carbon dioxide gas is evolved. After an hour or two, when the rate has apparently increased, it can be shown that the additional amount of gas released by the algae is hydrogen (191, 207).

In the course of 1–4 days, *Chlorella pyrenoidosa* changes its fermentation, which begins as a production of lactic acid, into one comprising the evolution of hydrogen (106). After adaptation in helium or nitrogen a weak illumination causes a faster rate of hydrogen evolution. The photoproduction of hydrogen in such algae as *Scenedesmus*, *Ankistrodesmus*, or *Chlamydomonas*, increases with the light intensity until other photochemical reactions counteract this unusual light effect. Feeding with glucose or inhibition of carbon dioxide reduction by dinitrophenol enhance the effect. Photoreduction of carbon dioxide, when the latter is present, or early deadaptation brought about by the relatively poor supply of reducing agents (which otherwise keep the hydrogenase active) tend to depress or even abolish the effect. Thus, the production of hydrogen by light in algae shows a maximum when plotted against light intensity. Under one atmosphere of hydrogen the evolution of hydrogen is suppressed and changed into an absorption.

TABLE XIX
PHOTOPRODUCTION OF HYDROGEN FROM MALATE[a]

$$8\,H_2O + 8\,X + 8\,Y \xrightarrow{n.h\nu} 8\,HX + 8\,YOH$$
$$C_4H_6O_5 + 4\,HX \longrightarrow C_4H_8O_4 + H_2O + 4\,X$$
$$\tfrac{1}{2}\,C_4H_8O_4 + 8\,YOH \longrightarrow 2\,CO_2 + 6\,H_2O + 8\,Y$$
$$\tfrac{1}{2}\,C_4H_8O_4 \longrightarrow (CH_2O)_2$$
$$4\,HX \longrightarrow 2\,H_2 + X$$

$$C_4H_6O_5 + H_2O \xrightarrow{n.h\nu} (CH_2O)_2 + 2\,CO_2 + 2\,H_2$$
$$\tfrac{1}{3}\text{ Hexose}$$

[a] According to Kamen *et al.* (281).

In purple bacteria (55, 281) the photoproduction of hydrogen can be several times larger, comparatively, than in the algae, and it is always accompanied by a production of carbon dioxide (223–225) (see reaction scheme in Table XIX). The evolution of hydrogen and carbon dioxide in the light is strong only when the bacteria have been freshly grown in yeast extract media without another nitrogen source. The addition of a substrate like malate starts the reaction at a high rate only with cells which are not completely "resting." As in many other instances mentioned in this chapter, a certain steady concentration of carbon dioxide is also a requirement for the production of H_2 and CO_2. This is particularly true with those substrates whose decomposition does not immediately produce carbon dioxide by decarboxylation. Fatty acids, dicarboxylic acids, keto acids—in other words the usual substrates for Athiorhodaceae—give good rates of hydrogen evolution; alcohols, only after 1 or 2 days of adaptation. Carbohydrates are not attacked. The addition of ammonium chloride immediately stops this rather wasteful type of photometabolism and shifts it into normal photoreduction (Fig. 95). Nitrogen gas has the same effect, only less pronounced, because all purple bacteria are nitrogen fixers. The bacteria grow fairly well in organic media containing amino acids, but

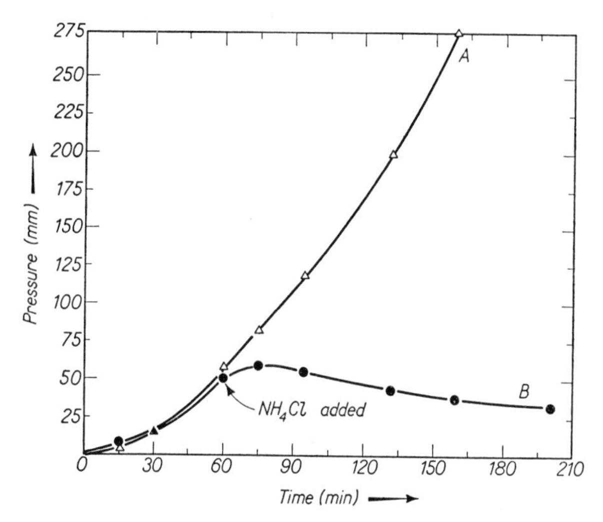

FIG. 95. Pressure changes due to the evolution of hydrogen (and carbon dioxide) by *Rhodospirillum rubrum* in the light under helium. The photochemical evolution of hydrogen stops when ammonium chloride is added to the suspension medium which is free of ammonium salts or nitrate. Nitrogen gas produces the same effect. Thus it was found that purple bacteria fix N_2 in the light. From Kamen (281, 282).

freshly fixed nitrogen or ammonia is apparently necessary to synthesize the particular enzymes needed for a more efficient assimilation of organic hydrogen donors in the light.

As a tentative explanation of this photoeffect in algae and bacteria, one may propose a dehydrogenation of endogenous or added organic compounds by the (YOH) produced in the photolysis of water without a corresponding utilization of the (XH). The excess of photohydrogen then finds its way to the hydrogenase, which, working in reverse, releases it as free gas. There is here a problem where experimentation with deuterium or tritium could give a definite answer. Kamen's scheme for the photodecomposition of malic acid is shown in Table XIX.

Figure 96 is a scheme intended to show how the hydrogenase fits into the mechanism of photosynthesis. Line *1* represents the reduction of carbon dioxide, line *2* the path of oxygen under aerobic conditions. Lines *3*, *4*, *5*, and *6* indicate the reactions that come into play when the hydrogenase has been activated. Reaction *3* interferes with *2* to give photoreduction. Line *4* represents the oxyhydrogen reaction. It proceeds in the dark with external oxygen and in the light with the oxygen of photosynthesis to the extent that YOH is not captured by reaction *3*. Line *5* pictures the carbon dioxide reduction coupled with *4* and line *6* the (hypothetical) way by which hydrogen gas can be released photochemically whenever other hydrogen donors are being oxidized

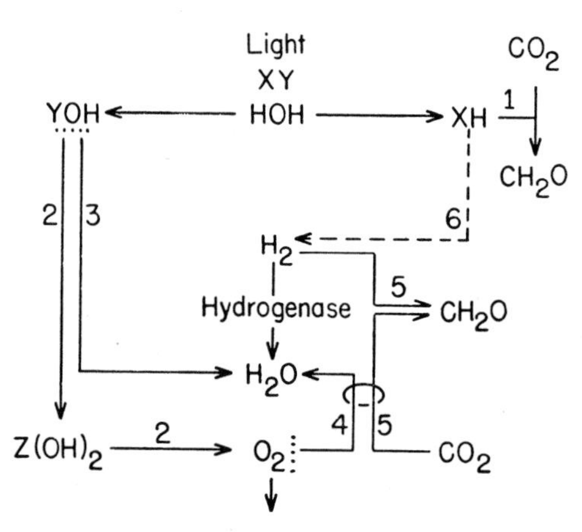

FIG. 96. Scheme showing the coupling of hydrogenase with the photochemical mechanism in adaptive algae. The main metabolic pathways are numbered *1–6*: *1*, fixation of CO_2 (Section X); *2*, path of oxygen; *3*, reduction of oxidized intermediate YOH; *4*, oxyhydrogen reaction; *5*, fixation of CO_2 coupled with reaction *4*; *6*, photoproduction of hydrogen (cf. 210).

via reaction *3*. As long as reaction *2* is not blocked by fermentation products, manganese deficiency, or specific poisons, reactions *1*, *2*, *3*, *4*, and *5* may conceivably proceed simultaneously. Too high a concentration of $Z(OH)_2$ or of oxygen inactivates the hydrogenase and enforces a return to aerobic conditions (cf. 210).

D. NITRATE, NITRITE, AND NITROGEN REDUCTION IN THE LIGHT

1. The Reduction of Nitrate and Nitrite

Many living cells obtain their nitrogen by the enzymatic reduction of nitrate with organic metabolites. A systematic study of the accelerating influence of light on the reduction of nitric acid to ammonia in *Chlorella* sp. was published by Warburg and Negelein (562) in 1920. Their results can be roughly summarized by saying that they proved the complexity of the phenomenon. It is apparently mediated by the normal process of carbon dioxide fixation, and the absence of carbon dioxide depresses the rate of nitrate reduction. Either the end products or the intermediates of photosynthesis serve as reducing agents for the nitrate molecule (102, 489).

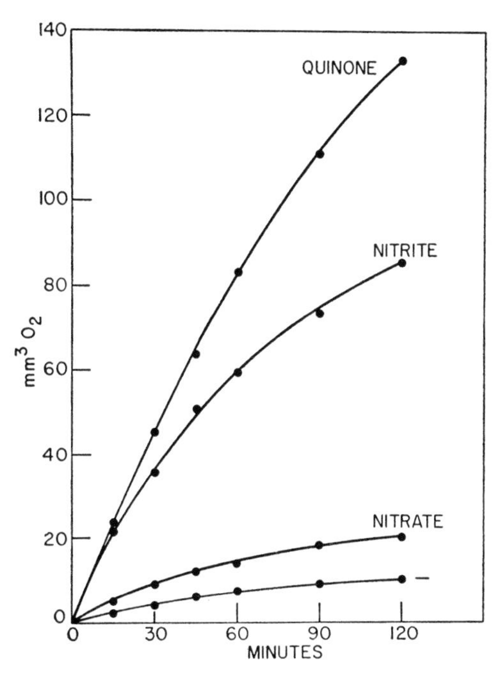

FIG. 97. Comparison of nitrite and nitrate as Hill reagents. *Ankistrodesmus braunii* photoreduces nitrite under nitrogen in the absence of carbon dioxide approximately like quinone. Abscissa: time. Ordinate: oxygen evolved. According to Kessler (306, 310).

More recently the question has come up whether nitrate might not be a true Hill reagent—that is, whether it, too, could be reduced directly, like certain dyestuffs, in suspensions of illuminated chloroplasts or chloroplast fragments. Nitrate is reduced in many nonphotosynthetic organisms. The influence of light, therefore, can be indirect as well as direct, and discrepancies in the observations from several laboratories might be explained on that basis (156, 157).

Obviously, the transformation of nitric acid into ammonia must proceed via several steps. One intermediate was shown to be nitrite.

Further tests with nitrite revealed that it is reduced in the light more like a direct oxidant for the photochemical reaction, a behavior not seen with nitrate (304–311). Figure 97 compares the rate of oxygen evolution in the light as the consequence of the addition of nitrate or nitrite or quinone to a suspension of *Ankistrodesmus braunii* at pH 6.5, under nitrogen, in the absence of carbon dioxide. Though initially the rates of O_2 evolution due to quinone and nitrite reduction are identical, the rate with the latter declines, and cannot be increased by adding more nitrite. The photochemical nitrite reduction, obviously, depends on some exhaustible supply of either an intermediate reducing compound or of a substance which combines with the ammonia produced. Isolated chloroplasts reduce neither nitrate nor nitrite directly. (A reduction of nitrate achieved by chloroplasts in the light which depends upon the presence of TPN plus nitrate reductase is quite indirect and probably different from the observation we are discussing here.)

Despite the prompt action which light has on the conversion of nitrite to ammonia, one has to conclude that some other photoproduct —perhaps energy-rich phosphate—is necessary to keep the reaction going. The influence of carbon dioxide, the inhibiting effect of dinitrophenol, and the low saturation rate are the reasons given. In this connection one might ask to what extent light energy contributes to the immediate synthesis of proteins. The experiences gained with nitrite show why amino acids are among the earliest products containing labeled carbon, since the necessary reduced nitrogen (ammonia) can be delivered right on the spot (see Section X).

Nitrite is such a reactive substance in the cell that even under anaerobic conditions in the dark it is reduced at a measurable rate. Light increases this rate five to ten times, and the presence of carbon dioxide doubles it again. The values found for disappearance of nitrite and the corresponding gas exchange at high light intensity satisfied the following over-all equations:

$$\text{Anaerobic in } N_2\text{: } HNO_2 + H_2O \xrightarrow{\text{light}} NH_3 + 1.5\ O_2 \tag{s}$$

$$\text{Anaerobic in } H_2\text{: } HNO_3 + 3H_2 \xrightarrow{\text{dark or light}} NH_3 + 2\ H_2O \tag{t}$$

In the dark and in the absence of oxygen, nitrite was found to be the simplest reagent to establish the presence of an active hydrogenase (Fig. 98). In adapted algae nitrite is immediately reduced in the dark by an equivalent amount of hydrogen, if this gas is present. The rate of this reduction increases with the duration of the preceding anaerobic incubation and is thus a measure of the degree to which adaptation has progressed with time. In this way, it could be confirmed

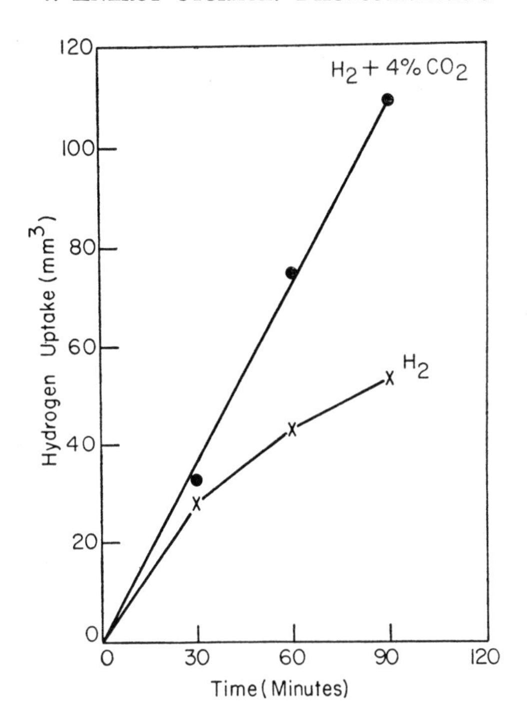

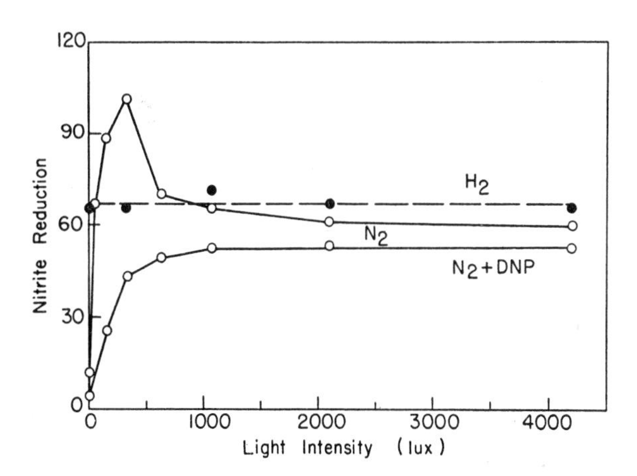

FIG. 98. (Top) Enzymatic reduction of nitrite with hydrogen in the dark by adapted *Ankistrodesmus braunii*. Presence of CO_2 insures a sustained rate (308, 311).

FIG. 99. (Bottom) Influence of light intensity on the rate of nitrite reduction by *Ankistrodesmus braunii*. ●—● in hydrogen; rate is independent of light. ○—○, in nitrogen; rate has a maximum at 300 lux. Dinitrophenol abolishes the maximum completely while interfering only slightly with the saturation rate. Saturation is always reached at the relatively low intensity of 1000 lux (308).

that in *Scenedesmus* sp. it may take several hours to produce a fully activated hydrogenase system. For reduction of nitrite with molecular hydrogen in adapted algae no light is necessary. The reaction proceeds at its maximum rate without an external supply of energy. Carbon dioxide exerts a similar effect upon the rate and the stoichiometry of the nitrite reduction by hydrogen as it does in the oxyhydrogen reaction. As long as (a rather high) concentration of carbon dioxide is present, the reduction continues at a steady pace and the amount of hydrogen taken up per molecule nitrite reduced corresponds exactly to the formation of ammonia. In the absence of carbon dioxide both rate and ratio begin to drop. Contrary to the oxyhydrogen reaction, no fixation of carbon dioxide takes place when the latter is present. This could be tested by using radioactive $C^{14}O_2$. In parallel experiments, *Ankistrodesmus braunii* fixed only 50% more CO_2 than the control in pure hydrogen when nitrite was reduced to ammonia, while it took up sixteen times more CO_2 when oxygen was reduced to water. Aerobically, however, nitrite—or, better, ammonia—induced a strong respiratory fixation of carbon dioxide.

The reduction of nitrite with hydrogen in *Ankistrodesmus* or *Chlorella* is particularly sensitive to poisoning with dinitrophenol. This fact helps to explain a very unusual observation in regard to the light dependency of the nitrite reduction under nitrogen. From the low anaerobic dark value, the rate of reduction rises steeply to a maximum which is reached at the comparatively low intensity of 300 lux and falls off again to a lower saturation value with a further rise in light intensity. This peculiar maximum disappears in the presence of dinitrophenol (see Fig. 99). It is the ability of *Ankistrodesmus braunii* to evolve hydrogen at low intensities (see the preceding paragraph) which provides the answer to the puzzle. At low light intensities nitrite is reduced, under nitrogen, not according to one, but to both, reactions shown above, the necessary hydrogen for the second reaction being mobilized by light. (About the probable role of photophosphorylation, see Section XIII.) The complexity and interdependence of these metabolic reactions is the consequence of the variety of reactions which may occur simultaneously in adapted algae (see Fig. 96).

Purple bacteria have no difficulty in reducing nitrate rapidly during their photometabolism. Nitrate competes with carbon dioxide for organic hydrogen donors; and in an atmosphere of hydrogen, the ratio of hydrogen absorbed to nitrate reduced is exactly 4, as required by the equation:

$$HNO_3 + 4\ H_2 \xrightarrow{\text{light}} NH_3 + 3\ H_2O \qquad \text{(u)}$$

2. *Fixation of Elementary Nitrogen*

Among the photosynthetic organisms some species of blue-green algae—mainly the Nostocaceae—have long been known to be capable of fixing nitrogen from the air. This property is said to be important for the fertilization of rice fields in India, where blue-green algae grow abundantly (157, 605).

Kamen *et al.* recently discovered that the purple bacteria, both Athiorhodaceae and Thiorhodaceae, also belong to the nitrogen fixing microorganisms (55, 282, 333, 334). This is of special interest here because it was found that the photochemical production of hydrogen by

TABLE XX
EFFECT OF NITROGEN ON OXYGEN EVOLVED BY *Anabaena cylindrica*[a]

Gas	O_2 Evolved (mg/$h\nu$/100 ml suspension)
$-CO_2$ $+A$	0.064
$-CO_2$ $+N_2$	0.960
$+CO_2$ $+A$	0.928
$+CO_2$ $+N_2$	2.184

[a] According to Fogg (157).

TABLE XXI
PHOTOSYNTHETIC NITROGEN FIXATION IN THE BLUE-GREEN ALGA *Anabaena cylindrica*[a]

Nitrogen source	Increase in dry weight of cells (mg/100 ml)	O_2 Evolved (mg/100 ml)	C Fixed (mg/100 ml)	Photosynthetic quotient ($\Delta O_2 : \Delta C$)	Nitrogen assimilated (mg/100 ml)
N_2	1.08	0.774	0.316	0.92	0.089
NH_4^+	1.30	0.480	0.244	0.74	0.358

[a] According to Fogg (157).

purple bacteria (see above) is depressed in nitrogen but not in helium. The occurrence of a hydrogenase in a photosynthetic cell is not, *per se*, an indication of an ability to fix nitrogen. The green algae which can be adapted to photoreduction do not fix elementary nitrogen and differ in this respect from the hydrogenase-containing purple bacteria and Nostocaceae. A direct coupling between the fixation of elementary nitrogen and the photochemistry of *Anabaena* has been found by Fogg. In contrast to argon, nitrogen causes the evolution of "extra oxygen" in the light (see Tables XX and XXI).

XII. Photosynthesis with Cell Extracts: Chloroplast Reactions

Complete photosynthesis is possible outside the intact living cell (13, 16, 516, 517). Molisch said as much in 1904 after he saw oxygen evolution in extracts from air dried leaves while performing experiments similar to those of Beijerinck, who, in 1901, used luminous bacteria as indicator. During the last forty years a great many investigators have vainly tried to find photosynthesis in cell extracts. Others found some indications that were not reproducible.

The problem could be solved only after it had been recognized that photosynthesis consists of a series of interlocked metabolic systems or cycles each depending for proper function upon a number of soluble protein factors, coenzymes, or metal activators. It has required skill and improved technique, after each successful step in isolating partial reactions, to retain or to add those components which are usually lost or destroyed in the process of breaking up green cells. Not only are the various constituents easily lost during the preparation procedures, but the "life time" of a successful chloroplast extract is severely limited. Clendenning found that it makes a difference whether chlorophyll extracts are stored above or below —40°C, an indication that certain reactions still proceed while the preparations are completely frozen and incapable of any kind of the known enzymatic reactions (cf. 423).

Willstätter and Stoll in 1918 gave up their attempt to extract either juices or particles which could still do photosynthesis because the broken cells showed no trace of carbon dioxide reduction. If we repeat these experiments today and use the same material [sunflower (*Helianthus*), *Cyclamen*, or *Pelargonium* leaves] their negative results can still be confirmed. The reason is that not all green leaves are equally suited to produce active extracts or chloroplast preparations. The leaves of the sunflower, *Helianthus annuus*, have been used extensively in photosynthesis experiments (see Fig. 1). When the structure is disrupted, the photosynthetic activity becomes inhibited by compounds (saponins, tannins) which exist in the same cell (94, 97). On the other hand, spinach (as normally purchased), and a number of other plants such as Swiss chard (*Beta vulgaris* var. *cicla*), *Phytolacca* sp., etc., apparently lack such destructive constituents and have, in recent years, been the mainstay of the research on cell-free photochemical reactions (470). The proof that chloroplasts preserve the essential feature of photosynthesis—the capacity to evolve oxygen in the light (as seen in vestigial amounts by Beijerinck and Molisch)—goes back to a discovery by R. Hill in 1939 (252–256, 601).

A. REDUCTION OF SPECIAL REAGENTS

Green extracts from leaves of *Stellaria media* or *Lamium album* ground in appropriate buffers, though they showed no trace of photosynthesis, could still evolve oxygen in the light if certain oxidizing substances were present. In 1940, Hill and Scarisbrick established that the evolution of oxygen by illuminated chloroplasts continues, in a mixture of potassium ferric oxalate and potassium ferricyanide, until all ferrisalts are reduced to ferrous salts (254). The oxygen evolved is equivalent to the amount of iron salt reduced to the ferrous level. In spinach preparations the oxalate can be omitted. Ferricyanide alone is reduced immediately in the light, and the rate of the reaction is comparable to photosynthesis.

Provided Hill's reaction is not a complete artifact, these early experiments established that the photochemical activity of the natural chlorophyll can be separated from the reactions leading to the reduction of carbon dioxide and that the photochemistry indeed consists of a kind of photolysis of water (compare Section I,C; see equation d in Fig. 2). Carbon dioxide as a hydrogen acceptor is here replaced by an artificial substrate which is reduced at the expense of the hydrogen derived from water. The oxygen is set free just as in photosynthesis. The final proof that the photolysis of water is at the heart of the process was furnished by using isotopic oxygen in heavy water.

The illumination of chloroplasts in a Hill medium leads to exactly the same result as the decomposition of water by an electric current

TABLE XXII

THE ISOTOPIC COMPOSITION OF OXYGEN EVOLVED BY ILLUMINATED CHLOROPLASTS AS COMPARED WITH THAT OF THE SUSPENDING WATER (186)

Water used	Oxidant	Ratio $O^{18}O^{16}:O^{16}O^{16} \times 100$ — Method of O_2 production: Photochemical	Electrolytic
Normal	0.02 *M* ferricyanide	0.39	0.38
Normal	0.02 *M* ferricyanide	0.39	0.38
Enriched	0.02 *M* ferricyanide	1.4	1.3
Enriched	0.02 *M* ferricyanide	0.84	0.8
Enriched	0.0067 *M* quinone	0.62	0.61
Enriched	0.0035 *M* indophenol	0.57	0.62
Enriched	Dil. 2,6-dichlorophenolindophenol	0.54	(0.57–0.49)
Enriched	0.00221 *M* K_2CrO_4	0.52	0.49

(262) (see Table XXII). Hill's discovery was soon confirmed and extended by other workers, and it was found that a great range of substances could be reduced photochemically. At first it seemed that only easily reducible compounds like quinone and certain dyes (e.g. 2,6-dichlorophenolindophenol) were suitable to demonstrate the chloroplast activity, and these were unphysiological substances. Quinone in particular [first used by Warburg and Lüttgens; eq. (v); Fig. 100]

$$\left.\begin{array}{c} 4\ H_2O \xrightarrow[\text{chloroplasts}]{h\nu} 4\ [H] + 4\ [OH] \\ 2\ \text{quinone} + 4\ [H] \rightarrow 2\ \text{hydroquinone} \\ 4\ [OH] \rightarrow 2\ H_2O + O_2\uparrow \end{array}\right\} \quad (v)$$

though otherwise most practical for such tests, destroys essential enzymes in the photosynthetic system. These strong oxidants usually give quantitative results (18, 263, 567, 568). Since the reduced products upon reoxidation release a certain amount of free energy, the reduction of iron salts or of dyes constitutes a "synthesis," though not a very efficient one. A physiological, ever-present, strong oxidant is the oxygen of the air. Illuminated chloroplasts reduce it to hydrogen peroxide. Mehler proved this by coupling the reduction with the known oxidation of ethanol to acetaldehyde by means of the peroxidatic activity of high concentrations of catalase (363, 364). The reaction sequence may be written:

$$2\ HOH + 2\ XY \xrightarrow{\text{light}} 2\ XH + 2\ YOH \quad (w)$$

$$O_2 + 2\ XH \longrightarrow 2\ X + H_2O_2 \quad (x)$$

$$2\ YOH \longrightarrow 2\ Y + H_2O + \tfrac{1}{2}\ O_2 \quad (y)$$

$$H_2O_2 + CH_3CH_2OH \xrightarrow{\text{catalase}} CH_3CHO + 2\ H_2O \quad (z)$$

Since one molecule of oxygen disappears in reactions (x) plus (z) and only one-half molecule of oxygen is evolved by reaction (y), the chloroplast reaction can be followed manometrically. Without ethanol as acceptor the gas exchange balances because one-half molecule of oxygen results from the catalytic decomposition of the hydrogen peroxide (236). Yet, with the aid of isotopic oxygen and a mass spectrometer, it was possible to show that chloroplasts promote, indeed, the reactions (w), (x), and (y) in the light (61, 66). This photoreduction of free oxygen by chloroplasts is considerably accelerated by traces of another Hill oxidant, namely, quinone. Figure 101 gives an example. Curve *1* is the quantitative evolution of oxygen due to the reduction of a small amount of quinone by spinach chloroplasts in the light. Curve *2* results from the balance of oxygen exchange by the same chloroplast preparation containing ethanol and catalase. This gas exchange is accelerated to give the slope of curve 3 when quinone, catalase, and ethanol are combined. The action of the quinone is catalytic and depends on the reduction of quinone at the chloroplast surface. Addition of hydroquinone does not produce the same effect (curve 3).

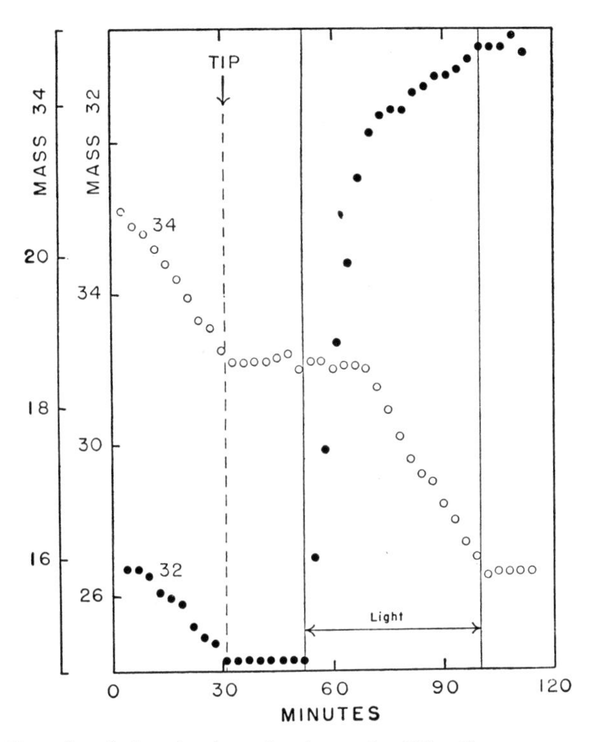

FIG. 100. Photochemical reduction of quinone in *Chlorella* sp., as seen by Brown *et al.*, with the isotope tracer method in presence of air enriched with oxygen of mass 34. Compare Fig. 32. Addition of quinone stops respiration. In light normal O_2 (32) is evolved during quinone reduction. After exhaustion of quinone a photochemical exchange of oxygen takes place because oxygen itself is a "Hill" reagent. O_2 (34) is reduced [together with O_2 (32)]. Simultaneously, O_2 (32) is evolved from water. (See Fig. 101.)

Just as the intact cell is not necessary in principle for the process of photosynthesis, so the entire chloroplast is not necessary for the Hill reaction (186, 187, 432). Experiments with repeatedly washed whole chloroplasts are needed to prove that a certain reaction does not depend on substances or particles found outside the chloroplasts, or, conversely, to demonstrate that certain factors have to be added again to restore any lost functions. Otherwise the difference between whole chloroplasts and chloroplast fragments, grana, or smaller particles is merely a question of stability of the preparation or inactivation by dilution of soluble factors. "Damaged or fragmented chloroplasts are stabilized by potassium chloride but not by media of high osmotic pressure. Whole chloroplasts are stabilized by media of high osmotic pressure (sucrose solution), but not by chloride." The Hill reaction itself is not influenced by either of these factors. The absolute reaction rates are approximately the same as the rates measured for whole-cell photosynthesis (94, 97, 145, 148, 238, 244, 303, 459).

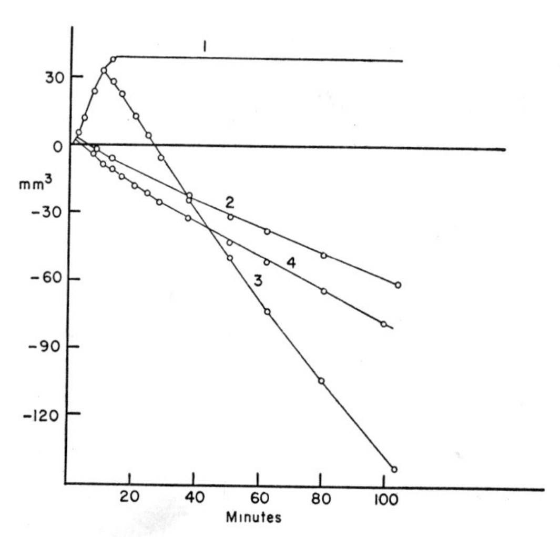

FIG. 101. Oxygen as "Hill" reagent in suspensions of chloroplast material. Manometric observations. Experiment *1*: Oxygen evolved during reduction of quinone. Experiment *2*: Oxygen consumed in presence of added catalase and alcohol. Experiment *3*: Like experiment *2*, but after reduction of quinone. Rate of oxygen uptake is twice as fast. Experiment *4*: Like experiment *2*, with hydroquinone. From Mehler (364).

The good rates dispose of an old argument that the mechanism of the photochemical reduction of artificial substrates in chloroplasts must be different from photosynthesis because neither the quantum yield nor the saturation rate seemed to approach that found in photosynthesis. Hill *et al.* could show that the rate of methemoglobin reduction by chloroplast preparations from peas (*Pisum sativum*) compares very well with that of photosynthesis in *Chlorella* sp. for high, as well as low, light intensities (110, 256). Only at medium intensity is the yield of the cell-free preparation lower. This can be interpreted by assuming greater losses due to back or side reactions in the cell-free preparations.

The "chloroplast" or "Hill" reaction is defined as the reduction of an artificially added hydrogen acceptor by illuminated chloroplasts or their fragments with the simultaneous evolution of oxygen, which has been shown to come from water. If we summarize this description in the equation:

$$2\ H_2O + 2\ A \xrightarrow[\text{chloroplast}]{\text{light}} 2\ H_2A + O_2 \qquad \text{(aa)}$$

the oversimplification is nearly as great as in the much misused short expression for photosynthesis. In reality there exist a whole array of sometimes very dissimilar processes which have one thing in common: they are driven by the same source of energy—the photolysis of water (40, 352, 478). Consequently, they are all inhibited by such substances as hydroxylamine, *o*-phenanthroline, DCMU, and others, which hinder the liberation of free oxygen. Inhibitors specific for the reduction of carbon dioxide, as for instance, cyanide, have little or no effect on typical chloroplast reactions (39, cf. 436).

On the other hand, different oxidants require different intermediate factors, soluble or insoluble, in order to become efficiently reduced by illuminated chloroplasts. Compared with complete photosynthesis some of these couplings are rather simple; the fewer the intermediate steps which exist between the primary photochemical process and the added reagent, the more the particular chloroplast reactions assume the characteristics of a photochemical reaction (39, 40). The influence of temperature, for instance, upon the over-all rate will become smaller. Thus some Hill reactions retain their high rate at temperatures which are so low as to depress normal photosynthesis severely.

The reaction map—the scheme of Fig. 4 (p. 15)—does not cover all possible types of chloroplast reactions because it was drawn to fit the ways of the living cell. In particular, one set of reactions among those observed with chloroplasts and cell extracts is still missing: a "Hill" reduction without the evolution of oxygen similar to the photoreduction of purple bacteria and adapted algae. To accomplish this, all that is required is to replace the dismutation of (YOH) to oxygen by an artificial reduction with an added hydrogen donor. Some beginnings have been made in this respect. At least with chromatophores of the purple bacterium *Rhodospirillum rubrum*, a photochemical reduction of DPN can be brought about in the light by the simultaneous and stoichiometric dehydrogenation of flavin nucleotide, $FMNH_2$ (193, 551). This reaction competes with photophosphorylation (see Section XIII). But purple bacteria lack, anyhow, the capacity to evolve oxygen. A "Hill" photoreduction with preparations from aerobic plants seems more difficult. The reduction of the oxygen of the air by chloroplast preparations (in the presence of traces of quinone as an accelerating factor) is mainly an exchange according to equation:

$$O_2 + 4\ HO^*H \xrightarrow{\text{light}} 2\ H_2O_2 + 2\ H_2O^* + O_2^* \quad \text{(bb}$$

where O* means oxygen marked by the isotope O^{18}. It becomes less of an exchange in the presence of ascorbic acid; more oxygen is taken up and less oxygen is developed. The easiest interpretation is to say that ascorbate reduces the photohydroxyls, YOH (246) (see Section XI Fig. 96).

Kamen and Vernon discovered a specific photooxidation of cytochrome in extracts from *Rhodospirillum rubrum* (285, 549). What makes this reaction less interesting is that molecular oxygen must be present (258); what makes it more interesting is its typical enzymatic specificity (cf. 396). Thus, it cannot be dismissed as one of the usual photosensitized chemical oxidations, of which so many entirely artificial examples are known (cf. 436).

For a long time it was believed that the Hill reagents were reduced directly in contact with the photochemical mechanism, since they evidently did not require intermediate hydrogen transfer agents such as those necessary for the reduction of phosphoglyceric acid or other organic acids. Lately it has become apparent that the dissimilar behavior of chloroplast preparations from different plants toward the same dye or quinone or iron salts might be explained by a difference in the sensitivity, solubility, or concentration of certain intermediate protein factors in these plants. The existence of such factors was recognized when it was found that the reduction of methemoglobin or of cytochrome by chloroplast preparations depended on them (111, 601).

B. Reduction of Carbon Dioxide

The repeated failures to find true photosynthesis in chloroplasts, while quinones and cytochromes—i.e., substances with a high potential—became reduced at a great rate, led to a discussion of the reducing power of excited chlorophyll in terms of oxidation-reduction potentials. As we shall see below, the later findings that pyridine nucleotides, DPN, and TPN can not only be reduced in a coupled reaction, but even accumulated in their reduced forms in cell-free preparations, and thus are true Hill reagents, has rendered a good deal of this critical speculation obsolete.

The first deliberate experiment to achieve a photochemical reduction of carbon dioxide by chloroplasts was due to Vishniac and Ochoa (552–554) (Fig. 102). They combined chloroplasts with the enzymes capable of performing a carboxylation reaction (Fig. 102). The decisive intermediate step is the reduction of pyridine nucleotides (Fig. 102). Independently, Tolmach, who had tried to achieve a direct reduction of phosphoglyceric acid by chloroplasts, observed that oxygen evolution increased upon addition of the coenzyme (521–523)

$$4\ H_2O \xrightarrow[\text{chloroplasts}]{h\mu} 4\ [H] + 4\ [OH]$$
$$4\ [OH] \rightarrow 2\ H_2O + O_2\uparrow$$
$$4\ [H] + 2\ TPN \rightarrow 2\ TPNH_2$$
$$2\ CH_3COCOOH + 2\ C^*O_2 + 2\ TPNH_2 \xrightarrow[\text{enzyme}]{\text{"malic"}}$$
$$HOOCCHOHCH_2C^*OOH + 2\ TPN$$

FIG. 102. First light-induced fixation of carbon dioxide seen in a cell-free system. The enzymes added to a chloroplast suspension channel the carbon dioxide into malic acid. From Vishniac and Ochoa (552, 554).

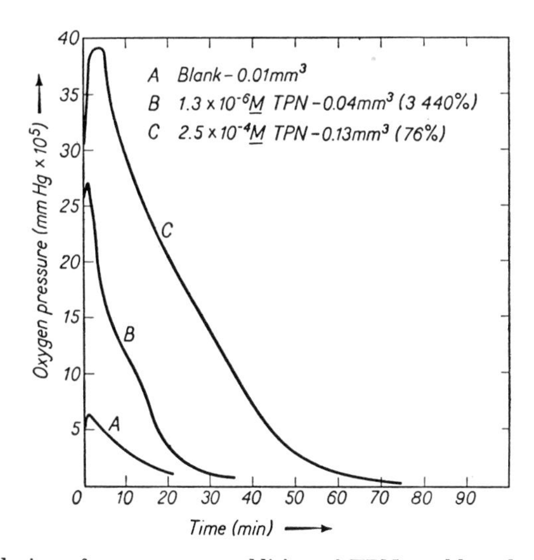

FIG. 103. Evolution of oxygen upon addition of TPN to chloroplasts under anaerobic conditions. Curve *B* shows that TPN must act catalytically since much more oxygen is evolved than the amount equivalent to that of the TPN added. From Tolmach (521, 522).

(Fig. 103). More model reactions of this kind were tried in quick succession because it had become obvious that illuminated chloroplasts could be used as a source of hydrogen by coupling them to any kind of biochemical enzyme system that depended on reduced coenzymes for their specific synthetic achievements (17, 248, 439). The most elegant artificial system of this kind is that invented by Racker, who pointed out how in this way the photosynthetic production of carbohydrates from molecular hydrogen and carbon dioxide is possible (440). Compared with photosynthesis, however, such working models still have some drawbacks. The products are not the right ones and yield, for instance, malic acid instead of carbohydrates; the carbon dioxide partial pressure must be kept unusually high, and in the case of Racker's reaction, we have the cooperation of enzymes which do not work in this way in the green plant. Those factors which would enable us to reconstruct complete photosynthesis, from chloroplasts and from the enzymes which have been extracted and identified as components of the pentose cycle are apparently the easiest to lose.

TABLE XXIII
PHOTOSYNTHETIC ACTIVITY OF FRAGMENTS FROM *Spirogyra* CHLOROPLASTS[a]

	Photosynthetic activity[b]				
Respiration (μl/hr)	Oxygen evolution (μl/hr)	Carbon dioxide consumption (μl/hr)	$Q_{O_2}^{chl} \times 10^3$	$Q_{CO_2}^{chl} \times 10^3$	A.Q.
187	302	316	—	—	0.9
174	465	510	—	—	0.91
435	768	607	—	—	1.2
180	104	682	1.1	7.4	0.1
265	522	1034	3.5	7.0	0.51
292	607	1312	4.1	8.9	0.47

[a] From Thomas *et al.* (517).
[b] $Q_{O_2}^{chl}$ and $Q_{CO_2}^{chl}$: maximal oxygen evolution and carbon dioxide consumption in μl/mg chlorophyll/hour.
[c] A.Q.: Assimilatory quotient.

Tolbert showed how opening a large cell like those of *Nitella* and squeezing out chloroplasts together with surrounding plasma gives cell-free preparations capable of assimilating carbon dioxide (for a short time). Chloroplast fragments from *Spirogyra* sp. (algae which were collected by Thomas *et al.* from their natural habitat) appear so far to be the least fragile. Suspended in phosphate buffer at pH 7.2 they gave, in the light, a normal photosynthesis at normal rates (Table XXIII). Arnon and co-workers found a somewhat diminished photosynthesis in washed, unbroken chloroplasts from spinach, which, however, produced starch like the complete cell. The identity of this cell-free carbon dioxide assimilation with photosynthesis has been confirmed, not only because others have also seen a synthesis of starch, but because the distribution of tracer carbon in the carbohydrates formed was found to be the same (230, 295).

A not unimportant similarity in the behavior of intact cells and chloroplasts concerns the secretion of glycolic acid. In Section IX it was stated that an insufficient supply of carbon dioxide induces illuminated algae to release some glycolic acid into the medium. Presumably, this stems from the cleavage of RuDP or a precursor carbohydrate into C_3 and C_2 compounds when the RuDP is not entirely used up in the carboxylation reaction. The same happens with intact chloroplasts from Swiss chard. Under conditions which favor photosynthesis in the presence of some $C^{14}O_2$ as a tracer but at a light intensity far above saturation (2500 foot-candles), Tolbert found an excretion of glycolic acid into the medium while the normal products of photosynthesis were retained within the chloroplasts (519).

Rupture of the chloroplast by treatment with distilled water results in the loss of the photosynthetic capacity. The latter can be partially restored by adding back to the fragments a water extract from whole chloroplasts. Furthermore, addition of adenosine triphosphate plus coenzyme II (ATP + TPN) brings about a four times larger fixation of carbon dioxide (measured with the radioactive carbon technique) (17).

It has been discussed at length whether the chloroplasts contain within their structure all the necessary cofactors (cf. 43) or whether the latter are partially dissolved in the surrounding protoplasm of the cell. This may be a meaningless question since we do not know how permeable the chloroplast membranes are in respect to the individual components of the complete photosynthetic mechanism. The fact that some of them can be so easily lost speaks against their being fixed at the lamellar structure like the pigments, and it seems irrelevant whether they are dissolved only in the liquid inside the chloroplast or in some larger parts of the cell. It should be remembered that photosynthetic bacteria and blue-green algae have no chloroplasts. *Spirogyra* chloroplasts, at least, appear to be complete and self sufficient (516, 517). Chloroplast fragments are capable of producing the same results provided none of the necessary cofactors are lost during the extraction procedure.

This final experimental demonstration of photosynthesis in cell extracts does not automatically rehabilitate all earlier, unconfirmed claims for cell-free photosynthesis. The majority of these observations have too weak an experimental basis and the alleged results remain implausible. Among the exceptions may be the experiments of Gerretsen (221) and of Franck (169). Gerretsen studied changes of pH and of reduction potentials in crude *Avena sativa* chloroplast suspensions under anaerobic conditions. Here, added carbon dioxide produced changes which he interpreted as a reduction of CO_2. Franck saw, by means of the very sensitive oxygen analyzer, that a residual evolution of oxygen in chloroplast preparations was considerably enhanced if the nitrogen stream contained some carbon dioxide. Later Franck and Brown, using the tracer method, found no significant fixation of carbon dioxide in these chloroplasts and the earlier observation was dismissed as an unspecified catalysis (58). Since these two sets of experiments were performed at different times, the method of preparation may have been sufficiently different to cause the discrepancy in the results.

C. Reduction of Coenzymes I and II

Of all the known natural catalysts which have been seen to react with, or in the presence of, illuminated chloroplasts, the pyridine nucleotides, DPN and TPN, are by far the most interesting ones. In the reduced state they are known to react with phosphorylated carboxyl groups to give aldehyde and oxidized coenzyme. In other words, a combination of phosphorylation agents (such as ATP) and reduced coenzymes may reverse the main steps in glycolysis. The observation by Arnon *et al.*, mentioned above, that ATP and TPN enhance carbon dioxide reduction with chloroplast fragments, is a result long hoped for—seemingly another proof that photosynthesis is indeed the reversal of glycolysis, to be considered together with the discoveries concerning the formation of phosphoglyceric acid and the function of the pentose cycle (17). On these pillars the reversal hypothesis seems to rest quite firmly (Fig. 108, Section XIII). San Pietro and Lang found conditions under which TPN not only is reduced as a member of a functioning complete enzyme system, but accumulates in analyzable amounts. A certain soluble protein factor extractable from chloroplasts has to be present, and the illumination has to be a long one. This pyridine nucleotide reductase is specific for TPN and, perhaps, indirectly for DPN. It has no effect on the rate of other Hill reactions, nor is its activity with chloroplasts and TPN enhanced by the addition of thioctic acid. All this supports the notion that former attempts to find reduced TPN failed because of loss of enzyme, back reactions, and an inefficient coupling with the photochemical mechanism (451, 452).

The experiments with chloroplasts have proved beyond doubt that as long as a minimum amount of structure is preserved, the ability to perform a photochemical decomposition of water is retained and that this is one of the most stable features of the photosynthetic system (511). The efficiency of the various reactions which can be coupled with the photochemical mechanism depends on the extent to which back reactions can be avoided. The dilution or destruction of any one of several intermediate transfer agents will favor such back reactions. It is, therefore, not surprising that strong oxidants like quinone guarantee better yields. They are better able to compete with the back reaction for the photohydrogen than, say, the coenzymes which can be so readily reoxidized. The detrimental effect of oxygen, provided this picture is correct, is equally obvious. As has been said so often, one amazing achievement of the intact cell is indeed the fact that the numerous possible side reactions can be so successfully held in check.

From the standpoint of the schemes of Figs. 4 and 108, it is easy to explain why certain chloroplast preparations catalyze one photochemical reaction in preference to another. If we assume specific links for most of the Hill reagents so far known, the presence or absence of one specific factor changes the over-all character of the process. Given a high concentration of natural (or artificial) connecting links, the rate of a normal partial reaction like photophosphorylation may, in chloroplasts, approach or surpass that of carbon dioxide reduction in plants. It is a question of eliminating all competing processes and of favoring the particular reaction which we now assume to be the source of energy-rich phosphates. It would be erroneous to conclude that such artificially increased rates of physiological reactions also prevail in the living cell. One should beware of the assumption that, because the activity of chloroplasts can be combined successfully with certain other enzyme systems known to exist in living cells, this combination is in fact part of the carbon dioxide fixation mechanism. In each case the proof has to come by a careful comparison of the cell-free system with the reaction in the intact organisms (cf. 111, 116).

XIII. Energy Transfer by Active Phosphate in Photosynthesis

A. ENERGY-RICH PHOSPHATE BOND (~P)

A major chapter in cell physiology concerns the capture of the energy released during the degradation of foodstuffs. The reactions which make it possible for the living cell to save about 60% of the free energy released in many intermediate steps of respiration and glycolysis revolve around the enzymatic transfer not only of hydrogen (or electrons), but also of phosphoric acid groups from one molecule to another. The more it became known how similar some intermediary steps in photosynthesis were to those in general metabolism the more obvious it appeared that phosphate transfer also played a decisive role in the capture of light energy.

Phosphoric acid as a factor in the fermentation of sugars was discovered by Harden and Young in 1905. After forty more years of biological research, we know that phosphate esters of organic metabolites are formed in the living cell wherever the free energy released by respiration and fermentation is to be used for synthetic reactions. In this way a good part of the energy can be saved which would be lost as heat if, for instance, the dehydrogenation of an aldehyde group to the free carboxyl occurred in the unphosphorylated form. The bond to phosphoric acid in the aldehyde.

$$\begin{array}{l} \qquad \mathrm{OH} \\ \quad / \\ \mathrm{R.C{-}H} \\ \quad \backslash \\ \qquad \mathrm{O{-}\textcircled{P}} \end{array}$$

becomes "energy rich" after dehydrogenation to the phosphorylated carboxyl:

$$\begin{array}{l} \qquad \mathrm{O} \\ \quad /\!/ \\ \mathrm{R.C{-}O{\sim}\textcircled{P}} \end{array}$$

$\textcircled{P}$ stands for

$$\begin{array}{l} \qquad \mathrm{OH} \\ \quad\ / \\ \mathrm{{-}P{=}O} \\ \quad\ \backslash \\ \qquad \mathrm{OH} \end{array}$$

and $\sim$ for the extra energy which is not lost as heat but is now held in the phosphate group. If the energy-rich compound is hydrolyzed with the release of inorganic phosphate the energy is dissipated and the reaction becomes essentially irreversible:

$$\begin{array}{l} \qquad \mathrm{O} \\ \quad /\!/ \\ \mathrm{R.C} \\ \quad \backslash \\ \qquad \mathrm{O{\sim}\textcircled{P}} \end{array} \quad + \mathrm{HOH} \rightarrow \mathrm{H_3PO_4} + \mathrm{RCOOH}\ (+\ \text{heat})$$

As long as the molecule

$$\begin{array}{l} \qquad \mathrm{O} \\ \quad /\!/ \\ \mathrm{R.C} \\ \quad \backslash \\ \qquad \mathrm{O{\sim}\textcircled{P}} \end{array}$$

holds on to its phosphate group, the dehydrogenation by means of one of the coenzymes (CoE = TPN or DPN) remains reversible:

$$\begin{array}{l} \qquad \mathrm{O} \\ \quad /\!/ \\ \mathrm{R.C} \\ \quad \backslash \\ \qquad \mathrm{O{\sim}P} \end{array} \quad + \mathrm{CoEH_2} \rightleftarrows \begin{array}{l} \qquad \mathrm{OH} \\ \quad / \\ \mathrm{R.C{-}H} \\ \quad \backslash \\ \qquad \mathrm{O{-}P} \end{array} \quad + \mathrm{CoE}$$

In other words, a phosphorylated acid group can be reduced by a metabolic reducing agent like $DPNH_2$.

Reduced coenzyme, $DPN(H_2)$, in its turn, if not used directly for synthetic reactions, may be oxidized through the flavoprotein-cytochrome system. The energy liberated in this respiratory chain of reactions leading to oxygen again is not lost, but saved, in large part, by the formation of more energy-rich phosphate bonds.

In order that the energy of oxidation (dehydrogenation) become available elsewhere for a similar reversed reaction, the cell uses agents which transfer phosphate groups in the energy-rich condition. Such an agent is adenosine diphosphate, ADP. It will add one more phosphate group and become ATP, adenosine triphosphate. A molecule of the general structure A—Ⓟ∼Ⓟ changes into one which can be written A—Ⓟ∼Ⓟ∼Ⓟ. The carboxyl group is left behind, unphosphorylated and on the way toward decarboxylation.

$$R.C\begin{matrix}{}^{\nearrow\!\!\!\!/\,O} \\ {}_{\searrow O\sim P}\end{matrix} + ADP \rightleftarrows R.C\begin{matrix}{}^{\nearrow\!\!\!\!/\,O} \\ {}_{\searrow OH}\end{matrix} + ATP$$

ATP is an "energy-rich" substance that can give its active phosphate groups to many compounds in the cell, which thus will become available for synthetic reactions. We shall not go further into the details of these energy transfers except to say that they happen on the surface of enzyme proteins whose specificity determines which one among several possible reactions should proceed. The amount of energy saved and transported by means of phosphorylation is 6 to 7 kcal per ∼Ⓟ, that is, one-sixth of the energy in the singlet excited state or one-fifth of that in the triplet state of chlorophyll (see Section IV).

ATP is the most common "energy coin" with which the cell pays for synthetic reactions, and which it regains by digesting food. Anything which stops the circulation of this "currency" may not always stop the breakdown reaction but will certainly stop synthesis and growth. For a detailed discussion of phosphorus metabolism and the problems involved see (338, 339, 348).

The question of the cycle of phosphates in connection with the problem of photosynthesis arose when it was recognized that the carbohydrates formed continuously in the light ought first to be phosphorylated in order to enter the general metabolism or to be stored away as starch and sucrose (1). After the enzymatic carboxylations in living cells had been discovered in 1936, one began to wonder whether those forces which brought about synthetic reactions in nonphotosynthetic organisms were somehow being used to promote also the reduction of carbon dioxide in the light. Ruben (449) specifically pointed out that phosphorylations might be necessary in order to make the reduction of a carboxyl group possible. By pursuing such analogies to their limits, photosynthesis became in the eyes of the biochemists but part of the then known "standard" carbohydrate metabolism (glycolysis according to Embden-Meyerhof) attached to a kind of photocell which provided the necessary flow of protons or electrons.

The central photochemical problem of photosynthesis was dismissed in brackets, given the symbol (H), and for the next ten years the attention of biochemists was mainly directed toward finding out which of the already known metabolic pathways would fit snugly and without experimental contradiction into a convincing scheme of photosynthesis. As has been said above in the section on carboxylation, none did. The solution of the problem came with the discovery of the carboxylation of ribulose diphosphate (see Section IX).

But long before any details of a photosynthetic phosphorus metabolism became known, certain assertions could be made. If photosynthesis needed a constant supply of some energy-rich phosphate, it was clear that the assimilatory mechanism in green plants and in purple bacteria had to provide for it and thus be self-supporting in that respect (212).

The known rates of respiration and of fermentation in the photosynthetic organs of plants are much too slow to deliver energy-rich phosphate at the pace required for photosynthesis at saturation (500). Direct measurements by Brown *et al.* (see Section V) confirmed that respiration does not speed up thirty times during illumination. Moreover, purple bacteria and adapted algae reduce carbon dioxide efficiently under completely anaerobic conditions.

The high over-all efficiency of photosynthesis, on the other hand, excludes any mechanism based on the assumption that all of the light energy is first converted into energy-rich phosphate. Experimentally, therefore, the task was to establish the existence of a specific phosphorylation cycle which serves photosynthesis (78, 222, 583). The evidence accumulated since 1948—first by measuring light-induced phosphate exchange in whole cells (119, 265, 266, 292, 467, 493, 553, 584, 607), and, since 1954, in chloroplasts—has proved the existence of such a photophosphorylation mechanism. Figure 108 is a composite scheme based mainly on recent discoveries by Arnon *et al.* (15–17), Wessels (592–595), and Jagendorf *et al.* (21a, 275). Before we discuss this scheme we have to review briefly the investigations which contributed to the present status of our knowledge of the problem.

B. LIGHT-INDUCED PHOSPHATE METABOLISM IN INTACT CELLS

The general scheme of photosynthesis (Fig. 3) indicates three ways in which $\sim$Ⓟ might be formed economically. First, during the breakdown of a photoperoxide leading to the evolution of free oxygen; second, during the dismutation of the initial XH· radical to produce a stable reduced intermediate XH_2 (69); third, by way of the back reaction between XH and YOH. [The fourth possibility of a direct photochemical process is demonstrably uneconomical (cf. 493).]

The existence and the role of adenosine triphosphate (ATP) as representative for the modern concepts in phosphorus metabolism was first recognized as the result of experimentation with animal tissues and heterotrophs like yeast. It took some special effort to demonstrate later that quite similar or even identical synthetic reactions, based on the transfer of energy-rich phosphate bonds, also took place in the cells of green plants (1).

The steady-state level of organic phosphate esters is likely to be higher in the light for two reasons. An increased turnover and greater production of sugars may require a faster production of ATP and a correspondingly higher concentration of phosphorylated intermediates (cf. 420, 424). The storage products are, of course, not phosphorylated and after an initial increase no more phosphate esters will be formed, while the accumulation of sucrose, starch, etc., continues. It depends on the model of carbohydrate synthesis selected as a basis for the calculation how much more organic phosphate should be found in the light. The second source of an increased phosphate turnover may be the phosphorylated intermediates required for energy transfer in the reduction process itself.

In both cases the level of organic phosphates is a function of the light intensity, but only the turnover will be directly proportional to the rate of photosynthesis. Nearly the entire change from the dark state to the light state ought to occur during the transient periods. Once adjustment to the new conditions has taken place, there is no reason to expect further changes. An accumulation of phosphorylated compounds such as ATP or other polyphosphates can be expected only in the presence of an excess of phosphate acceptors and under conditions where the normal reduction process is either eliminated or at least partly inhibited. From this point of view it is not surprising, therefore, that the later experiments with nonphotosynthesizing chloroplasts turned out to be such a successful method of proving the existence of a light-driven phosphorylation.

The methods employed to prove that a true photophosphorylation exists have steadily gained in refinement and complexity. The firs approach was to determine the relative levels of organic and inorgani phosphates present in green cells in the dark and in the light (cf. 424) (Figs. 104, 105). The next was to watch the shifting between the tw kinds of phosphate during the induction periods—the transient period immediately after light or after darkness. This was rightly considere to be more revealing than steady-state experiments which could not tel much about the rate of the actual phosphate turnover (see Fig. 114 Section XV). The introduction of radioactive P^{32} was a refinement tha allowed experiments of short duration and, in combination with chro matography, gave results quite similar to those which turned out to b so revealing in the chromatography with the radioactive carbon iso type, C^{14} (265, 266, 292–294, 467–470, 585–589, 607–609).

ATP specifically is usually assayed either in a cell-free enzym mixture which promotes the formation of glucose-6-phosphate or i one where the light emission of firefly extracts indicates the amoun of ATP present (494, 495).

Figures 104–107 are representative of the research done with intac cells. All these experiments more or less clearly supported the notio that the light energy absorbed in the chloroplasts could directly in duce the transformation of inorganic into organic phosphates, i.e. without the aid of some kind of oxygen-requiring respiratory system Particularly surprising were the findings of Wassink and Winter mans and of Kandler because in their experiments regular photo synthesis was either suppressed or quantitatively unimportant.

Figures 104–106 show Wintermans' and Wassink's observation tha the absence of carbon dioxide enhances the uptake of phosphate b illuminated *Chlorella* sp. suspended in acid medium. This points to phosphorylation mechanism which competes with carbon dioxide fixa tion for the absorbed light energy. Typical for a phosphorylation, th reaction is inhibited by dinitrophenol (DNP). It is of special interes that the degree of inhibition becomes less with increasing light in tensity (Fig. 106). Kandler discovered that at least part of the photo phosphorylation is insensitive to large doses of cyanide and thus ca counteract the dephosphorylation which takes place in the dark upo the addition of cyanide (Fig. 107). Here light replaces the role c respiration in furnishing the energy to phosphorylate glucose in orde that the cell can take it up from the medium and store it as reserv material. Aerobically in the dark, 7% of the glucose which disappear from the medium is respired and 93% stored. In the dark, but i nitrogen, the *Chlorella* is unable to deal with extracellular glucose Under these circumstances an illumination so low in intensity that i

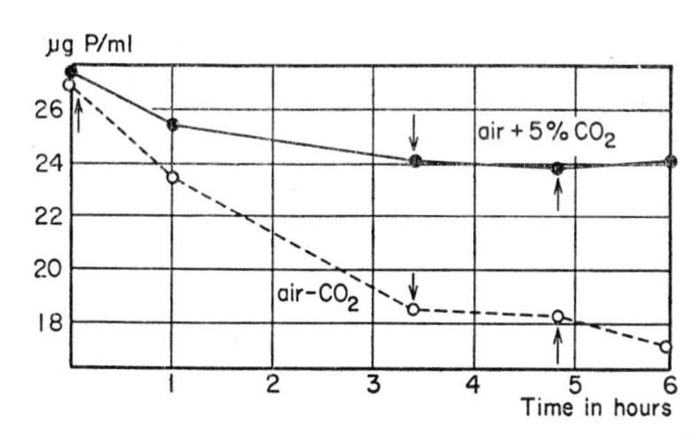

FIG. 104. Changes in the TCA-soluble phosphate of a suspension of *Chlorella* sp. at pH 4.0, in light and darkness, and in the presence and absence of CO_2. ↑ Shift to light, ↓ shift to darkness. From Wintermans and Wassink (584, 607).

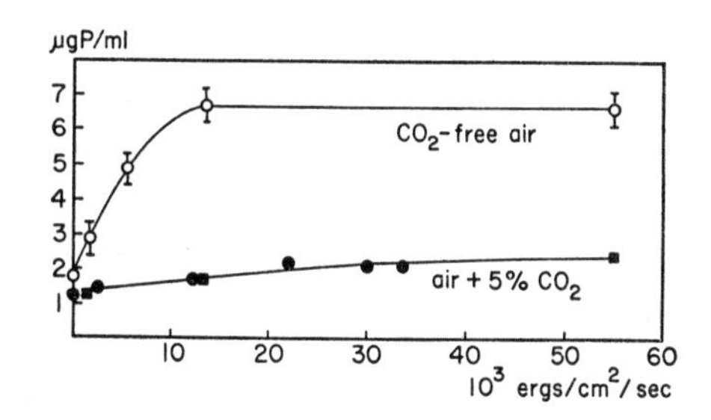

FIG. 105. Fixation of orthophosphate by *Chlorella* sp. at different light intensities in the presence and in the absence of CO_2. pH, ± 4.0; 25°C; ± 5 mm³ cells per milliliter; illumination for about 3 hours. From Wintermans and Wassink (608).

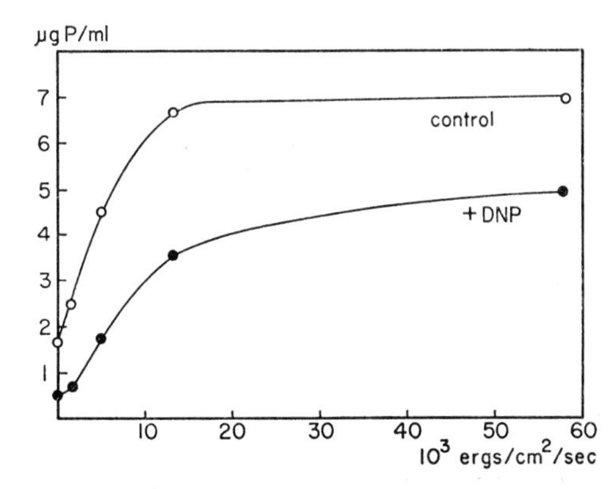

FIG. 106. Phosphate fixation by *Chlorella* sp. in CO_2-free air at various light intensities, as influenced by dinitrophenol (0.4 µg/ml, pH 4.0). From Wintermans (609).

would not cause the release of enough oxygen to serve respiratior enables the alga to translocate the glucose from the medium into th cells. The success of this experiment depends somewhat on the condi tion of the algae. They have to be depleted first of their usual endog enous storage material by a prolonged period of aeration in the dark

These and other experiments with intact cells left little doubt as t the existence of a directly light-induced phosphorylation. Wintermans and Wassink's studies on the kinetics of polyphosphate accumulation ir the presence and absence of carbon dioxide and Kandler's observatio on the insensitivity to cyanide of phosphate uptake in the light indicat that photophosphorylation precedes or initiates carbon dioxide fixatio and may occur in more than one way.

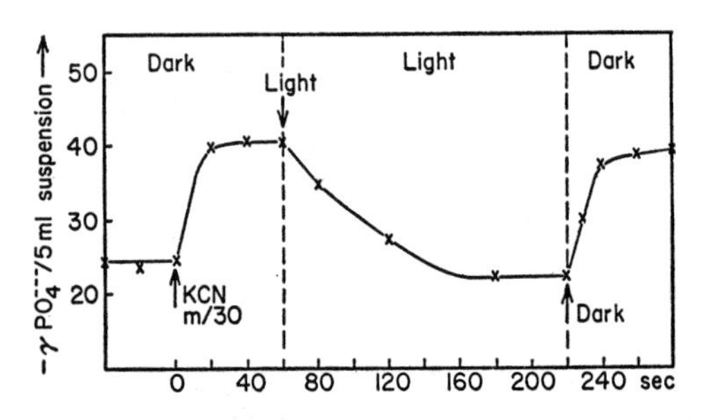

FIG. 107. Changes of inorganic phosphate in a suspension of *Chlorella* sp. Upo addition of KCN (*M*/30) in the dark, oxidative phosphorylation is inhibited, dephos phorylation continues, and the level of inorganic phosphate rises. Light phosphoryla tion, insensitive to cyanide, restores former level but only as long as illuminatio continues. From Kandler (294).

To explain the photoproduction of energy-rich phosphate, most in vestigators have preferred to think in terms of an oxidative phosphory lation as a model (compare Holzer's scheme (1951) in ref. 265). Thi left an internal cycle between the reducing and oxidizing ends of th chlorophyll complex as the only possibility, since phosphorylation with free oxygen could be excluded for the reasons mentioned above

The observations with whole cells and most of the tentative ex planations have been fully confirmed by the work with chloroplasts only that the latter have added a discovery of great importance— phosphorylation built into the process of carbon dioxide fixation itsel

C. PHOSPHORYLATION BY CHLOROPLASTS AND CHLOROPLAST FRAGMENT

Experiments with chloroplasts, on account of greater flexibility, ar obviously superior to those with intact cells. First, chloroplast studie provided the incontestable evidence that the photochemical mechanisr itself can transform ADP and inorganic phosphate into ATP (553). Since 1954, in quick succession, reports have appeared about the power of cell particles to produce energy-rich phosphate in the light: for instance, chromatophores from purple bacteria (3, 192, 291, 292); chloroplasts from spinach (14, 597); chloroplast fractions, grana, and even subgrana (cf. 15). The yield in phosphorylated substrates, mostly ATP from ADP, was very poor in the beginning, until it was learned that a number of cofactors, catalysts, and specific proteins had to be added to enhance it (11–17, 21a, 22, 275, 594, 595, 598).

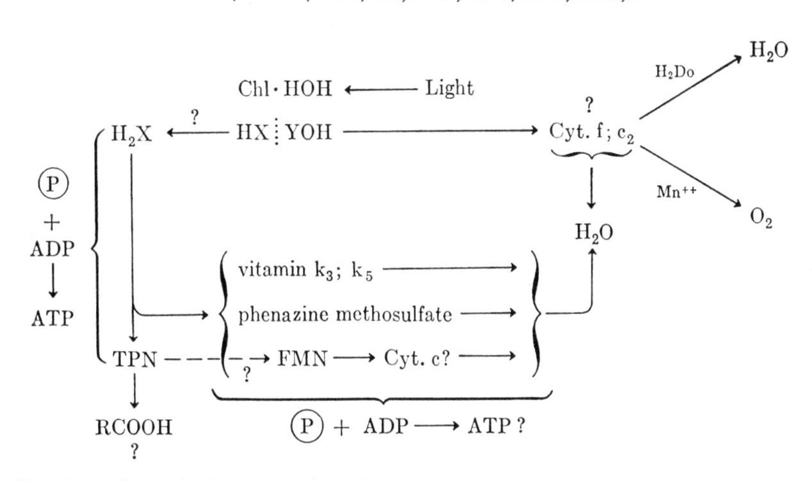

FIG. 108. General scheme of photophosphorylation as found in chloroplast preparations. Inorganic phosphate can be esterified under the influence of light with and without a concomitant normal evolution of oxygen. Reduction of TPN coupled with the evolution of oxygen gives an equivalent amount of ATP. An artificial shortcut by adding naphthoquinone derivatives, or dyestuffs, or flavin produces a cyclic phosphorylation which may induce an additional phosphorylation as indicated at the bottom of the scheme. After Wessels (595), Arnon (15), and Jagendorf *et al.* (22, 275).

The yields have become comparable to those of other chloroplast reactions. As in all work with chloroplasts, the species of the plant, the condition of the leaves, and the skill in the extracting procedure determine the quality of the material, on which the success of the experiment depends. Such unsolved minor questions as the degree of specificity for either one of the two pyridine nucleotides or the presence or absence of extractable intermediate enzymatic factors are unlikely to change much of the over-all aspect of the photophosphorylation problem.

The available experimental evidence strongly supports a mechanism for phosphorylation shown schematically in Fig. 108. The upper two

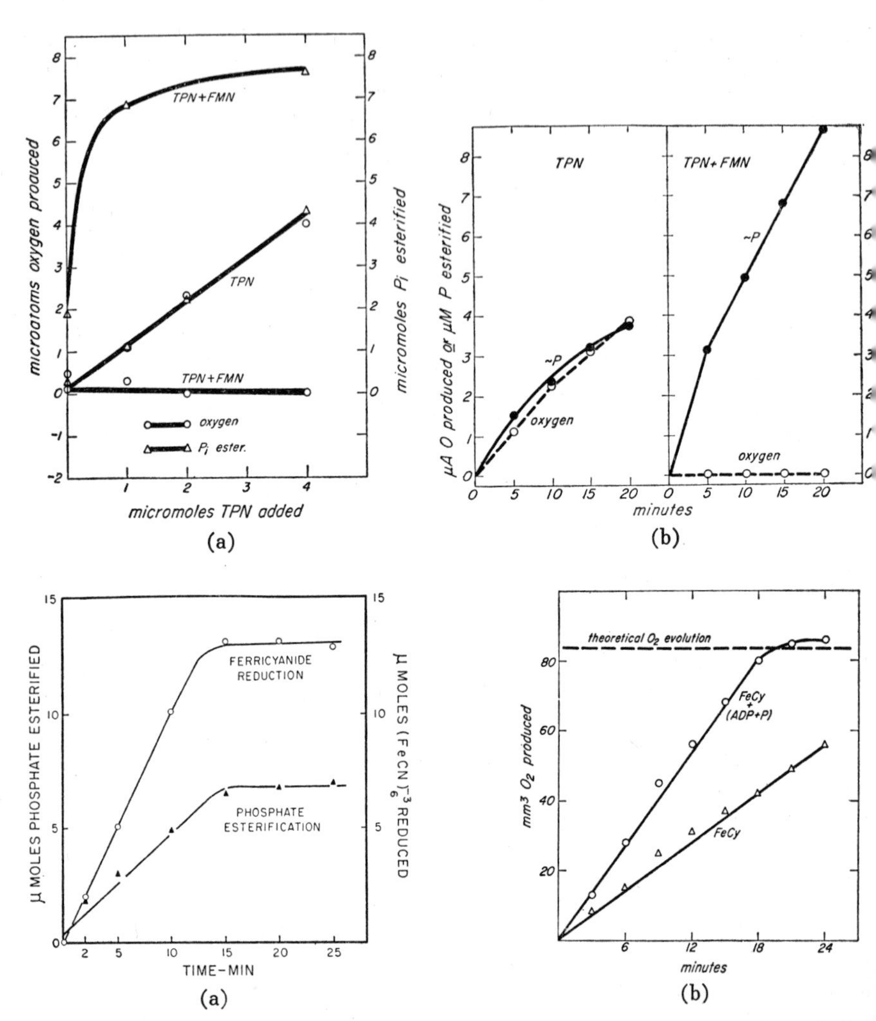

FIG. 109a. (Top left) Equivalence of TPN reduction, oxygen evolution, and phosphate esterified in chloroplast preparations (middle curve) and change of photosynthetic phosphorylation to cyclic phosphorylation after the addition of flavin mononucleotide. Oxygen evolution disappears and rate of phosphorylation increases. See the general scheme of Fig. 108. From Arnon *et al.* (17).

FIG. 109b. (Top right) The time courses of photosynthetic phosphorylation with oxygen evolution (left) and of cyclic phosphorylation in the presence of FMN (right). From Arnon *et al.* (17).

FIGS. 110a and b. (Bottom) Coupling of phosphorylation with ferricyanide reduction. a. Esterification proceeds only as long as ferricyanide is reduced. After Jagendorf (275). b. The rate of the reduction is increased in the presence of phosphate acceptors. From Arnon *et al.* (17).

lines symbolize the photolysis leading to reduced and oxidized intermediates, as usual (compare Figs. 3, 4, 124). Going counterclockwise we follow a reaction which ends in the reduction of TPN. Presumably, this is the same process, the Hill reaction with TPN, which we have described in the preceding section. This reduction is not a direct reaction between XH and TPN since we know already that it requires an extractable special enzyme. Once the TPN has been reduced it may be utilized in turn as a general reducing agent in all those processes for which specific coupling enzymes exist in or around the chloroplast; or it may be reoxidized in a back reaction running on the pattern of a respiratory chain, with the only difference that the ultimate oxidizing agent is not free oxygen but an early precursor in the line which starts with YOH. It is this back reaction which had been discussed earlier as the likely energy source for a coupled phosphorylation. A production of energy-rich phosphate (specifically ATP from ADP) in the cycle between XH and YOH in this manner does indeed exist (see below). While the cycle functions, the oxygen of photosynthesis will be intercepted and reduced to water. The gas exchange in the light becomes smaller because this kind of phosphorylation must necessarily compete with carbon dioxide reduction (compare the experiments shown in Figs. 104–106). Whether the intermediate steps between reduced TPN and YOH are truly points of coupling with the phosphorylation enzymes has, however, become questionable. Arnon *et al.* made the quite fundamental discovery that a phosphorylation is possible without an internal back reaction. The steps from XH to TPN release sufficient energy to promote the synthesis of ATP entirely on the reducing end of the photochemical mechanism. Part of the experimental evidence is shown in Figs. 109a and 109b. Upon illumination of chloroplast preparations in the presence of TPN, ADP, and inorganic phosphate Ⓟ, three products appear simultaneously: oxygen, reduced TPN, and ATP. In other words, the reagents necessary for the reduction of a typical carboxyl group like that in PGA are produced together and not in competition with each other. But it is only necessary to add still another ingredient, flavin mononucleotide (FMN), in order to close the circuit of the oxidative pathway discussed above. With FMN present, the oxygen evolution is abolished and the rate of esterification of inorganic phosphate shoots up instead (Fig. 109a). The time course of these reactions is shown in Fig. 109b. So there are two types of photophosphorylation—synthetic and cyclic. The over-all process of the new synthetic photophosphorylation is given by equation (cc):

$$2\ ADP + 2\ P + 2\ TPN + 4\ H_2O \xrightarrow[\text{Chl.}]{\text{light}} 2\ ATP + 2\ TPNH_2 + 2H_2O + O_2 \qquad \text{(cc)}$$

Another means to produce a shift from synthetic to cyclic phosphorylation is vitamin K (K_3, K_5). Wessels had earlier pointed out that the naphthoquinones might be catalysts for photophosphorylation in living cells (592). His own experiments (43, 594, 595) and those just described seem to confirm this idea, except that the natural quinone in question might not be of the vitamin K type but one of the newly found benzoquinones, coenzyme Q_{255} (103a).

It has been possible to analyze the mechanism of light-induced phosphorylation still further by the use of nonphysiological electron transfer agents or electron acceptors. Jagendorf *et al.* (275) found that a

TABLE XXIV

COMPOUNDS EFFECTIVE AS COFACTORS FOR PHOTOSYNTHETIC PHOSPHORYLATION[a]

Compound	Quantity (μmoles per 3 ml)	Activity[b] (μmoles P per mg chlorophyll per hour)	
		Experiment 1	Experiment 2
None		0	0
Phenazine methosulfate	0.06	735	555
FMN	0.10	158	123
Menadione	0.10	202	136
p-Phenylenediamine	0.20	15	31
Indigo carmine	0.20	175	159
Methyl viologen	0.10	156	110
Benzyl viologen	0.10	153	92

[a] From Jagendorf *et al.* (275, cf. 21a).

[b] Experiment 1, chloroplasts 0.047 mg per flask; standard short assay conditions. Experiment 2, chlorophyll 0.070 mg per flask; standard short assay conditions.

simple oxidoreduction dye, phenazine methosulfate, acted as a cofactor which gave the highest rates of photophosphorylation so far attained. This dye completely replaces FMN, as well as vitamin K_3 or K_5 (menadione). It is also important that the pyridine nucleotide is not required in the combination of chloroplast, phenazine methosulfate, and the phosphate donor and acceptors. The cyclic phosphorylation can bypass TPN. Reduction of TPN is also not necessary for photophosphorylation in the presence of oxygen evolution. Instead of TPN, ferricyanide can be used as an oxidant. This was discovered by Arnon *et al.* and confirmed by Jagendorf *et al.* Figure 110a shows that phosphate esterification continues as long as ferricyanide reduction proceeds, and Fig. 110b shows how the rate of ferricyanide reduction depends on the coupling with the phosphorylating mechanism. Presence of excess ADP and of inorganic phosphate nearly doubles the rate of ferricyanide reduction.

Table XXIV, taken from Jagendorf and Avron (21a, 275), shows that phenazine methosulfate is the most effective of catalysts. It is unlikely that it accumulates in the chloroplasts, hence the local concentration, according to these authors, must be only a fraction of the chlorophyll present (see also Hill and Walker, 261).

The experience with this particular substance as the most effective catalyst for cyclic phosphorylation has been confirmed for fragments of chromatophores obtained from the purple sulfur bacteria, *Chromatium* sp. Vernon and Kamen, while studying photophosphorylation in

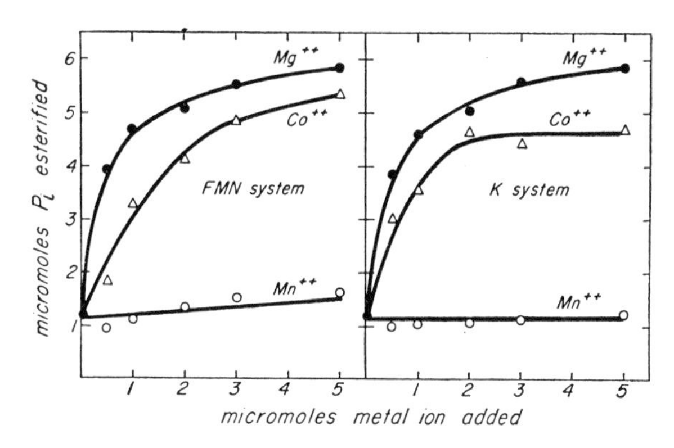

FIG. 111. Dependence of cyclic phosphorylation on magnesium or cobalt ion as cofactors. Manganese, which is necessary for oxygen evolution, cannot replace magnesium. From Arnon *et al.* (17).

such chromatophore fragments, observed that a number of other phenazine derivatives show no activity whatever.

The question remains whether it is at all necessary to postulate two different sites for photophosphorylation. Both types can be served by the same coupling to a reaction involving XH_2. Repeated washing severely diminishes the phosphorylation capacity of spinach chloroplasts with FMN or vitamin K as cofactors. A substance having enzyme characteristics and extractable from the same leaves restores the activity.

If we consider that it is necessary to add not only the substrates but several soluble factors (Fig. 111) to the chloroplast substance in order to obtain phosphorylation, we arrive again at a picture where the one immutable core is the chlorophyll complex—the mechanism capable of photolysis. To this core the phosphorylation system becomes attached, in the same manner as the enzymes necessary to release oxygen or to reduce pyridine nucleotides and other oxidants. The fact that it is possible to have normal oxygen evolution, together with phosphorylation but without a reduction of TPN (356), is, of course, important for the discussion of the role of phosphoglyceric acid as a true intermediate in the path of carbon.

XIV. Effect of Poisons

For a long time, inhibitors of either the complex-forming or competitive kind have been much used to influence biochemical reactions in living cells and cell extracts. The systematic use of poisons to pry into the mechanism of photosynthesis began with the experiments of Warburg (1919–1920) on the inhibition by cyanide and by phenylurethane. Since then so much has been added to this subject that a comprehensive review of all the effects discovered is not possible here. Fortunately, the present concept of photosynthesis, which to a great extent was developed with the aid of these observations, now permits the results to be classified and summarized.

In the general schemes of Figs. 3, 4, and 124, the separate parts correspond to basically different enzymatic reactions. It can be expected that the latter vary in their sensitivity toward entire classes of poisons. There are poisons which interfere with the carboxylation reaction; others which inhibit the evolution of oxygen; still others which act on photophosphorylation. To the first class belong cyanide, hydrogen sulfide, and probably azide; to the second, hydroxylamine, *o*-phenanthroline, phthiocol, vitamin K, and 3-(3,4-dichlorophenyl)-1,1-dimethylurea (DCMU). The third type is represented by dinitrophenol and perhaps fluoride. A fourth type has been designated as "unspecific narcotics," for instance phenylurethane. Since many of these poisons act upon other metabolic reactions as well, the over-all effect actually observed with the living cell may be the result of an interaction at more than one point. Therefore, it is useful to compare the action of the inhibitors upon the cell with that on the activity of cell-free extracts. This helps to localize the action in the photosynthetic mechanism. Hill reactions are not sensitive, or are only slightly sensitive, to cyanide poisoning. In intact cells, the initial oxygen evolution after a longer dark period, which must be attributed to the reduction of substrates already present, is also not affected by cyanide. This poison stops the production of PGA or of another corresponding intermediate in the carboxylation step of the Benson-Calvin cycle.

Other favorite metabolic inhibitors may influence photosynthesis in an indirect way. Carbon monoxide is one example. It is a strong poison for certain respiratory enzymes, e.g., cytochrome oxidase, and for hydrogenases in many organisms. Anaerobiosis under carbon monoxide is more harmful than under nitrogen because the functional reoxidation of oxidation-reduction catalysts in the light is suppressed. Photoreduction is inhibited in a mixture of hydrogen and carbon monoxide by the poisoning of the hydrogenase. Yet the mechanism of carbon assimilation as such is not affected (see Table XXV).

TABLE XXV
RELATIVE EFFECTS OF DILUTE POISONS ON VARIOUS PARTIAL REACTIONS[a]

Inhibitor	Type of reaction						
					Chlorophyll luminescence		
	O_2 Evolution	H_2 Absorption	CO_2 Fixation	ATP Formation	F[b]	C[b]	Respiration
Cyanide	−	+	+		incr.	incr.	+ or −
Hydrogen sulfide	−		+				+
Azide	−?		+			incr.	+
Iodoacetamide	−		+	−			+
Carbon monoxide	−	+	−				+
Hydrogen peroxide			+				
Hydroxylamine	+	−	−		incr.	incr. and decr.	−
o-Phenanthroline	+	−	−				−
Vitamin K	+		−				
Phthiocol	+?	−	−				−
Phenylurethane	−+	+	+			incr.	+
Dichlorophenol-dimethylurea	+	−	−				−
2,4-Dinitrophenol	+	+	+	+			incr.
Fluoride	−?		+?	+			+
Oxygen	−	+	+				−

[a] + Inhibition; − = no effect; incr. = increase; decr. = decrease.
[b] F = fluorescence; C = chemiluminescence.

There are numerous compounds which will inactivate proteins, and we can expect the over-all process of photosynthesis to be sensitive toward such agents. The amount of specific information which can be extracted from experiments with such agents is, however, scant.

Long before a definite picture of photosynthesis had emerged, it was customary to test whether a certain inhibitor would interfere with photosynthesis in dim, as well as in strong, light (compare Figs. 24, 26 in Section V). Those substances whose influence persisted at low light intensities were believed to stop the photochemical reaction (curve *c* in Fig. 24). The others, which lowered the saturation rate only, were said to interfere with the enzymatic steps preceding or following the appearance of the photoproducts (curve *b* in Fig. 24). On this classification, all the inhibitors which specifically stop the evolution of oxygen belong to those which supposedly interfere with the primary process because they inhibit strongly at low light intensities—in other words, because they depress the quantum yield. Further analysis has shown, without exception, that they seem not to act upon the photolysis of water itself but mainly on the dismutation of the oxidized waste product, YOH, to oxygen. In those algae which are adaptable to the bacterial type of photoreduction the inhibition due to these poisons either vanishes or becomes much less pronounced as long as the observed metabolism does not involve the evolution of oxygen (41, 206). Two examples are shown in Figs. 90 and 91. This fact is important since it shows that the removal of the hypothetical "hydroxylated" compound YOH is the key reaction which determines whether the utilization of the absorbed light energy will be successful or not. If we assume, for instance, that the hydroxyl group is formed directly at the reactive chlorophyll molecule (see Sections IV and XVI), failure to remove it in a normal way could have two consequences: either an immediate loss of the excitation energy as heat or an indirect loss by way of the back reaction:

$$XH + YOH \rightarrow XY + H_2O \qquad \text{(dd)}$$

This back reaction might be identical with the sequence of steps that is assumed to furnish the energy in cyclic photophosphorylation (see Section XIV). The rise of fluorescence and the decrease of chlorophyll luminescence produced by these same inhibitors indicates that the photolysis of water stops whenever the hydroxyl groups are not removed by reduction or dismutation (69) (compare Fig. 58, Section VI).

Cyanide, on the other hand, is typical of those inhibitors which stop reactions that are further removed from the chlorophyll molecule itself. All it does is to depress the saturation rate by interfering with the rate of the carboxylation reaction. This is supported by the observation that cyanide poisoning and removal of carbon dioxide have exactly the same effect upon the yield of chlorophyll fluorescence in illuminated cells (see Section VI, Figs. 51 and 54). Perhaps the most important observation connected with the effect of cyanide is one of the earliest, namely, the discovery by Warburg (560) that in an alga,

Chlorella sp., the compensation of respiration by light is insensitive to cyanide (see Section V). This requires, of course, that the respiration be less sensitive to cyanide than photosynthesis is (cf. 125, 132, 408). This happens to be the case in *Chlorella*, but need not be so in other organisms. Warburg interpreted his observation as a reduction of respiratory intermediates. This explanation, or the nearly identical one that light prevents decarboxylations, has remained the most reasonable one, and various recent experiments render it very likely that it is correct. Again, the physiology of algae is not uniform, and, therefore, we find quite different responses in different strains, or species, or genera toward treatment with the same concentrations of inhibitors under comparable external conditions. In the alga *Scenedesmus obliquus*, respiration is more sensitive to cyanide than is photosynthesis at low light intensities (203). It is possible, therefore, to shift the position of the compensation point by diminishing the rate of those dark reactions which light must first compensate, or balance, before a net reduction of carbon dioxide is seen (see Table XXVI).

TABLE XXVI
SHIFT OF COMPENSATION POINT DUE TO INHIBITION OF RESPIRATION BY CYANIDE IN *Scenedesmus obliquus* D_3

Experimental conditions	Respiration and photosynthesis in mm³ O_2 absorbed or produced			
	Control	*M*/50,000 HCN	*M*/10,000 HCN	*M*/2,000 HCN
Dark 20 min (respiration)	−54	−27	−13	− 2
Light 15 min, dark 5 min	−23	+11	+18	+29
Photosynthesis in 15 min corr.	+31	+38	+31	+31

Besides typical enzyme poisons, various metals are detrimental to plants because they interfere with the course of photosynthesis. The effects of the salts of copper and mercury are well known. In most such cases it is not quite known what happens. Probably, sulfhydryl groups become oxidized. Not all plants are equally sensitive to metal poisoning. Horwitz showed (270) that mercury vapor from a drop of mercury in the side-arm of a Warburg vessel is sufficient to double the rate of respiration and to depress photosynthesis in *Scenedesmus* sp. This is typical for results obtained with dinitrophenol as a poison. Other plants are rather resistant to mercury, so that the dropping mercury electrode can even be used for measuring photosynthesis without noticeable damage to the cells.

The so-called "narcotic" or unspecific poisons are compounds which cannot be shown to combine with a definite, active group of a well-identified class of enzymes. Chloroform, ether, alcohol, urethane, and phenylurethane belong to this category. Supposedly, they interfere with enzymatic reactions by their adsorption to the protein surface. However, the distinction between nonspecificity and quite specific

TABLE XXVII
INHIBITION OF HILL REACTION
BY SUBSTITUTED PHENYLURETHANES AND PHENYLUREAS

Poison	Concentration to produce 50% inhibition	Relative inhibitory capacity
Phenylurethane C_6H_5—N(H)—C(=O)—OC_2H_5	5×10^{-4} *M*	1
3-4 Dichlorophenylurethane Cl—C_6H_3(Cl)—N(H)—C(=O)—OC_2H_5	2×10^{-5} *M*	25
3-(4-Chlorophenyl)-1-1-dimethylurea (CMU) Cl—C_6H_4—N(H)—C(=O)—N(CH_3)(CH_3)	4×10^{-6} *M*	125
3-(3,4-Dichlorophenyl)-1,1-dimethylurea (DCMU) Cl—C_6H_3(Cl)—N(H)—C(=O)—N(CH_3)(CH_3)	2×10^{-7} *M*	2500

effects is not an absolute one (27). Instances are known where a typical narcotic like trichlorobutyl alcohol will inhibit one enzyme reaction much more strongly than another; and among the urethanes the herbicide DCMU shows one of the most specific effects ever encountered (41, 593).

Table XXVII shows how chemical substitutions change phenylurethane, the classical "narcotic," into 3-(3,4-dichlorophenyl)-1,1-dimethylurea, or DCMU, which turned out to be the most powerful specific inhibitor for photosynthesis. DCMU is technically used as an herbicide. It acts by interfering with the evolution of oxygen. Figure 91 is a comparison of the effects of DCMU on photosynthesis and on photoreduction in *Scenedesmus* sp. after 16 hours' adaptation to hydrogen. 5×10^{-7} *M* DCMU inhibits photosynthesis about 50%. It does not interfere with adaptation but cannot prevent deadaptation at higher light intensities. 3×10^{-6} *M* DCMU abolishes photosynthesis completely and correspondingly stabilizes photoreduction against any deadaptation in

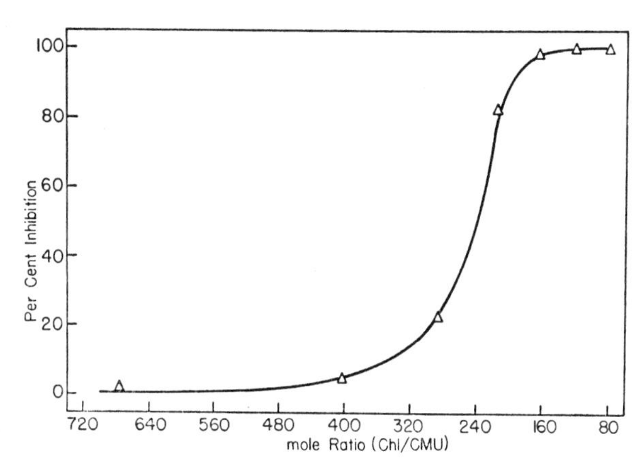

FIG. 112. The concentration of the herbicide CMU in a green cell, which inhibits photosynthesis 100%, is only a small fraction of the concentration of the chlorophyll present. [Chl] = 0.115 μM; 50% inhibition = 240 Chl/CMU; 100% inhibition = 160 Chl/CMU. Range for three separate experiments = 160–210 (100%). Compare Fig. 91, Section XI.

strong light. The results are the same as those first seen with hydroxylamine and *o*-phenanthroline. DCMU, however, seems to be amazingly specific. It does not interfere with respiration or fermentation, adaptation, or photoreduction, or with the action of catalase (cf. 565). This last result confirms earlier conclusions that catalase has no particular role to play in the mechanism of photosynthesis.

By using radioactive CMU and determining how much of it is actually present in cells showing the first signs of inhibition, Bishop found that one molecule of CMU suffices to inactivate about two hundred molecules of chlorophyll (see Fig. 112).

The action of iodoacetate on photosynthesis is, like that of most of the sulfhydryl-destroying compounds, nonreversible and time dependent. Iodoacetate or iodoacetamide strongly inhibit glycolysis by stopping the action of triosephosphate dehydrogenase. It should, therefore, serve well for testing the hypothesis that reduction steps following the carboxylation are simply the reverse of the glycolytic pathway. We still have to wait for a definitive answer. Early unpublished experiments by Stepka showed a stronger inhibition of the reduction of PGA than of the fixation of carbon dioxide in carbohydrate (cf. 1).

How destructive hydrogen peroxide is for the mechanism of photosynthesis usually escapes attention because of the presence of catalase in the living cell and in the chloroplast. If catalase, however, is first inactivated by cyanide, a few minutes of treatment with 10^{-4} M H_2O_2

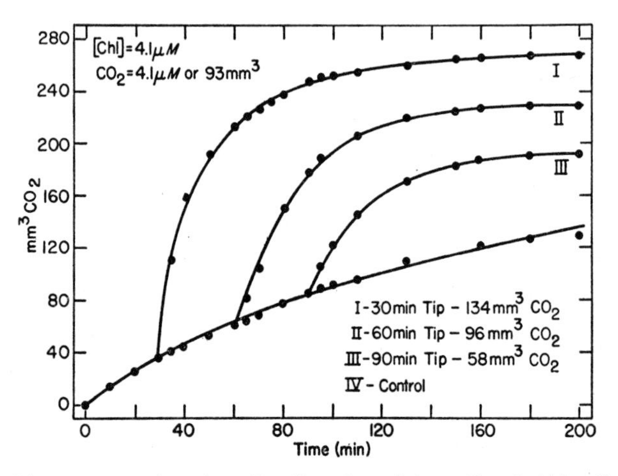

FIG. 113. The amount of carbon dioxide released by cells of *Chlorella* sp. under the influence of 4×10^{-3} M sodium fluoride depends on the metabolic condition of the cells. Here it decreases with increasing lengths of fermentation period. Temperature, 25°C; pH of medium, 4.3; N_2. Curve *I*, addition of NaF after 30 minutes; curve *II*, addition of NaF after 60 minutes; curve *III*, addition of NaF after 90 minutes (42).

suffice to lower the saturation rate of photosynthesis quite appreciably. There is no immediate recovery; the damage, however, is repaired in the course of hours or a couple of days (203).

As examples of competitive inhibition we may mention the action of heavy water on photolysis (426, 427) (see Section V), and of organic compounds upon the uptake of hydrogen in photoreduction (205).

Fluoride acts as an inhibitor of photosynthesis provided it penetrates into the cell (466). This is a very slow process in neutral media. Penetration is accelerated by anaerobic conditions or by using acid media. In such a complex system as the complete photosynthetic mechanism, there are several places where fluoride can interfere with the course of events. Thus, the effectiveness of fluoride is not surprising. Fluoride as an inhibitor attracted some passing attention when Warburg claimed to have shown the existence of a functional chlorophyll-carbon dioxide complex by means of fluoride poisoning (576, 577). He found that in acid-grown *Chlorella* sp. addition of fluoride caused an evolution of carbon dioxide. The amount of carbon dioxide released was supposedly the exact equivalent of the chlorophyll present. When those experiments were repeated, the size of the carbon dioxide gush turned out to be a function of the general metabolism of the cell (42) (see Fig. 113) and due to a decarboxylation of glutamic acid (cf. 365).

Quite apart from their usefulness in tracing certain types of enzymes by means of inhibitors, the experiments mentioned above have been extremely valuable in the attempts to correlate optical observations—like fluorescence, luminescence, and absorption changes—with certain partial reactions known to be particularly sensitive to the one or other specific poison (69).

XV. Transient Effects (Induction Periods)

The phenomena described in the preceding sections are mainly seen when external conditions are deliberately kept as constant as possible. The plants are illuminated with the same light intensity (either low or high), kept in the same medium, at the same temperature, etc., for at least such a length of time that the influence of the preceding treatment becomes negligible.

In this section we shall describe how living plants react when external conditions are suddenly changed—when the light they are exposed to is turned on or off, the carbon dioxide is quickly removed or added, or air is replaced by nitrogen. That plants do not immediately photosynthesize at their full rate when they are exposed to strong light was probably noticed long ago. Osterhout and Haas started the *Journal of General Physiology* in 1918 with a paper entitled, "On the Dynamics of Photosynthesis" (403). Since then an unusual amount of work has been devoted to the analysis of the sequence of events which must occur during the period between the end of the constant metabolic rate in the dark and the time when photosynthesis has reached the rate which is in equilibrium with the newly prevailing conditions—that is, until a new steady state has been attained. Observations on induction periods have greatly contributed to the understanding of the complexity of the photosynthetic mechanism. The individual bits of information concerning transients now in the literature are far too numerous to be reviewed in detail. As the author himself points out, the chapter on induction phenomena in Rabinowitch's monograph is one of the longest, covering over a hundred pages (436). To this can be added another hundred pages of collected short papers on this subject in "Research in Photosynthesis" (1955) (see Biblio. Notes). Figures 114–123 are examples of transient metabolic events as they have been recorded by means of several entirely different methods.

The induction phenomena can be roughly divided into two classes: those which are seen when a short dark period interrupts a longer period of illumination (compare Fig. 38, Section V) and those that occur after very long dark periods. The first class reflects shifts or disturbances within the photosynthetic mechanism and its immediate milieu. The second class comprises, in addition to the first, the slower but more far-reaching changes due to a redistribution of metabolites throughout the cell. Theoretically, this division could be said to correspond to changes in the oxidation-reduction level of catalysts, and the appearance and disappearance of short-lived intermediates on the one hand and the slower depletion or replenishment of pools of metabolites on the other. The effects due to a long pretreatment of the plant in one way or another overlap the variations found in response to different culture conditions. We know that the latter determine not only the transients, but the following steady-state responses as well. This distinction has not always been recognized and it is often difficult to know where to draw the line between "short" and "long" induction effects.

Short induction effects, such as the adjustment of the metabolism after the light has been turned on or off under otherwise uniform experimental conditions, can be expected to be simpler and more revealing about the succession of reactions following the primary excitation of the chlorophyll complex. On the other hand, it is well established that the most interesting part of the short induction period lasts, on the average, hardly more than a minute. To quantitatively follow optical and metabolic changes within a matter of seconds has, therefore, been a challenge to the inventive experimenter (see Sections II and VI). The many observations based on the slow physical response of conventional gas manometers, for instance, are useful only if the delay and distortion inherent in these instruments are clearly recognized (140, 141, 389).

As long as only kinetic data on gas exchange or on shifts of fluorescence intensity were available, attempts to explain the shape of induction curves were either very superficial—i.e., applicable only to the experiment in question—or difficult, in that they required a painstaking comparison of all available information, since obviously one clearly contradictory fact invalidates a theory (69).

What causes the induction? Why does photosynthesis not start immediately upon illumination with the exact rate that corresponds to the steady state at the particular intensity but reaches it only after a period of one to several minutes? From the now-obsolete point of view that photosynthesis might be a direct photochemical decomposition of a chlorophyll-carbon dioxide complex, an induction period was indeed puzzling. But the very fact that it existed helped to shape our present concept of photosynthesis as a metabolic process of interlaced and individually variable partial reactions. It would be astonishing, given the knowledge we have, if no induction periods could be seen—and this also applies, of course, to the phenomena that happen after the light is suddenly turned off.

In the introductory section we have used the scheme in Fig. 4 to show how complicated the mechanism of photosynthesis actually is and how many different reactions may follow the initial photolytic act of the chlorophyll. The quantity of biochemical data on hand, certainly very incomplete, is yet sufficient to support many reasonable explanations for almost all of the curves shown in Figs. 114–123. A partial list of probable causes for induction and aftereffects follows: We have learned that ribulose diphosphate is not stable in the presence of carbon dioxide; it changes into phosphoglyceric acid. Lack of RuDP after a dark period must produce an induction effect, which will be the more pronounced, the greater the discrepancy between its initial and its steady-state concentration in the light.

In the absence of RuDP and, consequently, of the carboxylation product which is the normal substrate for reduction, other light-induced processes will take over. Among them are the synthetic and the cyclical phosphorylations and the reduction of respiratory intermediates via reduced pyridine nucleotides (358).

A slight excess of RuDP after an illumination causes the carboxylation reaction to continue in the dark. This leads to a momentary increase of PGA and a subsequent wave of respiratory processes. If the concentration of respiratory intermediates after a dark pause happens to be high, these will be reduced first and normal photosynthesis may not begin until much of these respiratory intermediates have been removed (219). (This presupposes, of course, a free interchange between the inside and the outside of the chloroplast in respect to general metabolites.) If it is true what some investigators believe, that PGA, as we isolate it, has already passed the state of its photochemical reactivity, studies of induction periods may be the tool to investigate this question further.

The more pronounced transients seen in intact plants must indeed be caused by the complexities of the carboxylation and phosphorylation cycles, because the Hill or chloroplast reactions with artificial oxidants do not show them. This confirms what could also be deduced from experiments with inhibiting poisons: the proximity of the mechanism for evolving oxygen to the photochemistry. There are, however, characteristic transient effects in the course of the oxygen production, particularly if the changes are measured in times of seconds rather than minutes. We have to assume—and spectroscopy supports this assumption—functional changes in the oxidation-reduction levels of various enzymes connected with the photochemistry and the mechanism of oxygen evolution (see Section VI). It follows that the oxidation of a catalyst during an aerobic (or its reduction during an

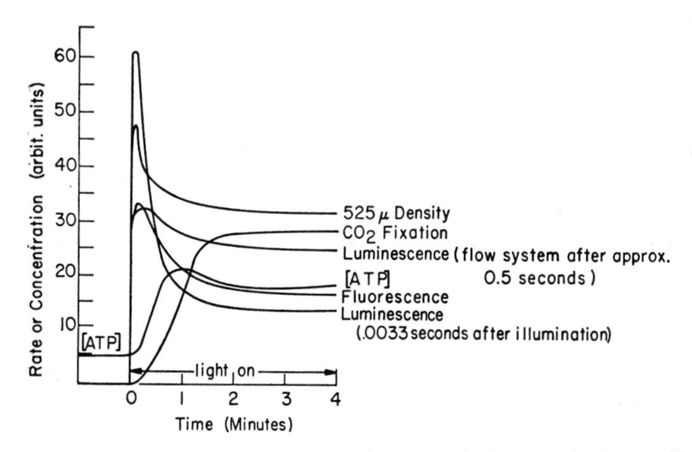

FIG. 114. Induction phenomena observed for several photosynthetic manifestations in living cells; so-called "short" induction period: it lasts about 1 minute. According to Strehler (497).

anaerobic) dark period leads to an initial delay of the over-all process until the proper oxidoreduction level has been re-established.

What we have discussed so far are the fundamental—one might say normal—causes of induction. Further variations of these are brought about by the influence of external factors. A limiting concentration of carbon dioxide may lead to a preponderance of other reductive carboxylations which proceed at lower partial pressures of CO_2, or to a photooxidative destruction of other metabolites. A high concentration of oxygen or its complete absence are bound to cause aberrations from the normal course of events. The number of "interesting" induction curves obtainable for CO_2, or O_2, or reduction products, or ATP changes, or fluctuations of luminescence with the aid of special pretreatment appears to be very great indeed (2, 47, 95, 204, 250, 317, 385, 480, 602).

Since it is virtually impossible to run experiments on photosynthesis without coming across some induction phenomena, the published examples are too numerous even to be listed (see, therefore, 436). Blinks and Skow were the first to employ a polarographic method, and they found that the response of a plant cell to sudden illumination is extremely rapid and rather abnormal. McAlister and Myers (361a)

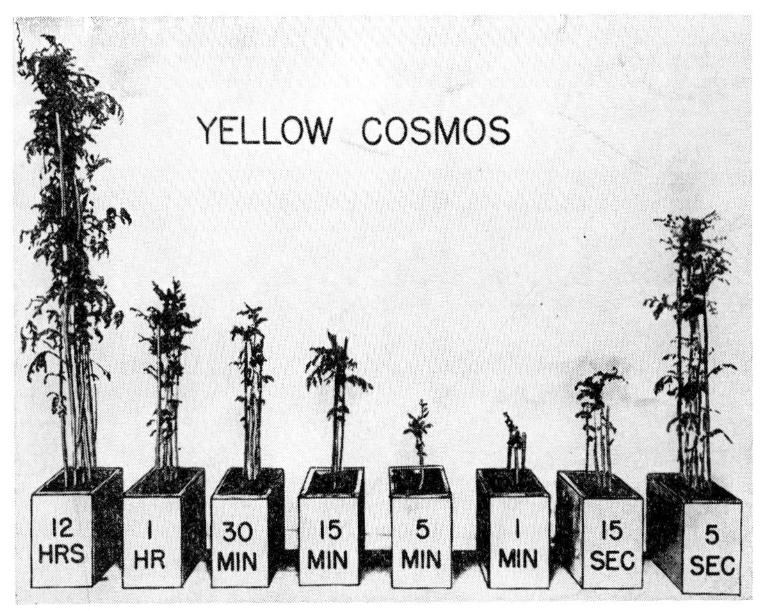

FIG. 115. Plants of yellow cosmos (*Cosmos sulphureus*) grown in intermittent light and dark periods. Complete suppression of growth at 1-minute intervals, due to induction phenomena. All plants have received the same total amount of light. According to Garner and Allard (220a).

observed the beginning of carbon dioxide reduction at the start of illumination and found a proportionality between intensity and the amount of carbon dioxide not reduced during the transient period. At very low light intensities these induction losses became negligible. These authors also showed that initial fluctuations in fluorescence intensities paralleled the carbon dioxide induction. Figure 114 is a composite picture due to Strehler demonstrating that there is hardly a reaction or process connected with photosynthesis that does not start with a short induction period when the light is suddenly turned on. The slowest process to reach a steady state is the reduction of carbon dioxide.

The fastest response is to be found among the processes directly connected with the photochemistry: fluorescence, luminescence, and spectral shifts. A great number of papers deal with the detailed study of each one of the induction curves summarized in Fig. 114. In addition, we have very typical transients in the oxygen gas exchange

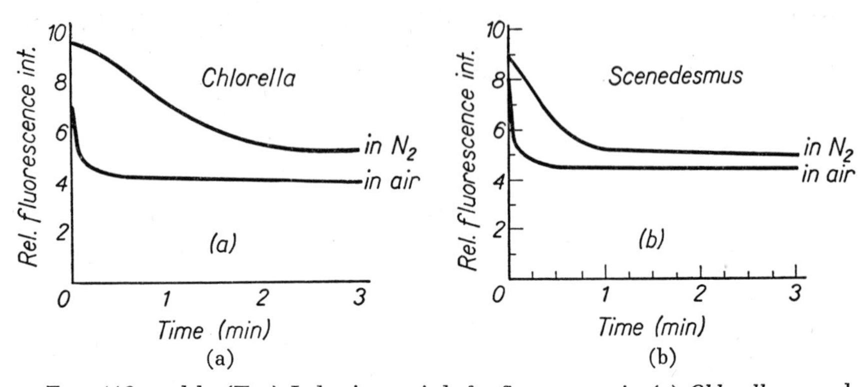

(a) (b)

FIGS. 116a and b. (Top) Induction periods for fluorescence in (a) *Chlorella* sp. and (b) *Scenedesmus* sp., at 25°C; 3×10^4 erg/cm²/sec incident light intensity. From Wassink *et al.* (580).

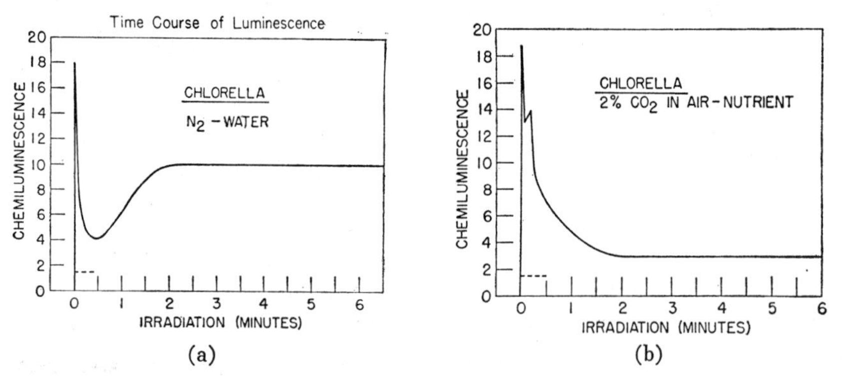

(a) (b)

FIGS. 117a and b. (Bottom) Examples of luminescence changes during the induction period in nitrogen and in air (68).

(260, 401, 461, 602), the reduction potentials in suspensions of microorganisms (587), in phosphorylation, or polyphosphate formation (588) in the reversible oxidation of cytochromes (89a, 118, 288).

Figures 116a and b are recordings of fluorescence intensities, (a) in *Chlorella* sp., (b) in *Scenedesmus* sp., both for either nitrogen or air.

Figures 117a and b show some variation of the initial luminescence intensity for *Chlorella* sp., (a) in nitrogen, (b) in air and carbon dioxide.

Recordings of the induction for oxygen evolution made independently in various laboratories show the same interesting pattern. A sharp initial burst of oxygen, a pause, a second maximum or step, and the final transition to the steady state of oxygen evolution in photosynthesis that parallels the assimilation of carbon dioxide. Figure 120 is a curve recorded by Allen (2) in the apparatus of Franck and Pringsheim,

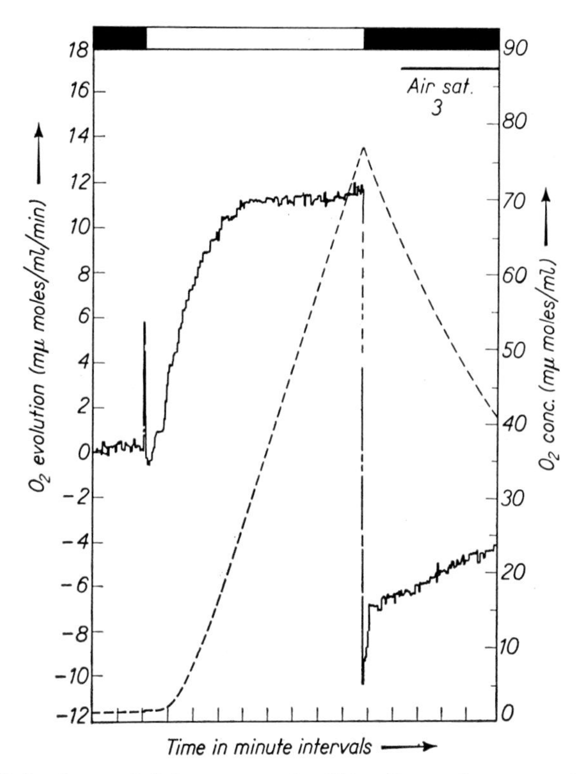

Fig. 118. Induction period for oxygen in *Chlorella* sp. Oxygen evolution always starts with an immediate gush, which may not be followed by continuous normal photosynthesis if carbon dioxide is absent. At "light off" a corresponding sharp intake of oxygen is seen. According to Olson *et al.* (401).

who first described this type of induction curve under anaerobic conditions (170). Figures 118 and 119 are from the work of Brackett and Olson (401). The curve in Fig. 118 shows how sharp the first oxygen peak becomes if the resolution of the recording apparatus is accurate enough to show this, and further that there is a similar phenomenon in reverse—a rapid but short-lived uptake of oxygen just after the light has been turned off. Figure 119 shows the inhibition of any response

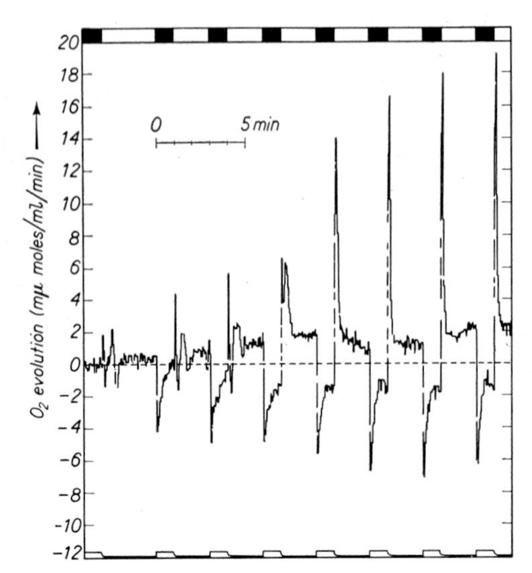

FIG. 119. Transients for oxygen caused by successive 1-minute light periods after anaerobiosis without carbon dioxide. Successive increase of a secondary maximum. Absence of photosynthesis (401).

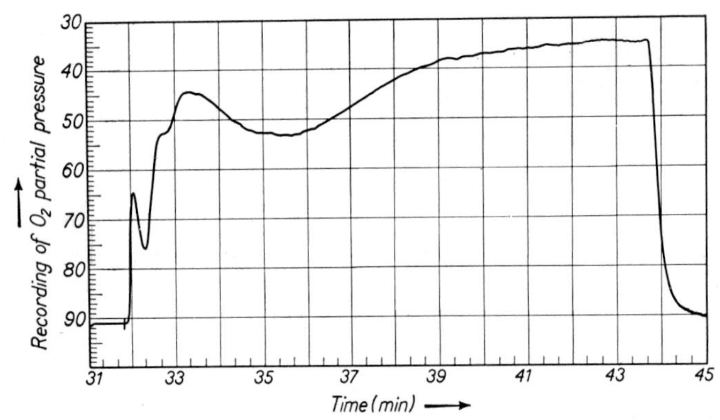

FIG. 120. Recording of oxygen transients produced by 3 mg of *Chlorella* sp. in a stream of nitrogen (4% CO_2) after half an hour of anaerobiosis in the dark. Illumination (820 lux) starts at about $T = 32$ minutes and ends 12 minutes later. From Allen, unpublished (cf. 2).

to light after an anaerobic period and the increase of the initial oxygen spike, etc., during intermittent illumination. Since in this experiment carbon dioxide was absent, the second phase seen in curve *b* did not develop. With *Oscillatoria* sp. grown at 35°C, Ivan Setlik obtained the recordings shown in Fig. 121. The curves are part of a series of transients seen with the same subject in medium of pH 7.5 aerated

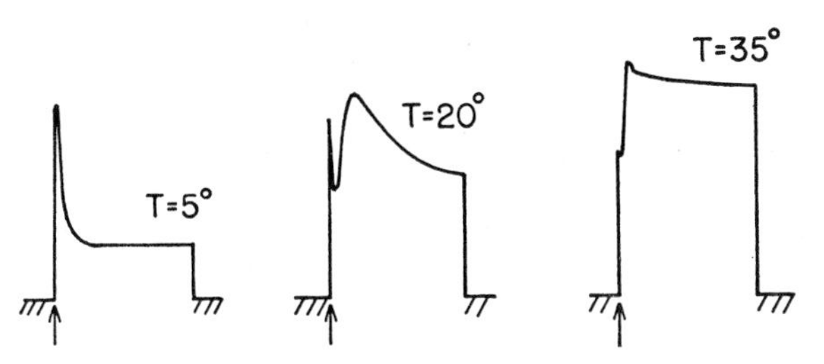

FIG. 121. Tracings of polarographic recordings of induction periods for oxygen in *Oscillatoria* sp. at increasing temperatures (5°C, 20°C, 35°C). Time of each illumination period: 10 minutes. Air: 1% CO_2. The first oxygen gush is much less affected by low temperature than the rate of steady-state photosynthesis. From Setlik (460).

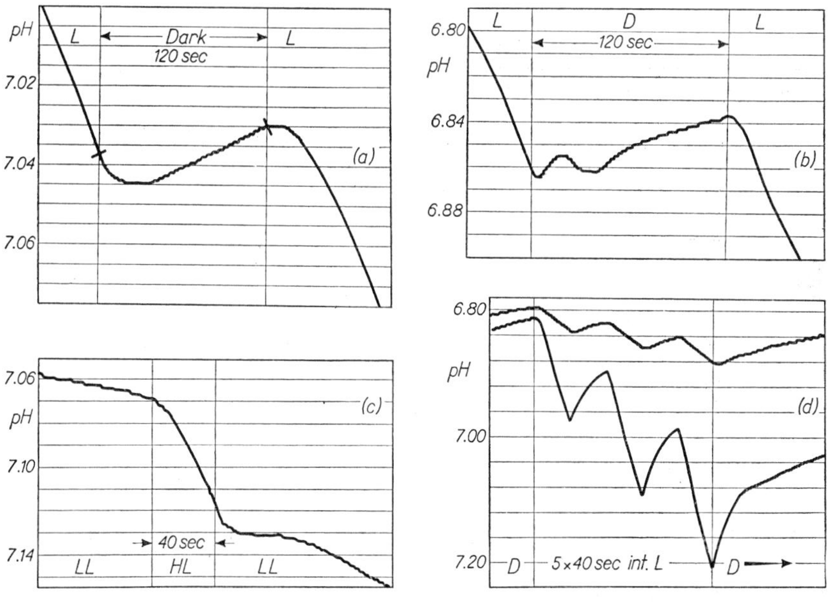

FIGS. 122a–d. Transients for carbon-dioxide. Glass electrode recordings of pH changes in bicarbonate suspensions of *Chlorella* sp. or *Scenedesmus* sp. (a) Aftereffect and induction period caused by a 2-minute dark pause under normal conditions, in air-carbon dioxide. (Compare Fig. 38, Section V.) (b) Complex aftereffects during transition from anaerobic to aerobic conditions. (c) Transients induced by 40 seconds of strong light during a period of photosynthesis at low light intensity. (d) Intermittent illumination under conditions of limiting carbon dioxide concentration. This causes violent back reactions after 40 seconds of saturating light, no back reaction after 40 seconds in weak light (218).

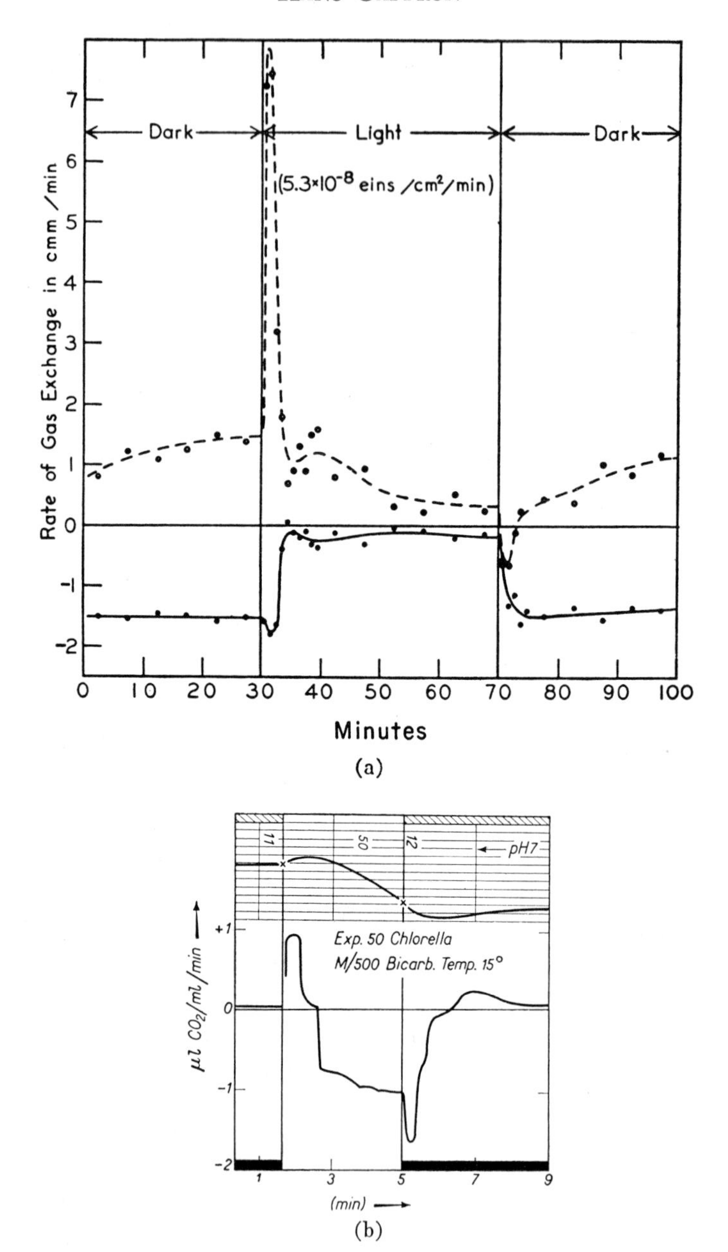

FIGS. 123a and b. Initial photochemical evolution of carbon dioxide and its reabsorption when light is turned off (Emerson effect). Characteristic for *Chlorella* sp. at high CO_2 concentrations. (a) Emerson and Lewis, gas manometer, dotted line above: CO_2. Solid line below: O_2 (135). (b) Gaffron, pH meter, pH changes above, derived rate of carbon dioxide exchange below (218, 219).

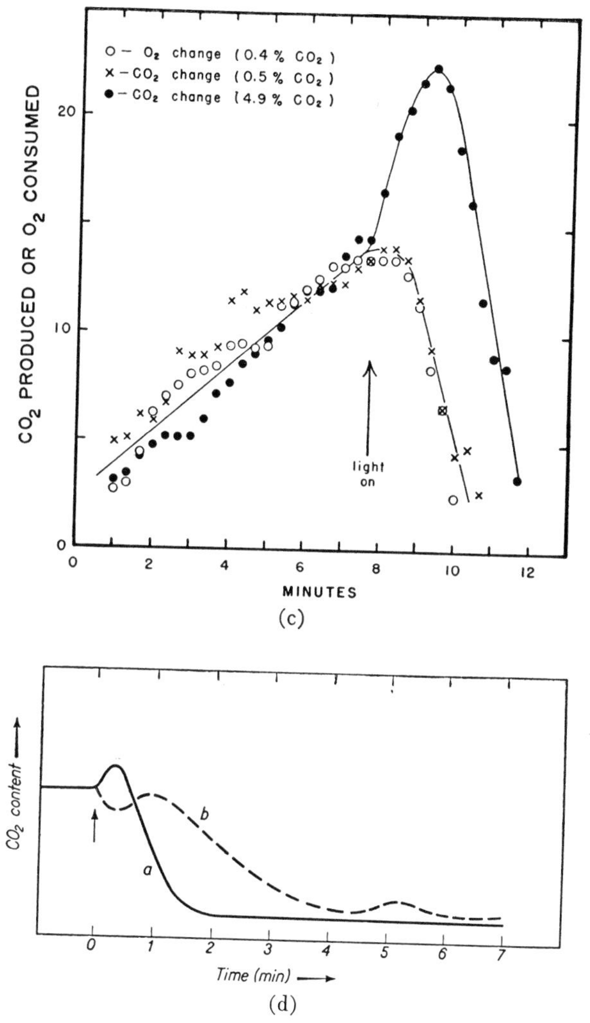

FIGS. 123c and d. Initial photochemical evolution of carbon dioxide and its reabsorption when light is turned off (Emerson effect). Characteristic for *Chlorella* sp. at high CO_2 concentrations. (c) Brown and Good, mass spectrometer (66). (d) Van der Veen, diaferometer (535, 536). Curve *a*: adaptation line of *Chlorella* in air with 3% CO_2. Curve *b*: adaptation line of a leaf in air with 3% CO_2.

with air, 1% CO_2, at increasing temperatures: curve *a*, 5°C; curve *b*, 20°C at one-fourth the recording width; curve *c*, 35°C at one-sixth the recording width. Light intensity was 6400 lux. Between 5° and 35°C the final rate of photosynthesis increased over ten times, the maximum rate of oxygen production during the induction less than four times.

Rapid and quantitative recordings of transient effects for the carbon dioxide exchange can be made with a glass electrode and algae suspended in bicarbonate solution (444, 445). Figures 122a–d are transients produced by a dark pause of 2 minutes during a period of prolonged photosynthesis (218, 219). Figure 122a shows the normal behavior of *Chlorella* sp. in $M/500$ bicarbonate and 4% CO_2 in air. The descending curve at the left corresponds to photosynthesis in the steady state. After the light has been turned off carbon dioxide continues to be picked up for about 20 seconds. Presently, respiration becomes manifest (ascending curve). When the light is turned on respiration is stopped immediately, while a net absorption of carbon dioxide begins 20 seconds later. The duration of the transients agree with those for oxygen in Figs. 118 and 119. The curve in Fig. 122b is an example of anomalies in the carbon dioxide gas exchange after darkening. They were caused in *Scenedesmus* sp. by a change from anaerobic to aerobic conditions. The curve in Fig. 122c shows transients caused by 40 seconds of saturating illumination in the midst of a period of photosynthesis at low light intensities. The rate at high light is seven times greater than at low light. The return to the lower intensity causes a temporary inhibition of photosynthesis. The two curves in Fig. 122d show that violent back reactions develop in the dark when cells of *Scenedesmus* sp. are illuminated quite strongly every 40 seconds. At low intensities the back reaction does not appear. The effect is brought about by a deficiency of carbon dioxide.

Figures 123a–d record four examples of the same unusual transition effect. This is an initial carbon dioxide gush. Since the existence of this effect has been disputed (578), it might be useful to point out that it has been seen independently of the method used for measuring the carbon dioxide exchange. Figure 123a is the original manometric observation by Emerson and Lewis; Fig. 123b is a recording with the glass electrode; Fig. 123c is the result obtained with a mass spectrometer; and Fig. 123d is a recording by van der Veen with the heat conductivity method first used by Aufdemgarten. The alga, *Chlorella* sp., seems particularly apt to give this anomalous light reaction. Whittingham has recently succeeded in separating this special effect from normal photosynthesis by inhibiting the latter with iodoacetamide. Having isolated it in this manner he could show by means of tracer carbon studies that the carbon dioxide gush consists of a reversible photodecarboxylation of aspartic acid (65, 76, 135, 140, 168, 219, 317, 535, 536).

The most astonishing example of what intermittent illumination causing a sequence of transient effects can produce in a plant is shown in Fig. 115. Garner and Allard varied the periods of light and darkness from the usual lengths of day and night down to 5 seconds each while the integrated total time of illumination remained constant. At about 1 minute dark and 1 minute light, the plant cannot grow. One minute of light is necessary to bring the photosynthetic mechanism into full gear and 1 minute of darkness is sufficient to cancel what has been achieved during the previous illumination. Thus, the plant never has a chance to get into photoproduction of foodstuffs. The example shown in Fig. 115 is the most striking which so far has been found, but other plants and also algae show the same effects to a lesser degree. It might be useful to remind the reader again that any conclusions as to the efficiency of photosynthesis, in other words, the quantum yield, can be based only on experiments where transient effects have been excluded, or have been corrected for, after careful analysis of the metabolic changes (220a).

XVI. Problems and Explanations

Research on photosynthesis has long passed the first level of scientific endeavors—the mere collection and description of facts. What is now known is to a high degree coherent and can be condensed into a theoretical pattern which is useful for evaluating the results of future investigations.

The basic framework into which any theory of photosynthesis has to fit was established many decades ago. In comparison with other unsolved metabolic problems, there has been little room for free speculation, because substrates and end products, the over-all gain in free energy, the smallness of the effective light quanta and their efficient utilization, the pigments involved, the principal division of the process into photochemical and purely enzymatic steps—all this has long been known. It is not surprising that there are today so few differences among those theories and schemes of photosynthesis which have a claim to be considered seriously. Nearly everything plausible has already been suggested, and later workers are often unaware that their supposedly new proposals had been considered twenty or more years ago—and not then pressed further for lack of evidence, which, thanks to their efforts, has now been supplied.

Figure 124 is a scheme summarizing what has been described in this chapter. Photosynthesis can be pictured as an assembly of semi-independent enzymatic systems—I, II, (IIa), III, V, and VI arranged around a core, IV, which contains the photochemical mechanism. We shall use this scheme to point out the nature of some of the unsolved problems. However, much has been written about photosynthesis which is plainly wrong or does not fit at all into any modern view of the process. Thus a few words about it should now be helpful, and particularly so since some of these ideas are faithfully copied from textbook to textbook without comment. "It is easy to get away with nonsense where everything is a specialty" (Barzun).

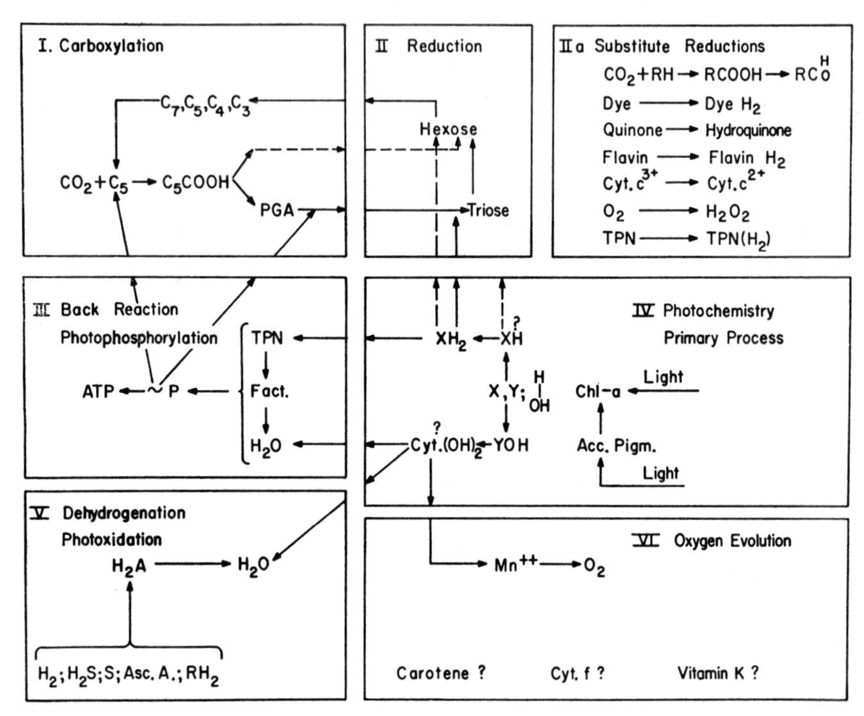

FIG. 124. Summary of present knowledge of photosynthesis as a set of at least five semi-independent reaction systems which have to cooperate in order to achieve the synthesis of organic matter from carbon dioxide.

A. OBSOLETE OR USELESS HYPOTHESES

In some textbooks the statement can still be found that plants specifically need *red light for photosynthesis,* because chlorophyll absorbs in the red. This unqualified notion is certainly wrong (see Section VI). The relationship of photoperiodism to red light is, however, a different story.

The *formaldehyde hypothesis* has survived, in one form or another, for a century, but it is certainly not true that formaldehyde is first formed in detectable amounts and then condensed to hexose (see Section IX).

There is no functional *chlorophyll-carbon dioxide compound* (as assumed by Willstätter and Stoll in 1918) and, hence, no mechanism to decompose such a compound photochemically. The recent revival of this idea by O. Warburg has no valid experimental justification. A "1-quantum process," the decomposition of an energy-rich chlorophyll-carbon dioxide complex into oxygen and reduced organic substances by a single light quantum followed by intense back reactions with oxygen, has been shown not to exist. Moreover, it is a theoretical impossibility (see Section VIII).

Instead of one *"Blackman"* or *"dark" reaction*, we have a whole range of enzymatic systems, and it is no longer feasible to treat them as if they were all of the same type (see Figs. 4 and 124).

Hydrogen peroxide has never been shown to appear as an intermediate in the path leading to the liberation of oxygen. But it is readily formed during the photochemical reduction of atmospheric oxygen in reactions of the "Hill" type (see Fig. 101, page 198).

Quantum yields between 0.25 and 0.35—that is, quantum numbers as low as 4.0 to 2.8—have been recorded since the 1920's in the laboratory of O. Warburg and co-workers, and later by Dean Burk. All efforts to obtain confirmation of such high yields in other laboratories and by other methods than the two-vessel manometric arrangement have been in vain. Apart from this, such high yields violate principles of thermodynamics and appear to be impossible, considering the mechanism of photosynthesis as we know it at present (see Section VIII).

A reaction with *free molecular oxygen* has been proposed as a normal essential part of photosynthesis. This special respiration, supposedly proceeding in light at twice the rate of the net carbon dioxide uptake, has been experimentally disproved. Oxygen is needed by some plants, however, to remove inhibitions caused by anaerobiosis in the dark (Section V,E).

There are numerous other theoretical propositions in the literature, sometimes with *mathematical elaborations*, which have added very little to an understanding of the problem because they have not produced any insight which was not already evident from the experimental data at hand. Since they have not received widespread attention, it is not necessary to enumerate them individually.

B. CURRENT PROBLEMS

1. Carboxylation

We are not yet sure whether the carboxylation of RuDP remains entirely the same reaction when the cells are in the light. In the dark it certainly proceeds as a nonphotochemical, purely enzymatic reaction in green cells, in extracts, and in nonphotosynthetic organisms. The product is always phosphoglyceric acid (PGA). There is also no doubt that in a system composed of illuminated chloroplasts, TPN, ATP, and the necessary enzymes, PGA can be reduced to triose (12). Yet, through the years beginning with the earliest experiments involving the use of radioactive carbon (Section IX), some evidence has come up that in light in the intact cells the step leading to stable PGA is bypassed and that the normal photosynthesis path to hexose is not the reverse of the glycolytic pathway. Attempts to discover unstable CO_2 fixation products have failed (297a). In obligate photoautotrophic organisms the photosynthetic carbon cycle may differ from that of plants having a functional respiratory system (441a).

2. *Reduction*

Related to the foregoing problem is the question whether the reduction of pyridine nucleotides is an indispensable intermediate step for the reduction of carbon dioxide fixation products. We know that energy-rich phosphate appears in illuminated chloroplasts without the aid of TPN.

The reduction of TPN, important as it certainly is for a variety of light-induced reactions, can be bypassed without decline of the phosphorylating capacity of the chloroplast. A direct reduction, therefore, of a precursor to PGA by an unknown reductant XH_2 or in molecular contact with chlorophyll itself, as Franck has steadfastly maintained, is one of the important unsolved questions (Sections XII and XIII; see 89a, 399a).

3. *Photophosphorylation*

We are not yet sure of the extent to which the cyclic phosphorylation working on the pattern of an oxidative phosphorylation proceeds under steady-state conditions. Maybe it functions merely as a priming mechanism to provide some energy-rich phosphate after most phosphorylated intermediates have been lost during a long dark period. Induction periods for oxygen evolution show traits that support this view. A photophosphorylation coupled to photooxidations in enzyme preparations from chloroplasts requires free oxygen. Its existence and meaning in the intact cell is not known (see Section XIII,C and Fig. 108, page 213).

4. *Photoreduction*

The coupling with, and the action of, hydrogenase (Fig. 124, Box V) is easy to understand in principle. We have, however, the strongly depressing influence of organic substrates like glucose on the utilization of hydrogen in adapted algae and sometimes also on the gas exchange of normal photosynthesis. This problem of long standing has recently been solved (Bishop, unpub.). Glucose acts not as a competitive hydrogen donor but as a competitive acceptor for photophosphorylation. The inhibition disappears as soon as all the glucose has been removed via phosphorylation. From Fig. 124 it is easy to deduce that the reactions in Boxes I and II can only proceed when those in Box III are not deflected toward some other task. There is further the problem of the photoproduction of hydrogen from various substrates. What is the origin of this hydrogen?—is it in the substrate? or the water of photolysis? (see Section XI).

5. *Oxygen Evolution*

Our information about the mechanism of oxygen evolution is meager. The path of oxygen is identical in the beginning with that leading to photoreduction. This common part of the way is rather intimately connected with the primary photochemistry and has, therefore, been put into Box IV of our scheme in Fig. 124.

The dismutation to oxygen proceeds only in the presence of manganous ion. Of this catalytic step we have direct proof. That more than one cytochrome participates is an idea based mainly on spectral changes in illuminated cells. Equally vague is the idea of a role for carotenes. It is known that they are necessary to protect the photochemical mechanism against photooxidation under aerobic conditions. Much better evidence exists for methyl-phytyl-benzoquinone (coenzyme Q_{255})* as a catalyst in oxygen evolution (Section VIII,C).

In many plants anaerobic conditions seem to depress the efficiency of the enzymes ("photocatalase") responsible for the release of oxygen. Oxygen evolution is the step which makes the gain of energy achieved in photolysis semipermanent. The importance of this partial problem is, therefore, obvious (Sections III, V, and VI).

6. *Photochemistry—The Decomposition of Water*

Compared with the photolysis of water, the partial problems surveyed above now appear secondary in importance. This is the result of the research of the last thirty years, namely, that the mechanisms involved in the carboxylation, reduction, phosphorylation, and disposal of oxygen can be understood on the basis of current biochemical knowledge.

The photochemistry, however, is different. This is the unique reaction which sets photosynthesis apart from all the other metabolic reactions in living cells. So little definitive information do we have

* In the nomenclature of CoQ subscripts are used either to designate structure of the isoprenoid units, or, as in this case, the absorption spectrum maximum.

about this process that we cannot make an easy choice among several theories available at the present time.

In Section X we gave reasons why we prefer to continue the theoretical discussion of bacterial photosyntheses also on the basis of a primary decomposition of water. Of course, we have been reminded rather often that this is not called for in those cases where the over-all free energy change is negligible. Stanier *et al.*, in a paper referred to in Section X above, state again that it is not always necessary to postulate for the assimilation of organic compounds an electron coupling through photochemically generated oxidants and reductants as proposed by van Niel, by Gaffron, and by others. Cyclic phosphorylation, they point out, suffices as the sole light reaction to achieve, for instance, the interconversion of acetate into the polymer $(C_4H_6O_2)_n$. Stoichiometrically and energetically, such a simplified and "stripped" mechanism is quite acceptable. Its virtue is that it describes certain details of the process in terms of better known enzymatic reactions. Yet, this does in no way contradict or render superfluous and obsolete a more general formulation embracing all photosynthetic reactions. To the contrary the partial mechanism proposed by Stanier *et al.*, fits easily into any scheme in which photosynthesis is pictured as the consequence of a photochemical creation of oxidants and reductants; cyclic phosphorylation belongs right into this same set of reactions (Section XIII). Obviously, what we would like to have is a reliable value for the quantum efficiency of acetate assimilation.

Nearly all the experimental evidence concerned with the photochemical step supports the contention that it results in the opening of one of the bonds in H—O—H and that the rest of the photosynthetic process is a consequence of the reactions initiated by the substances which receive the separated components of water. All through this article we have designated them as XH and YOH. Of course, until it has been shown specifically—as in the case of hydrogen transfer from a molecule of alcohol to a molecule of DPN—that an individual atom has been transferred, and not an electron to form an ion, this is only one way of describing the reactions we know must happen. The other way—which postulates a separation of electrical charges within the protein-lipid "sandwich" seen in the grana—is an ancient hypothesis that recently received the attractive popular name of "solar battery." Plain enzyme chemistry alone does not suffice to solve the problem of the role of the activated pigments. The photosynthetic unit is a fact which cannot be ignored. The precise structural arrangement determines the optical characteristics of the pigment molecules and thereby their efficiency for capturing and holding the absorbed light energy.

It is easy to predict that the kind of investigations discussed in Sections IIIa, IV, VI, and VII will from now on determine the pace of progress in our efforts to understand photosynthesis (8, 9, 10, 84, 101).

As long as no particular advantage (or drawback) of the one or the other hypothesis is known, both descriptions are equivalent. No objection at all exists to the picture of the photochemical step as a transfer of hydrogen resulting in a pair of highly reactive chemical radicals. Some physicists, while agreeing that the modes of notation on paper are interchangeable for enzymatic reactions, contend that this is not so for a photochemical system when electrons should be moved in 10^{-12} seconds. For lack of prompt hydration the activation energies become too high. Such a process is not advantageous when the energy of

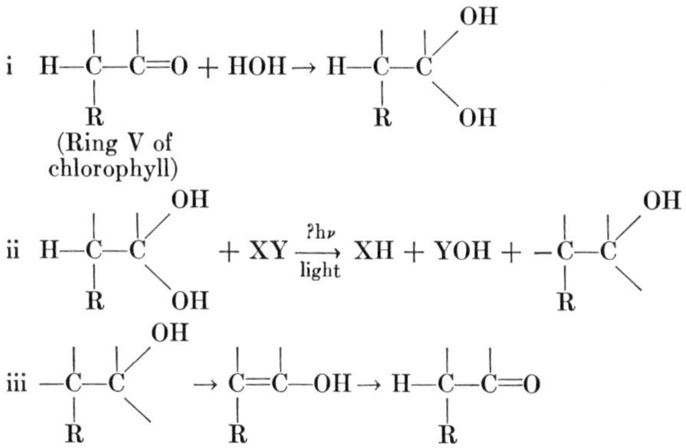

$$\text{i}\quad \text{H—}\underset{\text{R}}{\text{C}}\text{—C=O} + \text{HOH} \rightarrow \text{H—}\underset{\text{R}}{\text{C}}\text{—C}\begin{matrix}\text{OH}\\ \text{OH}\end{matrix}$$

(Ring V of chlorophyll)

$$\text{ii}\quad \text{H—}\underset{\text{R}}{\text{C}}\text{—C}\begin{matrix}\text{OH}\\ \text{OH}\end{matrix} + \text{XY} \xrightarrow[\text{light}]{?h\nu} \text{XH} + \text{YOH} + \text{—}\underset{\text{R}}{\text{C}}\text{—C}\begin{matrix}\text{OH}\\ \diagdown\end{matrix}$$

$$\text{iii}\quad \text{—}\underset{\text{R}}{\text{C}}\text{—C}\begin{matrix}\text{OH}\\ \diagdown\end{matrix} \rightarrow \underset{\text{R}}{\text{C}}\text{=C—OH} \rightarrow \text{H—}\underset{\text{R}}{\text{C}}\text{—C=O}$$

FIG. 125. Photochemical reaction of chlorophyll with water in ring V. According to Franck (178, 181).

each quantum is insufficient to make a direct hydrogen transfer possible. But after the first step has happened as a hydrogen transfer resulting in a radical, the reactions to follow may shift into typical electron transfer systems. We should not lose sight of the fact that in respiration we have both.

If cytochromes take part in the photochemical steps, there is little doubt that they will react as do the cytochromes in most other iron porphyrin-catalyzed reactions by a change of valency of the iron atom (549). Chance and Nishimura have recorded a very fast, light-induced, temperature-independent spectral change in *Chromatium* which corresponds to an oxidation of a cytochrome (89a). This may, indeed, be a primary step. The recent attempts to correlate the production of radicals and of free electrons in illuminated chloroplasts with the light absorption by chlorophyll have shown that both, radicals as well as electrons, are being formed (84, 402, 477, 530, 531).

The next question is whether the chlorophyll molecule itself undergoes chemical changes or is merely a sensitizer and thus does not participate directly in a chemical reaction. Figure 125 illustrates the short cycle of water decomposition directly at ring V of chlorophyll as discussed in great detail by Franck. The Russian school is inclined to take the reversible reduction of chlorophyll seen *in vitro* as a model which should guide our thinking about the process in the living cell (Section III). Experiments with tritium have shown that there are enzymes in chloroplasts which mobilize hydrogen atoms in chlorophyll.

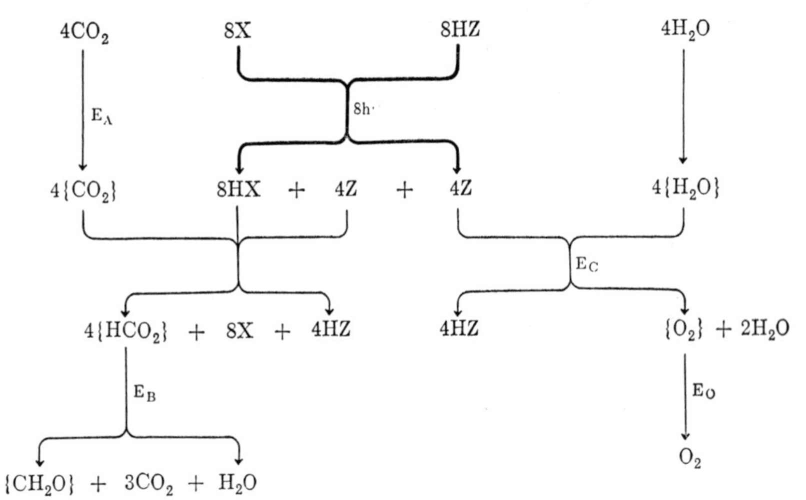

FIG. 126. Scheme of photosynthesis where water is decomposed at a place separated from the light absorbing pigment. According to Rabinowitch (436), p. 165.

The other extreme is the view that luminescence reactions in crystals and electromagnetic resonance point to ionizations (7, 8, 438).

A scheme for the oxidation of water at a place removed from chlorophyll a is Fig 126. The light enforces an electron transfer between the substance X and HZ, resulting in XH and Z. Half of the molecules oxidize water while the other half reinforce the reducing power of half of XH by means of the energy released in a back reaction with the other half of the XH. This scheme, among many others, was drawn by Rabinowitch in 1945 (436). It is easy to implement it in modern biochemical terms. The back reaction would be the phosphorylation needed for the reduction of the carboxylation product, etc.

7. *Quantum Yields*

Concerning the famous quantum-yield problem, it might help to clarify the issue if we restate it as follows:

The breaking of the O—H bond with one quantum of red light in a way that saves enough energy to proceed thence with synthetic reactions which require additional energy seems impossible. Since one quantum is not enough and since quanta are not dispensed in fractions but always as units, 2 quanta are the minimum which have to be expended initially per molecule of water decomposed. This leads automatically to an 8-quanta mechanism—with plenty of energy to spare. The explanation of higher quantum numbers than 8, i.e., a lower yield, is trivial. They must be attributed to heat losses. But how can we explain yields better than 8? This is possible but requires somewhat more involved assumptions. The creation of some energy-rich phosphate is a prerequisite for the reduction of carboxyl groups and is an integral part of the process. Assume now that the number of ATP molecules synthesized during the reduction process is one or two more than needed for the carboxylation cycle. In such a case the breaking of four hydrogen bonds leaves us not only with the equivalent of one carbon dioxide reduced and one oxygen liberated, but also with one or more ATP molecules in excess of immediate demand. It depends, of course, on the energy content of the energy-rich phosphate bonds and on the efficiency with which they are produced how much ATP can be saved. A surplus in phosphate energy diminishes either the phosphate requirement of the next cycle or enhances the rate of chemosynthetic reactions elsewhere in the cell. This leads to a condition in the steady state where the balance of respiration and photosynthesis in the light sum up to an over-all energy requirement averaging less than 2 quanta per hydrogen transfer, or less than 8 per carbon dioxide reduced. If photosynthesis could be influenced by outside factors in such a way that the hypothetical excess of ATP is not immediately drained away into the general metabolism but stored until a large reservoir has accumulated, and if this could be discharged at a certain moment by some external influence on the mechanism of photosynthesis, it would be possible to arrange a succession of alternating periods with unusually bad and unusually good quantum yields (cf. 419, 423). In the long run these fluctuating yields must average out to the normal steady-state yield of photosynthesis (see Section VIII).

8. Solar Energy Projects

A tremendous step forward in the development of the poorer regions on this earth would be the cheap and direct transformation of solar radiation into industrially suitable forms of energy. Discussions of future projects invariably bring up the question of a completely artificial photosynthesis. This might do away with the need to burn coal, oil, wood, and other products of photosynthesis or even with agriculture in all its ramifications (216).

The reader will now be familiar with the complexities of the natural process of photosynthesis. Only a part of this mechanism serves to convert radiant into chemical energy, and the foremost task would be to understand and reconstruct this particular part. It is rather obvious that the technical production of food in bulk must be left to the living plant (213). We hope that the complete artificial reconstruction of photosynthesis in the test tube may be achieved within a few years, but this is a goal for the laboratory scientist, not for the practical engineer.

The most versatile form of industrial energy is electricity. The problem of converting visible light into an electric current has been solved in principle and with good efficiency by the inorganic "solar battery." What remains to be done here is entirely a question of technology and economics.

The next promising invention may be a dye-sensitized, photochemical, 1-quantum process. This is a task which we already understand fully from the theoretical point of view, and we know precisely that the problem consists in separating the immediate energy-rich products of the photochemical primary process before they recombine. To construct such a device looks simpler at the time of this writing than to copy the 2-quanta process for splitting water. Considering the excess of light available, even a moderate yield of a 1-quantum process would mean a considerable gain. The chances for developing a technical photolysis of water with 2 quanta appear rather dim as long as the problem has not even been solved theoretically (48a, 107, 108).

BIBLIOGRAPHICAL NOTES

The list of references is necessarily incomplete. It may suffice, however, to point out the variety of phenomena observed during the last forty years which have formed our present view of photosynthesis. The great work of E. Rabinowitch [Photosynthesis, Vols. I, II, III, Interscience, New York (1945–1956)] covers practically the entire literature until 1955. Very often the student will find here a more detailed and profound analysis of a specific problem than in the original paper under discussion.

The second best source of information are the reviews which have appeared with great regularity in *Annual Review of Plant Physiology* since 1950 (350, 555). There are three smaller monographs: R. Hill and C. P. Whittingham, "Photosynthesis" (1955); G. E. Fogg, "The Metabolism of Algae" (1953), both published by Methuen, London, and Wiley, New York; J. A. Bassham and M. Calvin, "The Path of Carbon in Photosynthesis," Prentice-Hall, New Jersey (1957). (For other reviews see 20, 418, 543, 599.)

The following symposia reports contain a number of important papers: "Photosynthesis in Plants," Iowa State College Press, Ames, Iowa (1949); "Carbon Dioxide Fixation and Photosynthesis," 5th Symposium of the Society for Experimental Biology (1951); "Autotrophic Microorganisms," 4th Symposium of the Society for Microbiology (1954), both Cambridge (England) University Press; "Research in Photosynthesis," Papers and discussions presented at the Gatlinburg Conference, 1955, Interscience, New York (1957); "Biophysical Science, A Study Program," in *Reviews of Modern Physics* **31,** Nos. 1 and 2 (1959); "The Photochemical Apparatus, Its Structure and Function," 11th Symposium of the Brookhaven National Laboratory (1959), Office Tech. Services, Commerce Dept., Washington 25, D.C.; see also Daniels (107).

REFERENCES

1. Albaum, H. G. The metabolism of phosphorylated compounds in plants. *Ann. Rev. Plant Physiol.* **3,** 35–58 (1952).
2. Allen, F. L. Observations on photosynthesis and related systems. I. Influence of anaerobiosis on photosynthetic rates during continuous irradiation. *Arch. Biochem. Biophys.* **55,** 38–53 (1955).
3. Anderson, I. C., and Fuller, R. C. Photophosphorylation by isolated chromatophores of the purple sulfur bacteria. *Arch. Biochem. Biophys.* **76,** 168–179 (1958).
4. Arens, K. Photosynthese von Wasserpflanzen in Kaliumbikarbonatlösungen. *Jahrb. wiss. Botan.* **83,** 561–566 (1936).
5. Arnold, W. A calorimetric determination of the quantum yield in photosynthesis. *In* "Photosynthesis in Plants" (J. Franck and W. E. Loomis, eds.), pp. 273–276. Iowa State College Press, Ames, Iowa, 1949.
6. Arnold, W., and Oppenheimer, J. R. Internal conversion in the photosynthetic mechanism of blue-green algae. *J. Gen. Physiol.* **33,** 423–435 (1950).
7. Arnold, W., and Thompson, J. Delayed light production by blue-green algae, red algae, and purple bacteria. *J. Gen. Physiol.* **39,** 311–318 (1956).
8. Arnold, W., and Meek, E. S. The polarization of fluorescence and energy transfer in grana. *Arch. Biochem. Biophys.* **60,** 82–90 (1956).
9. Arnold, W., and Sherwood, H. K. Are chloroplasts semiconductors? *Proc. Natl. Acad. Sci. U.S.* **43,** 105–114 (1957).
10. Arnold, W. Decay of the delayed light emission in *Chlorella. In* "Research in Photosynthesis," pp. 128–133. Interscience, New York, 1957.
11. Arnon, D. I. Extracellular photosynthetic reactions. *Nature* **167,** 1008 (1951).
12. Arnon, D. I. Glyceraldehyde phosphate dehydrogenase of green plants. *Science* **116,** 635–637 (1952).
13. Arnon, D. I., Allen, M. B., and Whatley, F. R. Photosynthesis by isolated chloroplasts. *Nature* **174,** 394–396 (1954).
14. Arnon, D. I., Whatley, F. R., and Allen, M. B. Photosynthesis by isolated chloroplasts. II. Photosynthetic phosphorylation, the conversion of light into phosphate bond energy. *J. Am. Chem. Soc.* **76,** 6324–6329 (1954).
15. Arnon, D. I. Phosphorus metabolism and photosynthesis. *Ann. Rev. Plant Physiol.* **7,** 325–332 (1956).
16. Arnon, D. I., Allen, M. B., and Whatley, F. R. General concept of photosynthesis by isolated chloroplasts. *In* "Research in Photosynthesis," pp. 296–302. Interscience, New York, 1957.
17. Arnon, D. I., Whatley, F. R., and Allen, M. B. Assimilatory power in photosynthesis. *Science* **127,** 1026–1034 (1958).

18. Aronoff, S. Redox potentials and photoreduction by chloroplast granules. *Science* **104,** 503–505 (1946).
19. Aronoff, S. The absorption spectra of chlorophyll and related compounds. *Chem. Revs.* **47,** 175–195 (1950).
20. Aronoff, S. Photosynthesis. *Botan. Rev.* **23,** 65–107 (1957).
21. Arthur, W. E., and Strehler, B. L. Studies on the primary process in photosynthesis. I. Photosynthetic luminescence: Multiple reactants. *Arch. Biochem. Biophys.* **70,** 507–526 (1957).
21a. Avron, M., Jagendorf, A. T., and Evans, M. Photosynthetic phosphorylation in a partially purified system. *Biochim. et Biophys. Acta* **26,** 262–269 (1957).
22. Avron, M., Krogman, D. W., and Jagendorf, A. T. The relation of photosynthetic phosphorylation to the Hill reaction. *Biochim. et Biophys. Acta* **30,** 144–153 (1958).
23. Ballard, L. A. T. The depressant effect of carbon dioxide upon photosynthesis. *New Phytologist* **40,** 276–290 (1941).
24. Bandurski, R. S. Further studies on the enzymatic synthesis of oxalacetate from phosphorylenolpyruvate and carbon dioxide. *J. Biol. Chem.* **217,** 137–150 (1955).
25. Barker, H. A. Photosynthesis in diatoms. *Arch. Mikrobiol.* **6,** 141–156 (1935).
26. Barker, H. A. Studies upon the methane fermentation. *Antonie van Leeuwenhoek. J. Microbiol. Serol.* **6,** 201–220 (1940).
27. Barker, S. A., Bassham, J. A., Calvin, M., and Quarck, U. C. Sites of azaserine inhibition during photosynthesis by *Scenedesmus. J. Am. Chem. Soc.* **78,** 4632–4635 (1956).
28. Bartsch, R., and Kamen, M. D. On the new heme protein of facultative photoheterotrophs. *J. Biol. Chem.* **230,** 41–64 (1958).
29. Bassham, J. A., Shibata, K., and Calvin, M. Quantum requirement in photosynthesis related to respiration. *Biochim. et Biophys. Acta* **17,** 332–340 (1955).
30. Bassham, J. A., Barker, S. A., Calvin, M., and Quarck, U. C. Intermediates in the photosynthetic cycle. *Biochim. et Biophys. Acta* **21,** 376–377 (1956).
31. Bassham, J. A., and Calvin, M. Photosynthesis. *In* "Currents in Biochemical Research" (D. E. Green, ed.), pp. 29–69. Interscience, New York, 1956.
32. Bassham, J. A., and Calvin, M. "The Path of Carbon in Photosynthesis." Prentice-Hall, Englewood Cliffs, New Jersey, 1957.
33. Bassham, J. A., and Shibata, K. Mechanism of the initial steps in photosynthesis. *In* "Research in Photosynthesis," pp. 366–372. Interscience, New York, 1957.
34. Benson, A. A., Calvin, M., Haas, V. A., Aronoff, S., Hall, A. G., Bassham, J. A., and Weigl, J. W. C^{14} in Photosynthesis. *In* "Photosynthesis in Plants" (J. Franck and W. E. Loomis, eds.), pp. 381–402. Iowa State College Press, Ames, Iowa, 1949.
35. Benson, A. A., and Calvin, M. Carbon dioxide fixation by green plants. *Ann. Rev. Plant Physiol.* **1,** 25–42 (1950).
36. Benson, A. A. Identification of ribulose in $C^{14}O_2$ photosynthesis products. *J. Am. Chem. Soc.* **73,** 2971–2972 (1951).
37. Bergmann, F. H., Towne, J. C., and Borris, R. Assimilation of CO_2 by hydrogen bacteria. *J. Biol. Chem.* **230,** 13–24 (1958).
38. Bergmann, L. Stoffwechsel und Mineralsalzernährung einzelliger Grünalgen. II. Vergleichende Untersuchungen über den Einfluss mineralischer Faktoren bei heterotropher und mixotropher Ernährung. *Flora (Jena)* **142,** 493–539 (1955).
39. Bishop, N. I., and Spikes, J. D. Inhibition by cyanide of the photochemical activity of isolated chloroplasts. *Nature* **176,** 307–310 (1955).

40. Bishop, N. I., Lumry, R., and Spikes, J. D. The mechanism of the photochemical activity of isolated chloroplasts. I. Effect of temperature. *Arch. Biochem. Biophys.* **58**, 1–18 (1955).
41. Bishop, N. I. The influence of the herbicide, DCMU, on the oxygen-evolving system of photosynthesis. *Biochim. et Biophys. Acta* **27**, 205–206 (1958).
42. Bishop, N. I., and Gaffron, H. The inhibition of photosynthesis by sodium fluoride. I. The sodium fluoride-induced carbon dioxide burst from *Chlorella. Biochim. et Biophys. Acta* **28**, 35–44 (1958).
43. Bishop, N. I. Vitamin K, an essential factor for the photochemical activity of isolated chloroplasts. *Proc. Natl. Acad. Sci. U.S.* **44**, 501–504 (1958).
44. Bishop, N. I. The reactivity of a naturally occurring quinone (Q-255) in photochemical reactions of isolated chloroplasts. *Proc. Natl. Acad. Sci. U.S.* **45**, 1696–1702 (1959).
45. Bishop, N. I., Nakamura, H., Blatt, J., and Vennesland, B. Kinetics and properties of cytochrome c photooxidase of spinach. *Plant Physiol.* **34**, 551–557 (1959).
46. Blinks, L. R. The photosynthetic function of pigments other than chlorophyll. *Ann. Rev. Plant Physiol.* **5**, 93–114 (1954).
47. Blinks, L. R. Chromatic transients in photosynthesis of red algae. *In* "Research in Photosynthesis," pp. 444–449. Interscience, New York, 1957.
48. Blinks, L. R., and Skow, R. K. The time course of photosynthesis as shown by: The glass electrode, with anomalies in the acidity changes. A rapid electrode method for oxygen. *Proc. Natl. Acad. Sci. U.S.* **24**, 413–427 (1938).

48a. Blum, H. F. "Time's Arrow and Evolution," 2nd ed. Princeton Univ. Press, Princeton, New Jersey, 1955.

49. Bogorad, L. Factors associated with the synthesis of chlorophyll in the dark in seedlings of *Pinus jeffreyi. Botan. Gaz.* **111**, 221–241 (1950).
50. Bogorad, L. The enzymatic synthesis of porphyrins from porphobilinogen. Uroporphyrinogens as intermediates. *J. Biol. Chem.* **233**, 501–519 (1958).
51. Bold, H. C. The cultivation of algae. *Botan. Rev.* **8**, 69–138 (1942).
52. Brackett, F. S., Olson, R. A., and Crickard, R. G. Respiration and intensity dependence of photosynthesis in *Chlorella. J. Gen. Physiol.* **36**, 529–561 (1953).
53. Brackett, F. S., Olson, R. A., and Crickard, R. G. Time course and quantum efficiency of photosynthesis in *Chlorella. J. Gen. Physiol.* **36**, 563–579 (1953).
54. Bradbeer, J. W., Ranson, S. L., and Stiller, M. Malate synthesis in crassulacean leaves. I. The distribution of C^{14} in malate of leaves exposed to $C^{14}O_2$ in the dark. *Plant Physiol.* **33**, 66–70 (1958).
55. Bregoff, H. M., and Kamen, M. D. Studies on the metabolism of photosynthetic bacteria. XIV. Quantitative relations between malate dissimilation, photoproduction of hydrogen, and nitrogen metabolism in *Rhodospirillum rubrum. Arch. Biochem. Biophys.* **36**, 202–220 (1952).
56. Briggs, G. E. Experimental researches on vegetable assimilation and respiration. XX. The energetic efficiency of photosynthesis in green plants: Some new data and discussion of the problem. *Proc. Roy. Soc.* **B105**, 1–35 (1929).
57. Brody, S. S. New excited state of chlorophyll. *Science* **128**, 838–839 (1958).

57a. Brody, M., and Emerson, R. The effect of wavelength and intensity of light on the proportion of pigments in *Porphyridium cruentum. Am. J. Botany* **46**, 433–440 (1959); the quantum yield of photosynthesis in *Porphyridium cruentum* and the role of chlorophyll a in the photosynthesis of red algae. *J. Gen. Physiol.* **43**, 251–264 (1959).

58. Brown, A. H., and Franck, J. On the participation of carbon dioxide in the

photosynthetic activity of illuminated chloroplast suspensions. *Arch. Biochem.* **16**, 55–60 (1948).

59. Brown, A. H. The carbohydrate constituents of *Scenedesmus* in relation to the assimilation of carbon by photoreduction. *Plant Physiol.* **23**, 331–337 (1948).
60. Brown, A. H., Fager, E. W., and Gaffron, H. Assimilation of tracer carbon in the alga, *Scenedesmus. Arch. Biochem.* **19**, 407–428 (1948).
61. Brown, A. H., and Mehler, A. H. Studies on reactions of illuminated chloroplasts. III. Simultaneous photoproduction and consumption of oxygen studied with oxygen isotopes. *Arch. Biochem. Biophys.* **38**, 365–370 (1952).
62. Brown, A. H., and Weis, D. Relation between respiration and photosynthesis. *Plant Physiol.* **34**, 224–239 (1959).
63. Brown, A. H. The effects of light on respiration using isotopically enriched oxygen. *Am. J. Botany* **40**, 719–729 (1953).
64. Brown, A. H., and Webster, G. C. The influence of light on the rate of respiration of the blue-green alga, *Anabaena. Am. J. Botany* **40**, 753–758, 1753 (1953).
65. Brown, A. H., and Whittingham, C. P. Identification of the carbon dioxide burst in *Chlorella* using the recording mass spectrometer. *Plant Physiol.* **30**, 231–237 (1955).
66. Brown, A. H., and Good, N. Photochemical reduction of oxygen in chloroplast preparations and in green plants. *Arch. Biochem. Biophys.* **57**, 340–353 (1955).
67. Brugger, J. E. Fluorescence yield of chlorophyll in *Chlorella* as a function of light intensity. *In* "Research in Photosynthesis," pp. 113–117. Interscience, New York, 1957.
68. Brugger, J. E. Some observations on the chemiluminescence of algae. *In* "Research in Photosynthesis," pp. 131–141. Interscience, New York, 1957.
69. Brugger, J. E., and Franck, J. Experimental and theoretical contribution to studies of the afterglow of chlorophyll in plant materials. *Arch. Biochem. Biophys.* **75**, 465–496 (1958).
70. Bünning, E. Endogenous rhythms in plants. *Ann. Rev. Plant Physiol.* **7**, 1–90 (1956).
71. Burberg, R. V. Der Quantenbedarf bei der CO-Hämoglobinspaltung durch Licht. *Z. Naturforsch.* **10b**, 503–509 (1955).
72. Burk, D., Kendricks, S., Korzenovsky, M., Schocken, V., and Warburg, O. The maximum efficiency of photosynthesis: A rediscovery. *Science* **110**, 225–229 (1949).
73. Burk, D., Cornfield, J., and Schwartz, M. The efficient transformation of light into chemical energy in photosynthesis. *Sci. Monthly* **73**, 213–223 (1951).
74. Burk, D., and Warburg, O. Ein-Quanten-Reaktion und Kreisprozess der Energie bei der Photosynthese. *Z. Naturforsch.* **6b**, 12–22 (1951).

74a. Burlew, J. S., ed. Algal culture from laboratory to pilot plant. *Carnegie Inst. Wash. Publ.* **600** (1953).

75. Burma, D. P., and Mortimer, D. C. The fate of assimilated $C^{14}O_2$ in the sugar beet leaf studied by displacement with $C^{12}O_2$. *Can. J. Biochem. and Physiol.* **35**, 835–843 (1957).
76. Butler, W. L. Transient phenomena in leaves as recorded by a gas thermal conductivity meter. *In* "Research in Photosynthesis," pp. 399–405. Interscience, New York, 1957.

77. Calvin, M., and Benson, A. A. The path of carbon in photosynthesis. *Science* **107**, 476–480 (1948).
78. Calvin, M., and Aronoff, S. Phosphorus turnover and photosynthesis. *Plant Physiol.* **23**, 351–358 (1948).
79. Calvin, M., Bassham, J. A., and Benson, A. A. Chemical transformations of carbon in photosynthesis. *Federation Proc.* **9**, 524–534 (1950).
80. Calvin, M., Bassham, J. A., Benson, A. A., Lynch, V. H., Ouellet, C., Schou, L., Stepka, W., and Tolbert, N. E. Carbon dioxide assimilation in plants. *Symposia Soc. Exptl. Biol.* **5**, 284–305 (1951).
81. Calvin, M., Bassham, J. A., Benson, A. A., and Massini, P. Photosynthesis. *Ann. Rev. Phys. Chem.* **3**, 215–228 (1952).
82. Calvin, M., Bassham, J. A., Shibata, K., Steenberg, K., and Bourdon, J. The photosynthetic cycle and respiration. Light-dark transients. *J. Am. Chem. Soc.* **78**, 4120–4124 (1956).
83. Calvin, M., and Tollin, G. The luminescence of chlorophyll-containing plant material. *Proc. Natl. Acad. Sci. U.S.* **43**, 895–908 (1957).
84. Calvin, M., and Sogo, P. B. Primary quantum conversion process in photosynthesis: Electron spin resonance. *Science* **125**, 499–500 (1957).
85. Campbell, A. Synchronization of cell division. *Bacteriol. Revs.* **21**, 263–272 (1957).
86. Chance, B. Enzyme-substrate compounds. *Advances in Enzymol.* **12**, 153–190 (1951).
87. Chance, B. On the time sequence of reactions in the anaerobic light effect in *Rhodospirillum rubrum*. *In* "Research in Photosynthesis," pp. 184–188. Interscience, New York, 1957.
88. Chance, B., and Strehler, B. L. Effects of oxygen and red light upon the absorption of visible light in green plants. *Plant Physiol.* **32**, 536–548 (1957).
89. Chance, B., and Sanger, R. Oxygen and light induced oxidations of cytochrome, flavoprotein and pyridine nucleotide in a *Chlamydomonas* mutant. *Plant Physiol.* **32**, 548–561 (1957).
89a. Chance, B., and Nishimura, M. On the mechanism of chlorophyll-cytochrome interaction: The temperature insensitivity of light-induced cytochrome oxidation in *Chromatium*. *Proc. Natl. Acad. Sciences.* **46**, 19–24 (1960).
90. Chiau, Y. G., and Franck, J. Chlorophyll fluorescence and photosynthesis in algae, leaves and chloroplasts. *Arch. Biochem.* **14**, 253–295 (1947).
91. Claes, H. Biosynthese von Carotinoiden bei *Chlorella*. *Z. Naturforsch.* **11b**, 260–266 (1956).
92. Clendenning, K. A. Distribution of tracer carbon among the lipides of the alga *Scenedesmus* during brief photosynthetic exposures. *Arch. Biochem.* **27**, 75–88 (1950).
93. Clendenning, K. A., and Ehrmantraut, H. C. Photosynthesis and Hill reactions by whole *Chlorella* cells in continuous and flashing light. *Arch. Biochem.* **29**, 387–403 (1950).
94. Clendenning, K. A., and Gorham, P. R. Photochemical activity of isolated chloroplasts in relation to their source and previous history. *Can. J. Research* **C28**, 114–139 (1950).
95. Clendenning, K. A., and Haxo, F. T. Photosynthetic induction in marine algae. *Can. J. Botany* **34**, 214–230 (1956).
96. Clendenning, K. A., Brown, T. E., and Eyster, C. Comparative studies of

photosynthesis in *Nostoc muscorum* and *Chlorella pyrenoidosa*. *Can. J. Botany* **34**, 943–966 (1956).

97. Clendenning, K. A., Brown, T. E., and Walldov, E. E. Natural inhibitors of the Hill reaction. *In* "Research in Photosynthesis," pp. 274–284. Interscience, New York, 1957.
98. Cohen-Bazire, G., Sistrom, W. R., and Stanier, R. Y. Kinetic studies of pigment synthesis by non-sulfur purple bacteria. *J. Cellular Comp. Physiol.* **49**, 25–68 (1957).
99. Cohen-Bazire, G., and Stanier, R. Y. Specific inhibition of carotenoid synthesis in a photosynthetic bacterium and its physiological consequences. *Nature* **181**, 250–253 (1958).
100. Coleman, J. W., Holt, A. S., and Rabinowitch, E. I. Reversible bleaching of chlorophyll *in vivo*. *In* "Research in Photosynthesis," pp. 68–74. Interscience, New York, 1957.
101. Commoner, B., and Lippincott, B. B. Light-induced free radicals in FMN and flavoprotein enzymes. *Proc. Natl. Acad. Sci. U.S.* **44**, 1110–1116 (1958); Commoner, B., Lippincott, B. B., and Passonneau, J. V. Electron-spin resonance studies of free-radical intermediates in oxidation-reduction enzyme systems. *Ibid.* **44**, 1099–1109 (1958).
102. Cramer, M., and Myers, J. Nitrate reduction and assimilation in *Chlorella. J. Gen. Physiol.* **32**, 93–102 (1948).
103. Cramer, M., and Myers, J. Effects of starvation on the metabolism of *Chlorella. Plant Physiol.* **24**, 255–264 (1949).

103a. Crane, F. L. Internal distribution of coenzyme Q in higher plants. *Am. J. Botany* **34**, 128–131 (1959).

104. Cutinelli, C., Ehrensvärd, G., and Reio, L. Acetic acid metabolism in *Rhodospirillum rubrum* under anaerobic conditions. *Arkiv Kemi* **2**, 357–361 (1950).
105. Damaschke, K. Die Wasserstoffgärung von *Chlorella* im Dunkeln nach Anaerobiose unter Stickstoff. *Z. Naturforsch.* **12b**, 441–443 (1957).
106. Damaschke, K., and Lübke, M. Hemmung der Wasserstoffgärung von *Chlorella* p. durch Gifte. *Z. Naturforsch.* **13b**, 54–55 (1958).
107. Daniels, F. Principles and problems in the utilization of solar energy. *In* "Conference on the Use of Solar Energy: The Scientific Basis" (E. F. Carpenter, ed.), Vol. I. University of Arizona Press, Tucson, Arizona, 1955.
108. Daniels, F., and Duffie, J. A., eds. "Solar Energy Research." University of Wisconsin Press. Madison, Wisconsin, 1955.
109. Davenport, H. E., and Hill, R. The preparation and some properties of cytochrome f. *Proc. Roy. Soc.* **B139**, 327–345 (1952).
110. Davenport, H. E., Hill, R., and Whatley, F. R. A natural factor catalyzing reduction of methemoglobin by isolated chloroplasts. *Proc. Roy. Soc.* **B139**, 346–358 (1952).
111. Davenport, H. E. Coenzyme reduction by illuminated chloroplasts. *Biochem. J.* **73**, 45 P (1959).
112. Duggar, B. M., Stauffer, J. F., and Daniels, F. Quantum relations in photosynthesis with *Chlorella. Science* **99**, 435 (1934).
113. Dutton, H. J., and Manning, W. M. Evidence for carotenoid-sensitized photosynthesis in the diatom *Nitzschia closterium*. *Am. J. Botany* **28**, 516–526 (1941).
114. Dutton, H. J., Manning, W. M., and Duggar, B. B. Chlorophyll fluorescence

and energy transfer in the diatom *Nitzschia closterium*. *J. Phys. Chem.* **47**, 308–313 (1943).

115. Duysens, L. N. M. Energy transformations in photosynthesis. *Ann. Rev. Plant Physiol.* **7**, 25–50 (1956).
116. Duysens, L. N. M., and Amesz, J. Fluorescence spectrophotometry of reduced phosphopyridine nucleotide in intact cells in the near-ultraviolet and visible region. *Biochim. et Biophys. Acta* **24**, 19 (1957); Quantum requirement for phosphopyridine nucleotide reduction in photosynthesis. *Plant Physiol.* **34**, 210–213 (1959).
117. Duysens, L. N. M., and Sweep, G. Fluorescence spectrophotometry of pyridine nucleotide in photosynthesizing cells. *Biochim. et Biophys. Acta* **25**, 13–16 (1957).
118. Duysens, L. N. M. Methods for measurement and analysis of changes in light absorption occurring upon illumination of photosynthesizing organisms. *In* "Research In Photosynthesis," pp. 59–67. Interscience, New York, 1957.
119. Ebel, J. P. Recherches sur les polyphosphates contenus dans diverses cellules vivantes. I. Mise au point d'une methode d'extraction. *Bull. soc. chim biol.* **34**, 321–329 (1952).
120. Egle, K. Untersuchungen uber die Resistenz der Plastidenfarbstoffe. *Botan. Arch.* **45**, 93–148 (1944).
121. Egle, K., and Schenk, W. Untersuchungen über die Reassimilation der Atmungskohlensäure bei der Photosynthese der Pflanzen. *Beitr. Biol. Pflanz.* **29**, 75–105 (1952).
122. Elsden, S. R., Kamen, M. D., and Vernon, L. P. A new soluble cytochrome. *J. Am. Chem. Soc.* **75**, 6347 (1953).
123. Elsden, S. R. The utilization of organic compounds by photosynthetic bacteria. *In* "Autotrophic Micro-organisms," pp. 202–223. Cambridge Univ. Press, London and New York, 1954.
124. Elsden, S. R., and Ormerod, J. G. The effect of monofluoro acetate on the metabolism of *Rhodospirillum rubrum*. *Biochem. J.* **63**, 691–701 (1956).
125. Emerson, R. The effect of certain respiratory inhibitors on the respiration of *Chlorella*. *J. Gen. Physiol.* **10**, 469–477 (1927).
126. Emerson, R. The relation between maximum rate of photosynthesis and concentration of chlorophyll. *J. Gen. Physiol.* **12**, 609–622 (1929).
127. Emerson, R. Photosynthesis as a function of light intensity and of temperature with different concentrations of chlorophyll. *J. Gen. Physiol.* **12**, 623–639 (1929).
128. Emerson, R., and Arnold, W. A separation of the reactions in photosynthesis by means of intermittent light. *J. Gen. Physiol.* **15**, 391–420 (1932).
129. Emerson, R., and Arnold, W. The photochemical reaction in photosynthesis. *J. Gen. Physiol.* **16**, 191–205 (1932).
130. Emerson, R., and Green, L. Manometric measurements of photosynthesis in the marine alga *Gigartina*. *J. Gen. Physiol.* **17**, 817–842 (1934).
131. Emerson, R. The effect of intense light on the assimilatory mechanism of green plants, and its bearing on the carbon dioxide factor. *Cold Spring Harbor Symposia Quant. Biol.* **3**, 128–137 (1935).
132. Emerson, R., and Green, L. Nature of the Blackman reaction in photosynthesis. *Plant Physiol.* **12**, 537–545 (1937).
133. Emerson, R., and Green, L. Effect of hydrogen ion concentration on *Chlorella* photosynthesis. *Plant Physiol.* **13**, 157–168 (1938).

134. Emerson, R., and Lewis, C. M. Factors influencing the efficiency of photosynthesis. *Am. J. Botany* **26**, 808–822 (1939).
135. Emerson, R., and Lewis, C. M. Carbon dioxide exchange and the measurement of the quantum yield of photosynthesis. *Am. J. Botany* **28**, 789–804 (1941).
136. Emerson, R., and Lewis, C. M. The photosynthetic efficiency of phycocyanin in *Chroococcus* and the problem of carotenoid participation in photosynthesis. *J. Gen. Physiol.* **25**, 579–595 (1942).
137. Emerson, R., and Lewis, C. M. The dependence of the quantum yield of *Chlorella* photosynthesis on wave length of light. *Am. J. Botany* **30**, 165–178 (1943).
138. Emerson, R., Chalmers, R. V., and Cederstrand, C. Some factors influencing the long-wave limit of photosynthesis. *Proc. Natl. Acad. Sci. U.S.* **43**, 133–143 (1957).
139. Emerson, R., and Chalmers, R. V. On the efficiency of photosynthesis above and below compensation of respiration. *In* "Research in Photosynthesis," pp. 349–352. Interscience, New York, 1957.
140. Emerson, R., and Chalmers, R. V. Transient changes in cellular gas exchange. *In* "Research in Photosynthesis," pp. 406–408. Interscience, New York, 1957.
141. Emerson, R. The quantum yield of photosynthesis. *Ann. Rev. Plant Physiol.* **9**, 1–24 (1958).
142. Emerson, R. Yield of photosynthesis from simultaneous illumination with pairs of wavelengths. *Science* (1958).
143. Evans, E. A. The metabolism of pyruvate in pigeon liver. *Biochem. J.* **34**, 829–837 (1940).
144. Evans, E. A. Vennesland, B., and Slotin, L. The mechanism of carbon dioxide fixation in cell free extracts of pigeon liver. *J. Biol. Chem.* **147**, 771–784 (1943).
145. Eversole, R. A., and Wolken, J. J. Photochemical activity of digitonin extracts of chloroplasts. *Science* **127**, 1287–1288 (1958).
146. Eyster, C., Brown, T. E., and Tanner, H. A. Manganese requirement with respect to respiration and the Hill reaction in *Chlorella pyrenoidosa*. *Arch. Biochem. Biophys.* **64**, 240–241 (1956).
147. Eyster, C., Brown, T. E., and Tanner, H. A. Mineral requirements for *Chlorella pyrenoidosa* under autotrophic and heterotrophic conditions. *In* "Trace Elements" (C. A. Lamb, O. G. Bentley, and J. M. Beattie, eds.), pp. 157–174. Academic Press, New York, 1958.
148. Eyster, C. Chloride effect on the growth of *Chlorella pyrenoidosa*. *Nature* **181**, 1141–1142 (1958).
149. Fager, E. W., Rosenberg, J. L., and Gaffron, H. Intermediates in photosynthesis. *Federation Proc.* **9**, 535–542 (1950).
150. Fager, E. W., and Rosenberg, J. L. Phosphoglyceric acid in photosynthesis. *Science* **112**, 617–618 (1950).
151. Fager, E. W., and Rosenberg, J. L. Exchange reaction and phosphoglyceric acid in photosynthesis. *Arch. Biochem. Biophys.* **37**, 1–4 (1952).
152. Fager, E. W. Photochemical carbon dioxide fixation by cell-free leaf macerates. *Arch. Biochem. Biophys.* **37**, 5–14 (1952).
153. Fager, E. W. Photochemical carbon dioxide fixation by a cell-free system. *Arch. Biochem. Biophys.* **41**, 383–395 (1952).
154. Fager, E. W. Phosphoglyceric acid formation by carbon dioxide fixation in plant extracts. *Biochem. J.* **57**, 264–272 (1954).

155. Ferrari, A. G., Strehler, B. L., and Arthur, W. E. Dark- and light-activated chemiluminescence of chlorophyll *in vitro*. *In* "Research in Photosynthesis," pp. 45–49. Interscience, New York, 1957.
156. Fogg, G. E. Nitrogen fixation by blue-green algae. *Endeavour* **6**, 172–175 (1947).
157. Fogg, G. E., and Than-Tun. Photochemical reduction of elementary nitrogen in the blue-green alga *Anabaena cylindrica*. *Biochim. et Biophys. Acta* **30**, 209–210 (1958).
158. Fogg, G. E. "The Metabolism of Algae." Wiley, New York, 1953.
159. Fogg, G. E. Nitrogen fixation by photosynthetic organisms. *Ann. Rev. Plant Physiol.* **7**, 51–70 (1956).
160. Fogg, G. E. Photosynthesis and formation of fats in a diatom. *Ann. Botany (London)* [N.S.] **20**, 265–285 (1956).
161. Förster, T., and Livingston, R. The absolute quantum yields of the fluorescence of chlorophyll solutions. *J. Chem. Phys.* **20**, 1315–1320 (1952).
162. Förster, H. Das Wirkungsspektrum der Kopulation von *Chlamydomonas eugametos*. *Z. Naturforsch.* **12b**, 765–769 (1957).
163. Franck, J., and Livingston, R. Remarks on fluorescence, phosphorescence and photochemistry of dyestuffs. *J. Chem. Phys.* **9**, 184–190 (1941).
164. Franck, J., French, C. S., and Puck, T. T. Fluorescence of chlorophyll and photosynthesis. *J. Phys. Chem.* **45**, 1268–1300 (1941).
165. Franck, J., and Weller, S. Photosynthesis in flashing light. *J. Phys. Chem.* **45**, 1359–1373 (1941).
166. Franck, J., and Gaffron, H. Photosynthesis: Facts and interpretations. *Advances in Enzymol.* **1**, 199–262 (1941).
167. Franck, J., and French, C. S. Photoxidation processes in plants. *J. Gen. Physiol.* **25**, 309–324 (1941).
168. Franck, J. Carbon dioxide evolution during the induction period of photosynthesis. *Am. J. Botany* **29**, 314–317 (1942).
169. Franck, J. Photosynthetic activity of isolated chloroplasts. *Revs. Modern Phys.* **17**, 112–199 (1945).
170. Franck, J., Pringsheim, P., and Lad, D. T. Oxygen production by anaerobic photosynthesis of algae measured by a new micromethod. *Arch. Biochem.* **7**, 103–142 (1945).
171. Franck, J. The relation of the fluorescence of chlorophyll to photosynthesis. *In* "Photosynthesis in Plants" (J. Franck and W. E. Loomis, eds.), Chapter 16, p. 293. Iowa State College Press, Ames, Iowa, 1949.
172. Franck, J., and Loomis, W. E., eds. "Photosynthesis in Plants." Iowa State College Press, Ames, Iowa, 1949.
173. Franck, J. An interpretation of the contradictory results in measurements of the photosynthetic quantum yields and related phenomena. *Arch. Biochem.* **23**, 297–314 (1949).
174. Franck, J. A critical survey of the physical background of photosynthesis. *Ann. Rev. Plant Physiol.* **2**, 53–86 (1951).
175. Franck, J. The physical background of photosynthesis. *Symposia Soc. Exptl. Biol.* **5**, 160–175 (1951).
176. Franck, J. Participation of respiratory intermediates in the process of photosynthesis as an explanation of abnormally high quantum yields. *Arch. Biochem. Biophys.* **45**, 190–229 (1953).
177. Franck, J., and Platzman, R. Physical principles underlying photochemical, radiation-chemical, and radiobiological reactions. *In* "Radiation Biology" (Alex-

ander Hollaender, ed.), Vol. I, Part I, pp. 191–253. McGraw-Hill, New York, 1954.

178. Franck, J. Physical problems of photosynthesis. *Dædalus* **86**, 17–42 (1955).
179. Franck, J., and Allen, F. L. Photosynthetic evolution of oxygen by flashes of light. *Arch. Biochem. Biophys.* **58**, 124–143 (1955).
180. Franck, J. General remarks on chlorophyll-sensitized photochemical reactions *in vitro*. *In* "Research in Photosynthesis," pp. 19–30. Interscience, New York, 1957.
181. Franck, J. A theory of the photochemical part of photosynthesis. *In* "Research in Photosynthesis," pp. 142–148. Interscience, New York, 1957.
182. Franck, J., and Brugger, J. E. Experimental and theoretical contribution to studies of the afterglow of chlorophyll in plant materials. *Arch. Biochem. Biophys.* **75**, 465–496 (1958).
183. Franck, J. Remarks on the long-wave limits of photosynthesis and chlorophyll fluorescence. *Proc. Natl. Acad. Sci. U.S.* **44**, 941–948 (1958).
184. French, C. S. The rate of carbon dioxide assimilation by purple bacteria at various wave lengths of light. *J. Gen. Physiol.* **21**, 71–87 (1937).
185. French, C. S., and Rabideau, G. S. The quantum yield of oxygen production by chloroplasts suspended in solutions containing ferric oxalate. *J. Gen. Physiol.* **28**, 329–342 (1945).
186. French, C. S., Holt, A. S., Powell, R. D., and Anson, M. L. The evolution of oxygen from illuminated suspensions of frozen, dried, and homogenized chloroplasts. *Science* **103**, 505–506 (1946).
187. French, C. S., and Milner, H. W. The photochemical reduction process in photosynthesis. *Symposia Soc. Exptl. Biol.* **5**, 232–250 (1951).
188. French, C. S., and Young, V. K. The fluorescence spectra of red algae and the transfer of energy from phycoerythrin to phycocyanin and chlorophyll. *J. Gen. Physiol.* **35**, 873–890 (1952).

188a. French, C. S., Smith, J. H. C., Virgin, H. I., and Airth, R. L. Fluorescence spectrum curves of chlorophylls, pheophytins, phycoerythrins, phycocyanins and hypericin. *Plant Physiol.* **31**, 369–373 (1956).

189. French, C. S., Smith, J. H. C., and Virgin, H. I. Fluorescence spectra of protochlorophyll, chlorophylls c and d, and their pheophytins. *In* "Research in Photosynthesis," pp. 17–18. Interscience, New York, 1957.
190. Frenkel, A. W., Battley, E., and Gaffron, H. Photosynthesis and photoreduction by the blue-green alga, *Synechococcus elongatus*, Nag. *Biol. Bull.* **99**, 157–162 (1950).
191. Frenkel, A. W. Hydrogen evolution by the flagellate green alga, *Chlamydomonas moewusii*. *Arch. Biochem. Biophys.* **38**, 219–230 (1952).
192. Frenkel, A. W. Light-induced phosphorylation by cell-free preparations of *Rhodospirillum rubrum*. *In* "Research in Photosynthesis," pp. 303–310. Interscience, New York, 1957.
193. Frenkel, A. W. A bacterial analogue to the Hill-chloroplast reaction. *Plant Physiol.* **33**, xvii (1958).
194. Fuller, R. C., and Gibbs, M. Intracellular and phylogenetic distribution of ribulose 1,5-diphosphate carboxylase. *Plant Physiol.* **34**, 324–328 (1959).
195. Fuller, R. C., and Anderson, J. C. Suppression of carotenoid synthesis and its effect on the activity of photosynthetic bacterial chromatophase. *Nature* **181**, 253–254 (1958).

196. Gabrielsen, E. K. Photosynthesis in leaves at very low carbon dioxide concentrations. *Nature* **163**, 359 (1949).
197. Gaffron, H. Sauerstoff-Übertragung durch Chlorophyll und das photochemische Äquivalentgesetz. *Ber.* **60**, 755–766 (1927).
198. Gaffron, H. Uber den Stoffwechsel der schwefelfreien Purpurbakterien. *Biochem. Z.* **260**, 1–17 (1933).
199. Gaffron, H. Über den Stoffwechsel der Purpurbakterien. II. *Biochem. Z.* **275**, 301–319 (1935).
200. Gaffron, H. Über die Kohlensäureassimilation der roten Schwefelbakterien. II. *Biochem. Z.* **279**, 1–33 (1935).
201. Gaffron, H. Über die Unabhängigkeit der Kohlensäureassimilation der grünen Pflanzen von der Anwesenheit kleiner Sauerstoffmengen und über eine reversible Hemmung der Assimilation durch Kohlenoxyd. *Biochem. Z.* **280**, 337–359 (1935).
202. Gaffron, H., and Wohl, K. Zur Theorie der Assimilation. *Naturwissenschaften* **24**, 81–90, 103–107 (1936).
203. Gaffron, H. Wirkung von Blausäure und Wasserstoffperoxyd auf die Blackmansche Reaktion in *Scenedesmus. Biochem. Z.* **292**, 241–270 (1937).
204. Gaffron, H. Studies on the induction period of photosynthesis and light respiration in green algae. *Am. J. Botany* **27**, 204–216 (1940).
205. Gaffron, H. Carbon dioxide reduction with molecular hydrogen in green algae. *Am. J. Botany* **27**, 273–283 (1940).
206. Gaffron, H. The effect of specific poisons upon the photoreduction with hydrogen in green algae. *J. Gen. Physiol.* **26**, 195–217 (1942).
207. Gaffron, H., and Rubin, J. Fermentative and photochemical production of hydrogen in algae. *J. Gen. Physiol.* **26**, 219–240 (1942).
208. Gaffron, H. Reduction of carbon dioxide coupled with the oxyhydrogen reaction in algae. *J. Gen. Physiol.* **26**, 241–267 (1942).
209. Gaffron, H., and Rieke, F. F. Flash saturation and reaction periods in photosynthesis. *J. Phys. Chem.* **47**, 299–307 (1943).
210. Gaffron, H. Photosynthesis, photoreduction, and dark reduction of carbon dioxide in certain algae. *Biol. Revs. Cambridge Phil. Soc.* **19**, 1–20 (1944).
211. Gaffron, H. Some effects of derivatives of vitamin K on the metabolism of unicellular algae. *J. Gen. Physiol.* **28**, 259–285 (1945).
212. Gaffron, H. Photosynthesis and the production of organic matter on earth. *In* "Currents in Biochemical Research" (D. E. Green, ed.), pp. 25–48. Interscience, New York, 1946.
213. Gaffron, H. Photosynthesis and solar energy projects. *Office Naval Research, Research Revs.* pp. 7–12, October (1957).
214. Gaffron, H., Fager, E. W., and Rosenberg, J. L. Intermediates in photosynthesis: Formation and transformation of phosphoglyceric acid. *Symposia Soc. Exptl. Biol.* **5**, 262–283 (1951).
215. Gaffron, H., and Fager, E. W. The kinetics and chemistry of photosynthesis. *Ann. Rev. Plant Physiol.* **2**, 87–114 (1951).
216. Gaffron, H. Food from algae. *Research* (*London*) **6**, 222–230 (1953).
217. Gaffron, H. Mechanism of photosynthesis. *Symposium Soc. Gen. Microbiol.* **4**, 152–185 (1954).
218. Gaffron, H., and Rosenberg, J. L. Uber Rückreaktionen bei der Photosynthese. *Naturwissenschaften* **42**, 354–364 (1955).

219. Gaffron, H. Transients in the carbon dioxide gas exchange of algae. *In* "Research in Photosynthesis," pp. 430–443. Interscience, New York, 1957.

220. Gaffron, H. Photosynthesis and the origin of life. *In* "Rhythmic and Synthetic Processes in Growth" (D. Rudnick, ed.), pp. 127–154. Princeton Univ. Press, Princeton, New Jersey, 1957.

220a. Garner, W. W., and Allard, H. A. Effect of abnormally long and short alternations of light and darkness on growth development of plants. *J. Agr. Research* **42**, 645–650 (1931).

221. Gerretsen, F. C. Manganese in relation to photosynthesis. II. Redox potentials of illuminated crude chloroplast suspensions. *Plant and Soil* **2**, 159–193 (1950).

222. Gest, H., and Kamen, M. D. Studies on the phosphorus metabolism of green algae and purple bacteria in relation to photosynthesis. *J. Biol. Chem.* **176**, 299–318 (1948).

223. Gest, H., and Kamen, M. D. Studies on the metabolism of photosynthetic bacteria. IV. Photochemical production of molecular hydrogen by growing cultures of photosynthetic bacteria. *J. Bacteriol.* **58**, 239–245 (1949).

224. Gest, H. Anaerobic oxidation of malate and hydrogen in the dark by *Rhodospirillum rubrum. Bacteriol. Proc.* pp. 136–137 (1950).

225. Gest, H., Kamen, M. D., and Bregoff, H. M. Studies on the metabolism of photosynthetic bacteria. V. Photoproduction of hydrogen by *Rhodospirillum rubrum. J. Biol. Chem.* **182**, 153–170 (1950).

226. Gest, H. Metabolic patterns in photosynthetic bacteria. *Bacteriol. Revs.* **15**, 183–219 (1951).

227. Gest, H. Enzymatic oxidation of molecular hydrogen by bacterial extracts. *Federation Proc.* **10**, 188 (1951).

228. Gest, H. Properties of cell-free hydrogenases of *Escherichia coli* and *Rhodospirillum rubrum. J. Bacteriol.* **63**, 111–121 (1952).

229. Gibbs, M., and Kandler, O. Asymmetric distribution of carbon-14 in sugars formed during photosynthesis. *Proc. Natl. Acad. Sci.* **43**, 446–451 (1957).

230. Gibbs, M., and Cynkin, M. A. The photosynthetic carbon cycle in chloroplasts. *Plant Physiol.* **33**, xviii (1958).

231. Glass, B., ed. "Symposium on Inorganic Nitrogen Metabolism." Johns Hopkins Press, Baltimore, Maryland, 1956.

232. Glover, J., Kamen, M. D., and Van Genderen, H. Studies on the metabolism of photosynthetic bacteria. XII. Comparative light and dark metabolism of acetate and carbonate by *Rhodospirillum rubrum. Arch. Biochem. Biophys.* **35**, 384–408 (1952).

233. Goedheer, J. C. Optical properties and *in vivo* orientation of photosynthetic pigments. Ph. D. Thesis, 1957.

234. Goedheer, J. C. Investigations on bacteriochlorophyll in organic solutions. *Biochim. et Biophys. Acta* **27**, 478–490 (1958).

235. Goedheer, J. C., Horreus de Haas, G. H., and Schuller, P. Oxidation-reduction potentials of different chlorophylls in methanol. *Biochim. et Biophys. Acta* **28**, 278–283 (1958).

236. Good, N., and Hill, R. Photochemical reduction of oxygen in chloroplast preparations. II. Mechanism of the reaction with oxygen. *Arch. Biochem. Biophys.* **57**, 355–366 (1955).

237. Goodwin, R. H. Fluorescent substances in plants. *Ann. Rev. Plant Physiol.* **4**, 283–324 (1953).

237a. Goodwin, T. W. "Carotenoids: Their Comparative Biochemistry." Chemical Publ., New York, 1954.

238. Gorham, P. R., and Clendenning, K. A. Storage of isolated chloroplasts without loss of photochemical activity. *Can. J. Research Sect. C* **28**, 513–524 (1950).
239. Granick, S., and Gilder, H. The structure, function and inhibitory action of porphyrins. *Science* **101**, 540 (1945).
240. Granick, S. The chloroplasts: Their structure, composition, and development. *In* "Photosynthesis in Plants" (J. Franck and W. E. Loomis, eds.), pp. 113–132. Iowa State College Press, Ames, Iowa, 1949.
241. Granick, S. Biosynthesis of chlorophyll and related pigments. *Ann. Rev. Plant Physiol.* **2**, 115–144 (1951).
242. Granick, S. The enzymatic synthesis of porphyrins from porphobilinogen. *Proc. Natl. Acad. Sci. U.S.* **39**, 1176–1188 (1953).
243. Granick, S. Metabolism of heme and chlorophyll. *In* "Chemical Pathways of Metabolism" (D. M. Greenberg, ed.), Vol. II, pp. 287–331. Academic Press, New York, 1954.
244. Granick, S. Chloroplast structure and its relation to photosynthesis. *In* "Research in Photosynthesis," pp. 459–463. Interscience, New York, 1957.
245. Griffiths, M., Sistrom, W. R., Cohen-Bazire, G., Stanier, R. Y., and Calvin, M. Function of carotenoids in photosynthesis. *Nature* **176**, 1211–1215 (1955).
246. Habermann, H. M., and Brown, A. H. Certain effects of ascorbic acid on the reduction of oxygen in chloroplast preparations. *In* "Research in Photosynthesis," pp. 257–262. Interscience, New York, 1957.
246a. Halldal, P. Pigment formation and growth in blue-green algae in crossed gradients of light intensity and temperature. *Physiol. Plantarum* **11**, 401–420 (1958).
247. Haxo, F. T., and Blinks, L. R. Photosynthetic action spectra of marine algae. *J. Gen. Physiol.* **33**, 389–422 (1950).
248. Hendley, D. D., and Conn, E. E. Enzymatic reduction and oxidation of glutathione by illuminated chloroplasts. *Arch. Biochem. Biophys.* **46**, 454–464 (1953).
249. Hendley, D. D. Endogenous fermentation in Thiorhodaceae. *J. Bacteriol.* **70**, 625–634 (1955).
250. Hendley, D. D. Transients in acid production by purple sulfur bacteria. *In* "Research in Photosynthesis," pp. 450–458. Interscience, New York, 1957.
251. Hendricks, S. B. Control of growth and reproduction by light and darkness. *Am. Scientist* **44**, 229–247 (1956).
252. Hill, R. Oxygen produced by isolated chloroplasts. *Proc. Roy. Soc.* **B127**, 192–210 (1939).
253. Hill, R., and Scarisbrick, R. Production of oxygen by illuminated chloroplasts. *Nature* **146**, 61–62 (1940).
254. Hill, R., and Scarisbrick, R. The reduction of ferric oxalate by isolated chloroplasts. *Proc. Roy. Soc.* **B129**, 238–255 (1940).
255. Hill, R. Oxidoreduction in chloroplasts. *Advances in Enzymol.* **12**, 1–40 (1951).
256. Hill, R. Reduction by chloroplasts. *Symposia Soc. Exptl. Biol.* **5**, 222–231 (1951).
257. Hill, R., and Scarisbrick, R. The haematin compounds of leaves. *New Phytologist* **50**, 98–111 (1951).
258. Hill, R., and Bhagvat, K. Cytochrome oxidase in higher plants. *New Phytologist* **50**, 112–120 (1951).
259. Hill, R., and Hartree, E. F. Hematin compounds in plants. *Ann. Rev. Plant Physiol.* **4**, 115–150 (1953).

260. Hill, R., and Whittingham, C. P. The induction phase of photosynthesis in *Chlorella* determined by a spectroscopic method. *New Phytologist* **52**, 133–148 (1953).

261. Hill, R., and Walker, D. A. Pyocyanine and phosphorylation in chloroplasts. *Plant Physiol.* **34**, 240–245 (1959).

262. Holt, A. S., and French, C. S. Isotopic analysis of the oxygen evolved by illuminated chloroplasts. *Arch. Biochem.* **19**, 429–435 (1948).

263. Holt, A. S., and French, C. S. The photochemical liberation of oxygen from water by isolated chloroplasts. *In* "Photosynthesis in Plants" (J. Franck and W. E. Loomis, eds.), pp. 277–286. Iowa State College Press, Ames, Iowa, 1949.

264. Holt, A. S. The phase test intermediate and the allomerization of chlorophyll a. *Can. J. Biochem. and Physiol.* **36**, 439–456 (1958).

265. Holzer, H. Photosynthese und Atmungskettenphosphorylierung. *Z. Naturforsch.* **6b**, 424–430 (1951).

266. Holzer, H. Chemie und Energetik der pflanzlichen Photosynthese. *Angew. Chem.* **66**, 65–75 (1954).

267. Horecker, B. L., and Smyrniotis, P. Z. Transaldolase: The formation of fructose-6-phosphate from sedoheptulose-7-phosphate. *J. Am. Chem. Soc.* **75**, 2021–2022 (1953).

268. Horecker, B. L., and Smyrniotis, P. Z. The formation of sedoheptulose phosphate from pentose phosphate. *J. Biol. Chem.* **205**, 661–682 (1953).

269. Horecker, B. L., Hurwitz, J., and Jakoby, W. B. On the mechanism of carbon dioxide fixation leading to phosphoglyceric acid. *Biochim. et Biophys. Acta* **22**, 194–195 (1956).

270. Horwitz, L. Observations on the affect of metallic mercury upon some microorganisms. *J. Cellular Comp. Physiol.* **49**, 437–454 (1957).

271. Horwitz, L. Observations on the oxyhydrogen reaction in *Scenedesmus* and its relation to respiration and photosynthesis. *Arch. Biochem. Biophys.* **66**, 23–44 (1957).

272. Horwitz, L., and Allen, F. L. Oxygen evolution and photoreduction in adapted *Scenedesmus*. *Arch. Biochem. Biophys.* **66**, 45–63 (1957).

273. Hutner, S. H. Growth requirements of the photosynthetic bacterium, *Rhodospirillum rubrum*. *Arch. Biochem.* **3**, 439–444 (1944).

274. Hutner, S. H., Provasoli, L., Schatz, A., and Haskins, C. P. Some approaches to the study of the role of metals in the metabolism of microorganisms. *Proc. Am. Phil. Soc.* **94**, 153–170 (1950).

275. Jagendorf, A. T., and Avron, M. Cofactors and rates of photosynthetic phosphorylation by spinach chloroplasts. *J. Biol. Chem.* **231**, 277–290 (1958); Inhibitors of photosynthetic phosphorylation in relation to electron and oxygen transport pathways of chloroplasts. *Arch. Biochem. Biophys.* **80**, 246–257 (1959).

276. Jakoby, W. B., Brummond, D. O., and Ochoa, S. Formation of 3-phosphoglyceric acid by carbon dioxide fixation with spinach leaf enzymes. *J. Biol. Chem.* **218**, 811–822 (1956).

277. Johnson, F. H., ed. "The Luminescence of Biological Systems." American Association for the Advancement of Science, Washington, D.C., 1955.

278. Johnston, J. A., and Brown, A. H. The effect of light on the oxygen metabolism of the photosynthetic bacterium *Rhodospirillum rubrum*. *Plant Physiol.* **29**, 177–181 (1954).

279. Kamen, M. D. Some remarks on tracer researches in photosynthesis. *In* "Photo-

synthesis in Plants" (J. Franck and W. E. Loomis, eds.), pp. 365–380. Iowa State College Press, Ames, Iowa, 1949.

280. Kamen, M. D., Ajl, S. J., Ranson, A. S., and Siegel, J. M. Non-equivalence of methyl and carboxyl groups in photometabolism of acetate by *Rhodospirillum rubrum*. *Science* **113**, 302 (1951).

281. Kamen, M. D., and Siegel, J. M. Studies on the metabolism of photosynthetic bacteria. VII. Comparative studies on the photoproduction of hydrogen by *Rhodopseudomonas gelatinosa* and *Rhodospirillum rubrum*. *J. Bacteriol.* **61**, 215–228 (1951).

282. Kamen, M. D. Discoveries in nitrogen fixation. *Sci. American* **188**, 38–42 (1953).

283. Kamen, M. D., and Vernon, L. P. Existence of haem compounds in a photosynthetic obligate anaerobe. *J. Bacteriol.* **67**, 617–618 (1954).

284. Kamen, M. D., and Vernon, L. P. Enzymatic activities affecting cytochromes in photosynthetic bacteria. *J. Biol. Chem.* **211**, 663–675 (1954).

285. Kamen, M. D., and Vernon, L. P. Studies on the metabolism of photosynthetic bacteria. XVII. Comparative studies on simultaneous photoxidations in bacterial and plant extracts. *Arch. Biochem. Biophys.* **51**, 122–138 (1954).

286. Kamen, M. D. Bacterial heme proteins. *Bacteriol. Revs.* **19**, 250–262 (1955).

287. Kamen, M. D., and Takeda, Y. A comparative study of bacterial and mammalian cytochrome *c*. *Biochim. et Biophys. Acta* **21**, 518–523 (1956).

288. Kamen, M. D. Hematin compounds in the metabolism of photosynthetic tissues. *In* "Enzymes: Units of Biological Structure and Function," pp. 483–504. Academic Press, New York, 1956.

289. Kamen, M. D. Hematin compounds in the metabolism of photosynthetic tissues. *In* "Research in Photosynthesis," pp. 149–163. Interscience, New York, 1957.

290. Kamen, M. D., and Newton, J. W. Light-induced phosphorylation in extracts of purple sulfur bacteria. *In* "Research in Photosynthesis," pp. 311–312. Interscience, New York, 1957.

291. Kamen, M. D., and Newton, J. W. Photophosphorylation by subcellular particles from *Chromatium*. *Biochim. et Biophys. Acta* **25**, 464–474 (1957).

291a. Kanazawa, T. Synchronous culture of *Chlorella* with special reference to the processes of assimilation of potassium, magnesium and iron. *Tokugawa Inst. Biol. Research, Tokyo* **VIII**, 102–107 (1958).

292. Kandler, O. Über die Beziehungen zwischen Phosphathaushalt und Photosynthese. I. Phosphatspiegelschwankungen bei *Chlorella pyrenoidosa* als Folge des Licht-Dunkel Wechsels. *Z. Naturforsch.* **5b**, 423–437 (1950).

293. Kandler, O. Über die Beziehungen zwischen Phosphathaushalt und Photosynthese. II. Gesteigerter Glucoseeinbau im Licht als Indikator einer lichtabhängigen Phosphorylierung. *Z. Naturforsch.* **9b**, 625–644 (1954).

294. Kandler, O. Über die Beziehungen zwischen Phosphathaushalt und Photosynthese. III. Hemmungsanalyse der lichtabhängigen Phosphorylierung. *Z. Naturforsch.* **10b**, 38–46 (1955).

295. Kandler, O., and Gibbs, M. Asymmetric distribution of C^{14} in the glucose phosphates formed during photosynthesis. *Plant Physiol.* **31**, 411–412 (1956).

296. Kandler, O., and Schötz, F. Untersuchungen über die photooxydative Farbstoffzerstörung und Stoffwechselhemmung bei Chlorellamutanten und panaschierten Oenotheren. *Z. Naturforsch.* **11b**, 708–718 (1956).

297. Kandler, O. Über die Beziehungen zwischen Phosphathaushalt und Photosyn-

these. IV. Zur Frage einer stöchiometrischen Beziehung zwischen CO_2 Reduktion und Phosphatumsatz. *Z. Naturforsch.* **12b**, 271–280 (1957).

297a. Kasprzyk, Z., and Calvin, M. Search for unstable CO_2 fixation products in algae using low temperature liquid scintillators. *Proc. Natl. Acad. Sci.* **45**, 952–958 (1959).

298. Katz, E. Chlorophyll fluorescence as an energy flowmeter for photosynthesis. *In* "Photosynthesis in Plants" (J. Franck and W. E. Loomis, eds.), pp. 287–292. Iowa State College Press, Ames, Iowa, 1949.

299. Kautsky, H., and Hirsch, A. Energieumwandlungen an Grenzflächen. IV. Mitt.: H. Kautsky u.A. Hirsch, Wechselwirkung zwischen angeregten Farbstoffmolekülen und Sauerstoff. *Ber.* **64**, 2677 (1931).

300. Kautsky, H. Chlorophyllfluorescenz und Kohlensäureassimilation. *Angew. Chem.* **48**, 329 (1935).

301. Kautsky, H., and Hormuth, R. Messungen der Fluoreszenzkurven lebender Blätter. *Naturwissenschaften* **24**, 650–651 (1936).

302. Kautsky, H., and Franck, U. Fluoreszenzanalyse des Lichtenergiewechsels der grünen Pflanze. *Naturwissenschaften* **35**, 43 (1948).

303. Ke, B., and Clendenning, K. A. Properties of chloroplast dispersions in the presence of detergents. *Biochim. et Biophys. Acta* **19**, 74–83 (1956).

304. Kessler, E. Role of photochemical processes in the reduction of nitrate by algae. *Nature* **176**, 1069–1070 (1955).

305. Kessler, E. On the role of manganese in the oxygen-evolving system of photosynthesis. *Arch. Biochem. Biophys.* **59**, 527–529 (1955).

306. Kessler, E. Reduction of nitrite with molecular hydrogen in algae containing hydrogenase. *Arch. Biochem. Biophys.* **62**, 241–242 (1956).

307. Kessler, E. Stoffwechselphysiologische Untersuchungen an Hydrogenase enthaltenden Grünalgen. I. Uber die Rolle des Mangans bei Photoreduktion und Photosynthese. *Planta* **49**, 435–454 (1957).

308. Kessler, E. Untersuchungen zum Problem der photochemischen Nitratreduktion in Grünalgen. *Planta* **49**, 505–523 (1957).

309. Kessler, E. Manganese as a cofactor in photosynthetic oxygen evolution. *In* "Research in Photosynthesis," pp. 243–249. Interscience, New York, 1957.

310. Kessler, E. Contributions to the problem of photochemical nitrate reduction. *In* "Research in Photosynthesis," pp. 250–256. Interscience, New York, 1957.

311. Kessler, E. Stoffwechselphysiologische Untersuchungen an Hydrogenase enthaltenden Grünalgen. II. Dunkel-Reduktion von Nitrat und Nitrit mit molekularem Wasserstoff. *Arch. Mikrobiol.* **27**, 166–181 (1957).

312. Kessler, E., Arthur, W., and Brugger, J. E. The influence of manganese and phosphate on delayed light emission, fluorescence, photoreduction and photosynthesis in algae. *Arch. Biochem. Biophys.* **71**, 326–335 (1957).

313. King, N. K., and Winfield, M. E. The assay of soluble hydrogenase. *Biochim. et Biophys. Acta* **18**, 431–432 (1955).

314. Kok, B. A critical consideration of the quantum yield of *Chlorella*-photosynthesis. *Enzymologia* **13**, 1–56 (1948).

315. Kok, B. On the interrelation of respiration and photosynthesis in green plants. *Biochim. et Biophys. Acta* **3**, 625–631 (1949).

316. Kok, B. Photo-induced interactions in metabolism of green plant cells. *Symposia Soc. Exptl. Biol.* **5**, 211–221 (1951).

316a. Kok, B. Photosynthesis in flashing light. *Biochim. et Biophys. Acta* **21**, 245–258 (1956).

317. Kok, B., and Spruit, C. J. P. High initial rates of gas-exchange in respiration and photosynthesis of *Chlorella*. *Biochim. et Biophys. Acta* **19**, 212–223 (1956).
318. Kok, B., and Businger, J. A. Kinetics of photosynthesis and photo-inhibition. *Nature* **177**, 135–136 (1956).
319. Kok, B. Light induced absorption changes in photosynthetic organisms. *Acta Botan. Neerl.* **6**, 316–336 (1957).
320. Krasnovsky, A. A. Reversible photochemical reduction of chlorophyll by ascorbic acid. *Doklady Akad. Nauk S.S.S.R.* **60**, 421 (1948).
321. Krasnovsky, A. A., Evstigneef, V. B., Brin, G. P., and Gavrilova, V. A. Isolation of phycoerythrin from red algae and its spectral and photochemical properties. *Doklady Akad. Nauk S.S.S.R.* **82**, 947 (1952); *Chem. Abstr.* **46**, 7623 (1952).
322. Krasnovsky, A. A. *et al.* Fluorescence and photochemistry of chlorophyll. (Translated by E. I. Rabinowitch.) A.E.C. Technical Information Extension, Oak Ridge, Tenn., AEC-tr-2156, pp. 1–117 (1956).
323. Kunitake, G. M., Saltman, P., and Lang, A. The products of CO_2 fixation in leaves of long- and short-day treated *Kalanchoe blossfeldiana*. *Plant Physiol.* **32**, 201–203 (1957).
324. Kursanow, A. L. Recent advances in plant physiology in the U.S.S.R. *Ann. Rev. Plant Physiol.* **7**, 407–436 (1956).
325. Larsen, H. Photosynthesis of succinic acid by *Chlorobium thiosulphatophilum*. *J. Biol. Chem.* **193**, 167–173 (1951).
326. Larsen, H., Yocum, C. S., and van Niel, C. B. On the energetics of the photosynthesis in green sulfur bacteria. *J. Gen. Physiol.* **36**, 161–171 (1952).
327. Larsen, H. On the culture and general physiology of the green sulfur bacteria. *J. Bacteriol.* **64**, 187–196 (1952).
328. Larsen, H. The photolitho-autotrophic bacteria and their energy relations. *Symposium Soc. Gen. Microbiol.* **4**, 186–201 (1954).
329. Lascelles, J. The synthesis of porphyrins and bacteriochlorophyll by cell suspensions of *Rhodopseudomonas spheroides*. *Biochem. J.* **62**, 78–93 (1956).
330. Latimer, P., and Rabinowitch, E. Selective scattering of light by pigment containing plant cells. *In* "Research in Photosynthesis," pp. 100–106. Interscience, New York, 1957; *Arch. Biochem. Biophys.* **84**, 428–441 (1959).
331. Latimer, P., Bannister, T. T., and Rabinowitch, E. The absolute quantum yields of fluorescence of photosynthetically active pigments. *In* "Research in Photosynthesis," pp. 107–112. Interscience, New York, 1957.
332. Lautsch, W., Broser, W., and Godicke, V. Versuche zur Energieübertragung. *Z. Naturforsch.* **12b**, 303–307 (1957).
332a. Lavorel, J. Induction of fluorescence in quinone poisoned *Chlorella* cells. *Plant Physiol.* **34**, 204–209 (1959).
333. Lindstrom, E. S., Burris, R. H., and Wilson, P. W. Nitrogen fixation by photosynthetic bacteria. *J. Bacteriol.* **58**, 313–316 (1949).
334. Lindstrom, E. S., and Wilson, P. W. Photosynthesis and nitrogen fixation in *Rhodospirillum rubrum*. *Bacteriol. Proc.* p. 134 (1951).
335. Linschitz, H., and Sarkanen, K. The absorption spectra and decay kinetics of the metastable states of chlorophyll A and B. *J. Am. Chem. Soc.* **80**, 4826–4832 (1958).
336. Linschitz, H., and Rennert, J. Reversible photobleaching of chlorophyll in rigid solvents. *Nature* **169**, 193–194 (1952).
337. Linschitz, H., and Abrahamson, W. Reversible spectral changes in chlorophyll

solutions, following flash illumination. *In* "Research in Photosynthesis," pp. 31–36. Interscience, New York, 1957.

338. Lipmann, F., and Kaplan, N. O. Intermediary metabolism of phosphorus compounds. *Ann. Rev. Biochem.* **18**, 267–298 (1949).
339. Lipmann, F. Enzymatic group activation and transfer. *In* "Metabolism of the Nervous System" (D. Richter, ed.), pp. 329–340. Pergamon Press, New York, 1957.
340. Livingston, R., and Franck, J. Assimilation and respiration of excised leaves at high concentrations of CO_2. *Am. J. Botany* **27**, 449–458 (1940).
341. Livingston, R. The photochemistry of chlorophyll. *In* "Photosynthesis in Plants" (J. Franck and W. E. Loomis, eds.), pp. 179–196. Iowa State College Press, Ames, Iowa, 1949.
342. Livingston, R., and Franck, J. Remarks on intra- and inter-molecular migration of excitation energy. *Revs. Modern Phys.* **21**, 505–509 (1949).
343. Livingston, R., Watson, W. F., and McArdle, J. Activation of the fluorescence of chlorophyll solutions. *J. Am. Chem. Soc.* **71**, 1542–1550 (1949).
344. Livingston, R. Activation of the fluorescence of chlorophyll solutions. *Nature* **170**, 750 (1952).
345. Livingston, R. The photochemistry of chlorophyll *in vitro*. *In* "Research in Photosynthesis," pp. 3–12. Interscience, New York, 1957.
346. Livingston, R., and Fujimori, E. Interactions of chlorophyll in its triplet state with oxygen, carotene, etc. *Nature* **180**, 1036–1038 (1957).
347. Livingston, R. Intermolecular transfer of electronic excitation. *J. Phys. Chem.* **61**, 860–864 (1957).
348. Loomis, W. E., and Lipmann, F. Reversible inhibition of the coupling between phosphorylation and oxidation. *J. Biol. Chem.* **173**, 807–808 (1948).
349. Löwenhaupt, B. Active cation transport in submerged aquatic plants. *J. Cellular Comp. Physiol.* **51**, 199–219 (1958).
350. Lumry, R., Spikes, J. D., and Eyring, H. Photosynthesis. *Ann. Rev. Plant Physiol.* **5**, 271–340 (1954).
351. Lumry, R., Wayrynen, R. E., and Spikes, J. D. The mechanism of the photochemical activity of isolated chloroplasts. II. Quantum requirements. *Arch. Biochem. Biophys.* **67**, 453–465 (1957).
352. Lumry, R., and Spikes, J. D. Chemical-kinetic studies of the Hill reaction. *In* "Research in Photosynthesis," pp. 373–391. Interscience, New York, 1957.

352a. Lundegårth, H. On oxidation of cytochrome f by light. *Physiol. Plantarum* **7**, 375–382 (1954).

353. Lynch, V. H., and French, C. S. β-Carotene, an active component of chloroplasts. *Arch. Biochem. Biophys.* **70**, 382–391 (1957).
354. Magee, J. L., DeWitt, T. F., Smith, E. C., and Daniels, F. A photocalorimeter. The quantum efficiency of photosynthesis in algae. *J. Am. Chem. Soc.* **61**, 3529–3533 (1939).
355. Manning, W. M., Stauffer, F. S., Duggar, B. M., and Daniels, F. Quantum efficiency of photosynthesis in *Chlorella*. *J. Am. Chem. Soc.* **60**, 266–274 (1938).
356. Marre, E., and Forti, G. Lack of dependence of pyridine nucleotide reduction on high-energy phosphates in chloroplasts. *Science* **126**, 976–977 (1957).
357. Mason, H. S. Mechanisms of oxygen metabolism. *Advances in Enzymol.* **19**, 79–234 (1957).

358. Massini, P. Photosynthetic phosphorylation as an explanation for induction phenomena in photosynthesis. *Acta Botan. Neerl.* **6**, 434–444 (1957).
359. Mayaudon, J., Benson, A. A., and Calvin, M. Ribulose-1,5-diphosphate from and CO_2 fixation by *Tetragonia expansa* leaves extract. *Biochim. et Biophys. Acta* **23**, 342–351 (1957).
360. Mazelis, M., and Vennesland, B. Carbon dioxide fixation into oxalacetate in higher plants. *Plant Physiol.* **32**, 591–599 (1957).
361. McAlister, E. D. Time course of photosynthesis for a higher plant. *Smithsonian Inst. Publs. Misc. Collections* **95**, 1–17 (1937).
361a. McAlister, E. D., and Myers, J. The time course of photosynthesis and fluorescence observed simultaneously. *Smithsonian Inst. Publs. Misc. Collections* **99**, 1–37 (1940); *Science* **92**, 241–243 (1940).
362. McElroy, W. D., and Glass, B., eds. "Phosphorus Metabolism," Vols. I and II. Johns Hopkins Press, Baltimore, Maryland, 1951, 1952.
363. Mehler, A. H. Studies on reactions of illuminated chloroplasts. I. Mechanism of the reduction of oxygen and other Hill reagents. *Arch. Biochem. Biophys.* **33**, 65–77 (1951).
364. Mehler, A. H. Studies on reactions of illuminated chloroplasts. II. Stimulation and inhibition of the reaction with molecular oxygen. *Arch. Biochem. Biophys.* **34**, 339–351 (1951).
365. Meister, A. Metabolism of glutamine. *Physiol. Revs.* **36**, 103–123 (1956).
366. Menke, W., and Koydl, E. Direkter Nachweis des camellaren Feinbaus der Chloroplasten. *Naturwissenschaften* **27**, 29–30 (1939).
367. Metzner, H., Metzner, B., and Calvin, M. Labile products of early carbon dioxide fixation in photosynthesis. *Arch. Biochem. Biophys.* **74**, 1–6 (1958).
368. Miller, S. L. Production of some organic compounds under possible primitive earth conditions. *J. Am. Chem. Soc.* **77**, 2351–2361 (1955).
369. Milner, H. W. The fatty acids of *Chlorella. J. Biol. Chem.* **176**, 813–817 (1948).
370. Moore, W. E., and Duggar, B. M. Quantum efficiency of photosynthesis in *Chlorella. In* "Photosynthesis in Plants" (J. Franck and W. E. Loomis, eds.), pp. 239–250. Iowa State College Press, Ames, Iowa, 1949.
371. Mortimer, D. C. Evidence for an alternate pathway in photosynthetic assimilation. *Naturwissenschaften* **45**, 116–117 (1958).
372. Moses, V., Holm-Hansen, O., and Calvin, M. Response of *Chlorella* to a deuterium environment. *Biochim. et Biophys. Acta* **28**, 62–70 (1958).
373. Mothes, K., Baatz, I., and Sagromsky, H. Die Bedeutung der Carotinoide für die Lichtausnützung bei der Photosynthese. *Planta* **30**, 290–293 (1939).
374. Muller, F. M. On the metabolism of the purple sulfur bacteria in organic media. *Arch. Mikrobiol.* **4**, 131–166 (1933).
375. Myers, J., and Burr, G. O. Photosynthesis. Some effects of light of high intensity on *Chlorella. J. Gen. Physiol.* **24**, 45–67 (1940).
376. Myers, J. The growth of *Chlorella pyrenoidosa* under various culture conditions. *Plant Physiol.* **19**, 579–589 (1944).
377. Myers, J. Culture conditions and the development of the photosynthetic mechanism. II. Influence of light intensity on cellular characteristics of *Chlorella. J. Gen. Physiol.* **29**, 419–427 (1946).
378. Myers, J. Culture conditions and the development of the photosynthetic mechanism. V. Influence of the composition of the nutrient medium. *Plant Physiol.* **22**, 590–597 (1947).

379. Myers, J., and Cramer, M. Metabolic conditions in *Chlorella*. *J. Gen. Physiol.* **32**, 103–110 (1948).
380. Myers, J. The pattern of photosynthesis in *Chlorella*. *In* "Photosynthesis in Plants" (J. Franck and W. E. Loomis, eds.), pp. 349–364. Iowa State College Press, Ames, Iowa, 1949.
381. Myers, J., and Johnston, J. Carbon and nitrogen balance of *Chlorella* during growth. *Plant Physiol.* **24**, 111–119 (1949).
382. Myers, J. Physiology of the algae. *Ann. Rev. Microbiol.* **5**, 157–180 (1951).
383. Myers, J., Phillips, J. N., and Graham, J. R. On the mass culture of algae. *Plant Physiol.* **26**, 539 (1951).
384. Myers, J. Growth and photosynthetic characteristics of *Euglena gracilis*. *Arch. Mikrobiol.* **17**, 384–402 (1952).
385. Myers, J., and Phillips, J. N. Measurement of algal growth under controlled steady-state conditions. *Plant Physiol.* **29**, 148–152 (1954); Growth rate of *Chlorella* in flashing light. *Ibid.* **29**, 152–161 (1954).
386. Myers, J. Nutrition and growth of several blue-green algae. *Am. J. Botany* **42**, 282–287 (1955).
387. Myers, J., and Kratz, W. A. Photosynthesis and respiration of three blue-green algae. *Plant Physiol.* **30**, 275–280 (1955).
388. Myers, J., and Kratz, W. A. Relations between pigment content and photosynthetic characteristics in a blue-green alga. *J. Gen. Physiol.* **39**, 11–22 (1955).
389. Myers, J., and Matsen, F. A. Kinetic characteristics of Warburg manometry. *Arch. Biochem. Biophys.* **55**, 373–388 (1955).
390. Myers, J., and Killam, A. A special effect of light on the growth of *Chlorella vulgaris*. *Am. J. Botany* **43**, 569–572 (1956).
391. Myers, J., and Graham, J. The role of photosynthesis in the physiology of *Ochromonas*. *J. Cellular Comp. Physiol.* **47**, 397–414 (1956).
392. Myers, J. Algal cultures. *In* "Encyclopedia of Chemical Technology" (R. E. Kirk and D. F. Othmer, eds.), First Supplement Vol., pp. 33–51. Interscience, New York, 1957.
393. Myers, J. On uniformity of experimental material. *In* "Research in Photosynthesis," pp. 485–489. Interscience, New York, 1957.
394. Newton, J. W., and Newton, G. A. Composition of the photoactive subcellular particles from *Chromatium*. *Arch. Biochem. Biophys.* **71**, 250–265 (1957).
395. Newton, J. W., and Kamen, M. D. *Chromatium* cytochrome. *Biochim. et Biophys. Acta* **21**, 71–80 (1956).
396. Niemann, B. H., and Vennesland, B. Cytochrome c photooxidase of spinach chloroplasts. *Science* **125**, 353–354 (1957).
397. Nishimura, M. S., and Emerson, R. The quantum requirement of photosynthesis. *In* "Photosynthesis in Plants" (J. Franck and W. E. Loomis, ed.), pp. 219–238. Iowa State College Press, Ames, Iowa, 1949.
398. Nishimura, M. S., Whittingham, C. P., and Emerson, R. The maximum efficiency of photosynthesis. *Symposia Soc. Exptl. Biol.* **5**, 176–210 (1951).
399. Novelli, G. D. The role of cell fragments in metabolic reactions. *Bacteriol. Revs.* **21**, 255–256 (1957).
399a. Oh-Hama, T., and Miyachi, S. Effects of illumination and oxygen supply upon the levels of pyridine nucleotides in *Chlorella* cells. *Biochim. et Biophys. Acta* **34**, 202–210 (1959).
400. Olson, J. M., and Chance, B. Cytochrome reactions in *Chromatium*. *Biochim. et Biophys. Acta* **28**, 227–228 (1958).

401. Olson, R. A., Brackett, F. S., and Crickard, R. G. Transients in O_2 evolution by *Chlorella* in light and darkness. I. Phenomena and methods. II. Influence of O_2 concentration and respiration. *In* "Research in Photosynthesis," pp. 412–418. Interscience, New York, 1957.
402. Oster, G., and Mark, H. The production of organic free radicals by light. *J. Opt. Soc. Am.* **43**, 283–289 (1953).
403. Osterhout, W. J. V., and Haas, A. R. C. On the dynamics of photosynthesis. *J. Gen. Physiol.* **1**, 1–7 (1918).
404. Österlind, S. The retarding effect of high concentrations of carbon dioxide and carbonate ions on the growth of a green alga. *Physiol. Plantarum* **1**, 170–175 (1948).
405. Österlind, S. Inorganic carbon sources of green algae. I. Growth experiments with *Scenedesmus quadricauda* and *Chlorella pyrenoidosa. Physiol. Plantarum* **3**, 353–360 (1950).
406. Österlind, S. Inorganic carbon sources of green algae. II. Carbonic anhydrase in *Scenedesmus quadricauda* and *Chlorella pyrenoidosa. Physiol. Plantarum* **3**, 430–434 (1950).
407. Österlind, S. Inorganic carbon sources of green algae. IV. Photoactivation of some factor necessary for bicarbonate assimilation. *Physiol. Plantarum* **4**, 514–534 (1951).
408. Österlind, S. Inhibition of respiration and nitrate absorption in green algae by enzyme poisons. *Physiol. Plantarum* **5**, 292–297 (1952).
409. Österlind, S. Inorganic carbon sources of green algae. VI. Further experiments concerning photoactivation of bicarbonate assimilation. *Physiol. Plantarum* **5**, 403–408 (1952).
410. Packer, L., and Vishniac, W. The specificity of a diphosphopyridine nucleotide-linked hydrogenase. *Biochim. et Biophys. Acta* **17**, 153–154 (1955).
411. Packer, L., and Vishniac, W. Chemosynthetic fixation of carbon dioxide and characteristics of hydrogenase in resting cell suspesions of *Hydrogenomonas Ruhlandii* Nov. Spec. *J. Bacteriol.* **70**, 216–223 (1955).
412. Petering, H. G., Duggar, B. M., and Daniels, F. Quantum efficiency of photosynthesis in *Chlorella* II. *J. Am. Chem. Soc.* **61**, 3525–3529 (1939).
413. Pirson, A. Ernährungs- und stoffwechselphysiologische Untersuchungen an *Fontinalis* und *Chlorella. Z. Botan.* **31**, 193–267 (1937).
414. Pirson, A., and Wilhelmi, G. Photosynthese-Gaswechsel und Mineralsalzer-nährung. *Z. Naturforsch.* **5b**, 211–218 (1950).
415. Pirson, A., and Döring, H. Induzierte Wachstumsperioden bei Grünalgen. *Flora (Jena)* **139**, 314–328 (1952).
416. Pirson, A., Tichy, C., and Wilhelmi, G. Stoffwechsel und Mineralsalzernährung einzelliger Grünalgen. I. Mitteilung. 1. Vergleichende Untersuchungen an Mangelkulturen von *Ankistrodesmus. Planta* **40**, 199–253 (1952).
417. Pirson, A. Functional aspects in mineral nutrition of green plants. *Ann. Rev. Plant Physiol.* **6**, 71 (1955).
418. Pirson, A. Stoffwechsel organischer Verbindungen I. (Photosynthese). *Fortschr. Botan.* **19**, 235–262 (1957).
419. Pirson, A., and Schön, W. J. Versuche zur Analyse der Stoffwechselperiodik bei *Hydrodictyon. Flora (Jena)* **144**, 447–466 (1957).
420. Pirson, A., and Kuhl, A. Uber den Phosphathaushalt von *Hydrodictyon* I. *Arch. Mikrobiol.* **30**, 211–225 (1958).

421. Pirson, A., and Kuhl, A. Dependence on light of the reversible uptake of inorganic phosphate by *Hydrodictyon*. *Nature* **181**, 921–922 (1958).

422. Pirson, A., and Lorenzen, H. Periodizität von Nuklealreaktion und Kernteilung in *Chlorella*. *Ber.* **71**, 89–97 (1958).

423. Pirson, A., and Lorenzen, H. Ein endogener Zeitfaktor bei der Teilung von *Chlorella*. *Z. Botan.* **46**, 53–66 (1958).

424. Pirson, A. Mineralstoffe und Photosynthese. *In* "Encyclopedia of Plant Physiology" (H. Ruhland, ed.), pp. 355–381. Springer, Berlin, 1958.

425. Pollack, M., Pringsheim, P., and Terwoord, D. A method for determining small quantities of oxygen. *J. Chem. Phys.* **12**, 295 (1944).

426. Pratt, R., and Trelease, S. F. Influence of deuterium oxide on photosynthesis in flashing and in continuous light. *Am. J. Botany* **25**, 133–139 (1938).

427. Pratt, R. Influence of deuterium oxide on the growth of *Chlorella vulgaris*. *Am. J. Botany* **25**, 699–701 (1938).

428. Pratt, R. Studies on *Chlorella vulgaris*. IV. Influence of the molecular proportions of KNO_3, KH_2PO_4, and $MgSO_4$, in the nutrient solution on the growth of *Chlorella*. *Am. J. Botany* **28**, 492–497 (1941).

429. Pratt, R. Studies on *Chlorella vulgaris*. VII. Influence of age of the culture on rates of photosynthesis and respiration. *Am. J. Botany* **30**, 404–408 (1943).

430. Pratt, R. Studies on *Chlorella vulgaris*. IX. Influence on growth of *Chlorella* of continuous removal of chlorellin from the culture solution. *Am. J. Botany* **31**, 418–421 (1944).

431. Pringsheim, E. G. "Pure Culture of Algae." Cambridge Univ. Press, London and New York, 1946.

432. Punnett, T. Stability of isolated chloroplast preparations and its effect on Hill reaction measurements. *Plant Physiol.* **34**, 283–289 (1959).

433. Quayle, J. R., and Keech, D. B. Carbon dioxide and formate utilization by formate grown *Pseudomonas oxalaticus*. *Biochim. et Biophys. Acta* **29**, 223–224 (1958).

434. Quayle, J. R., Fuller, R. C., Benson, A. A., and Calvin, M. Enzymatic carboxylation of ribulose diphosphate. *J. Am. Chem. Soc.* **76**, 3610–3611 (1954).

435. Rabinowitch, E. Photosynthesis. *Ann. Rev. Plant Physiol.* **3**, 229–264 (1952).

436. Rabinowitch, E. I. "Photosynthesis and Related Processes," Vol. I, Vol. II Parts 1 and 2. Interscience, New York, 1945, 1951, 1956.

437. Rabinowitch, E. I. and Latimer, P. Selective scattering of light by pigment-containing plant cells. *J. Chem. Phys.* **24**, 480 (1956).

438. Rabinowitch, E. Primary photochemical and photophysical processes in photosynthesis. *Plant Physiol.* **34**, 213–218 (1959).

439. Racker, E. Mechanism of action and properties of pyridine nucleotide linked enzymes. *Physiol. Revs.* **35**, 1–56 (1955).

440. Racker, E. Synthesis of carbohydrates from carbon dioxide and hydrogen in a cell free system. *Nature* **175**, 249–251 (1955).

441. Rackow, B. Ist die pflanzliche photo-synthese eine licht reaktion mit rückläufiger dunkelreaktion? *Planta* **51**, 575–583 (1958).

441a. Richter, G. Comparison of enzymes of sugar metabolism in two photosynthetic algae: *Anacystis nidulans* and *Chlorella pyrenoidosa*. *Naturwissenschaften* **46**, 604 (1959).

442. Rieke, F. F. On the quantum efficiency of photosynthesis. *J. Chem. Phys.* **7**, 238–244 (1939).

443. Rieke, F. F. Quantum efficiencies for photosynthesis and photoreduction in green plants. *In* "Photosynthesis in Plants" (J. Franck and W. E. Loomis, eds.), pp. 251–272. Iowa State College Press, Ames, Iowa, 1949.
444. Rosenberg, J. L. Use of a glass electrode for measuring rapid changes in photosynthetic rates. *J. Gen. Physiol.* **37**, 753–774 (1954).
445. Rosenberg, J. L. On the measurement of carbon dioxide uptake with a glass electrode. *J. Gen. Physiol.* **40**, 827–831 (1957).
446. Rosenberg, J. L. Photochemistry of chlorophyll. *Ann. Rev. Plant Physiol.* **8**, 115–136 (1957).
447. Rosenberg, J. L., Takashima, S., and Lumry, R. Spectroscopy of flash-illuminated chloroplasts. *In* "Research in Photosynthesis," pp. 85–88. Interscience, New York, 1957.
448. Rothemund, P. Chlorophyll studies. *In* "Photosynthesis in Plants" (J. Franck and W. E. Loomis, eds.), pp. 197–208. Iowa State College Press, Ames, Iowa, 1949.
449. Ruben, S. Photosynthesis and phosphorylation. *J. Am. Chem. Soc.* **65**, 279–289 (1943).
450. Sagromsky, H. Zur Chlorophyllbildung bei Aurea-Formen I and II. *Z. Naturforsch.* **11b**, 548–569 (1956).
451. San Pietro, A., and Lang, H. M. Photosynthetic pyridine nucleotide reductase. *J. Biol. Chem.* **231**, 211–229 (1958).
452. San Pietro, A., Hendricks, S. B., Giovanelli, J., and Stolzenbach, F. E. Action spectrum for triphosphopyridine nucleotide reduction by illuminated chloroplasts. *Science* **128**, 845 (1958).
453. Scardovi, V. Studi sul metabolismo delle Athiorhodaceae. Metabolismo anaerobico del glucosio in *Rhodospirillum rubrum* e *Rhodopseudomonas vannielii* in assenza di energia luminosa. *Ann. Microbiol.* **6**, 151–166 (1955).
454. Scardovi, V. Studi sul metabolismo delle Athiorhodaceae. I. Ossidazioni corrispondenti al ciclo di Krebs nel metabolismo aerobico in oscurita di *Rhodopseudomonas vannielii.* Estratto dal Fascicolo III-IV-V-Vol. VI, p. 139 (1955).
455. Scardovi, V. Studi sul metabolismo delle Athiorhodaceae. II. Metabolismo anaerobico del glucosio in *Rhodospirillum rubrum* e *Rhodopseudomonas vannielii* in assenza di energia luminosa. Estratto dal Fascicolo III-IV-V-Vol. VI, pp. 151–166 (1955).
455a. Schenck, G. O. Photochemische Reaktionen I-V. *Ann.* **584**, 125–238 (1953).
456. Schlegel, H. G. Untersuchungen über den Phosphatstoffwechsel der wasserstoffoxydierenden Bakterien. *Arch. Mikrobiol.* **21**, 127–155 (1954).
457. Schlegel, H. G. Die Beeinflussung des Phosphathaushalts von Mikrooganismen durch Kohlendioxyd. *Arch. Mikrobiol.* **23**, 195–206 (1955).
458. Schön, W. J. Periodische Schwankungen der Photosynthese und Atmung bei *Hydrodictyon. Flora (Jena)* **142**, 347–380 (1955).
459. Schwartz, M. The photochemical reduction of quinone and ferricyanide by lyophilized *Chlorella* cells. *Biochim. et Biophys. Acta* **22**, 463–470 (1956).
460. Setlik, I. Transient phenomena in photosynthesis as revealed by the production of oxygen. *Rozpravy Československ. akad. věd, Řada mat a přirod. věd* **64** (3), 60–68 (1954).
461. Shemin, D. The biosynthesis of porphyrins; the succinate-glycine cycle. *In* "Currents in Biochemical Research" (D. E. Green, ed.), pp. 518–535. Interscience, New York, 1956.

462. Shibata, K. Spectrophotometry of intact biological materials. *J. Biochem. (Tokyo)* **45**, 599–623 (1958).
463. Siegel, J. M. The metabolism of acetone by the photosynthetic bacterium *Rhodopseudomonas gelatinosa. J. Bacteriol.* **60**, 595–606 (1950).
464. Siegel, J. M., and Kamen, M. D. Comparative studies on the photoproduction by *Rhodopseudomonas gelatinosa* and *Rhodospirillum rubrum. J. Bacteriol.* **61**, 215–228 (1951).
465. Siegel, J. M. The dark anaerobic metabolism of acetone and acetate by the photosynthetic bacterium *Rhodopseudomonas gelatinosa. J. Biol. Chem.* **228**, 41–47 (1957).
466. Simonis, W. Beobachtungen zur Hemmung der Photosynthese durch Natriumfluorid bei verschiedener Lichtintensität. *Z. Naturforsch.* **4b**, 109–114 (1949).
467. Simonis, W., and Grube, K. H. Untersuchungen über den Zusammenhang von Phosphathaushalt und Photosynthese. *Z. Naturforsch.* **7b**, 194–196 (1952).
468. Simonis, W., and Grube, K. H. Weitere Untersuchungen über Phosphathaushalt und Photosynthese. *Z. Naturforsch.* **8b**, 312–317 (1953).
469. Simonis, W., and Kating, H. Untersuchungen zur lichtabhängigen Phosphorylierung I. Die Beeinflussung der lichtabhängigen Phosphorylierung von Algen durch Glucosegaben. *Z. Naturforsch.* **11b**, 165–172 (1956).
470. Simonis, W., and Fürchtbauer, W. Beobachtungen zur Photosynthetischen Phosphorylierung isolieter chloroplasten. *Planta* **54**, 95–106 (1959).
471. Sironval, C., and Kandler, O. Photoxidation processes in normal green *Chlorella* cells. I. The bleaching process. *Biochim. et Biophys. Acta* **29**, 359–368 (1958).
472. Smith, E. L. The influence of light and carbon dioxide on photosynthesis. *J. Gen. Physiol.* **20**, 807–830 (1937).
473. Smith, J. H. C. Products of photosynthesis. *In* "Photosynthesis in Plants" (J. Franck and W. E. Loomis, eds.), pp. 53–94. Iowa State College Press, Ames, Iowa, 1949.
474. Smith, J. H. C. Processes accompanying chlorophyll formation. *In* "Photosynthesis in Plants" (J. Franck and W. E. Loomis, eds.), pp. 209–218. Iowa State College Press, Ames, Iowa, 1949.
475. Smith, J. H. C., Kupke, D. W., Loeffler, J. E., Benitez, A., Ahrne, I., and Giese, A. T. The natural state of protochlorophyll. *In* "Research in Photosynthesis," pp. 464–474. Interscience, New York, 1957.
476. Smith, L., and Chance, B. Cytochromes in plants. *Ann. Rev. Plant Physiol.* **9**, 449–482 (1958).
477. Sogo, P. B., Pon, N. G., and Calvin, M. Photo spin resonance in chlorophyll-containing plant material. *Proc. Natl. Acad. Sci. U.S.* **43**, 387–393 (1957).
478. Spikes, J. D., Lumry, R., Eyring, H., and Wayrynen, R. E. Potential changes in suspensions of chloroplasts on illumination. *Arch. Biochem.* **28**, 48–67 (1950).
479. Spoehr, H. A. "Photosynthesis." Chemical Catalog Co., New York, 1926; Stiles, W. "Photosynthesis." Longmans, Green, London, 1925.
480. Spruit, C. J. P., and Kok, B. Simultaneous observation of oxygen and carbon dioxide exchange during non-steady state photosynthesis. *Biochim. et Biophys. Acta* **19**, 417–424 (1956).
480a. Stanier, R. Y., Doudoroff, M., Kunisawa, R., and Contopoulon, R. The role of organic substrates in bacterial photosynthesis. *Proc. Natl. Acad. Sci.* **45**, 1246–1260 (1959).
481. Steemann-Nielsen, E. Experimental carbon dioxide curves in photosynthesis. *Physiol. Plantarum* **5**, 145–149 (1952).

482. Steemann-Nielsen, E. On detrimental effects of high light intensities on the photosynthetic mechanism. *Physiol. Plantarum* **5**, 334–344 (1952).
483. Steemann-Nielsen, E. Carbon dioxide as carbon source and narcotic in Photosynthesis and growth of *Chlorella pyrenoidosa. Physiol. Plantarum* **8**, 317 (1955).
484. Steemann-Nielsen, E. The interaction of photosynthesis and respiration and its importance for the determination of C^{14}-discrimination in photosynthesis. *Physiol. Plantarum* **8**, 945–958 (1955).
485. Steemann-Nielsen, E., and Jensen, P. K. Concentration of carbon dioxide and rate of photosynthesis in *Chlorella pyrenoidosa. Physiol. Plantarum* **12**, 170–180 (1958).
486. Stepka, W., Benson, A. A., and Calvin, M. The path of carbon in photosynthesis. II. Amino acids. *Science* **108**, 304–306 (1948).
487. Steward, F. C., and Pollard, J. K. Nitrogen metabolism in plants: ten years in retrospect. *Ann. Rev. Plant Physiol.* **8**, 65–114 (1957).
488. Stoppani, A. O. M., Fuller, R. C., and Calvin, M. Carbon dioxide fixation by *Rhodopseudomonas capsulatus. J. Bacteriol.* **69**, 491–501 (1955).
489. Stoy, V. Riboflavin-catalyzed enzymic photoreduction of nitrate. *Biochim. et Biophys. Acta* **21**, 395–396 (1956).
490. Strain, H. H. Functions and properties of the chloroplast pigments. *In* "Photosynthesis in Plants" (J. Franck and W. E. Loomis, eds.), pp. 133–178. Iowa State College Press, Ames, Iowa, 1949.
491. Strehler, B. L. The luminescence of isolated chloroplasts. *Arch. Biochem. Biophys.* **34**, 239–248 (1951).
492. Strehler, B. L., and Arnold, W. Light production by green plants. *J. Gen. Physiol.* **34**, 809–820 (1951).
493. Strehler, B. L. Photosynthesis—energetics and phosphate metabolism. *In* "Phosphorus Metabolisms" (W. D. McElroy and B. Glass, eds.), Vol. 2, pp. 491–502. Johns Hopkins Press, Baltimore, Maryland, 1952.
494. Strehler, B. L., and Totter, J. R. Firefly luminescence in the study of energy transfer mechanisms. *Arch. Biochem. Biophys.* **40**, 28–41 (1952).
495. Strehler, B. L. Firefly luminescence in the study of energy transfer mechanisms. II. Adenosine triphosphate and photosynthesis. *Arch. Biochem. Biophys.* **43**, 67–79 (1953).
496. Strehler, B. L., and Lynch, V. H. Absorption spectrum changes in *Chlorella* and the primary process. *In* "Research in Photosynthesis," pp. 89–99. Interscience, New York, 1957.
497. Strehler, B. L. Introductory remarks on the luminescence of photosynthetic organisms. *In* "Research in Photosynthesis," pp. 118–127. Interscience, New York, 1957.
498. Strehler, B. L., and Lynch, V. H. Studies on the primary process in photosynthesis. II. Some relationships between light-induced absorption spectrum changes and chemiluminescence during photosynthesis. *Arch. Biochem. Biophys.* **70**, 527–546 (1957).
499. Suzuki, I., and Werkman, C. H. Chemoautotrophic carbon dioxide fixation by extracts of *Thiobacillus oxidans*. I. Formation of oxalacetic acid. *Arch. Biochem. Biophys.* **76**, 103–111 (1958).
500. Syrett, P. J. Respiration rate and internal adenosine triphosphate concentration in *Chlorella. Arch. Biochem. Biophys.* **75**, 117–124 (1958).
501. Takashima, S., Morita, S., and Suzuki, K. On the cause of the S-shaped rate-

light intensity-relationship in the photosynthesis of purple bacteria. *J. Biochem.* **38**, 255–262 (1951).

502. Tamiya, H. Analysis of photosynthetic mechanism by the method of intermittent illumination. *Tokugawa Inst. Biol. Research*, **VI**, 1–129 (1949).
503. Tamiya, H., Iwamura, T., Shibata, K., Hase, E., and Nihei, T. Correlation between photosynthesis and light-independent metabolism in the growth of *Chlorella*. *Biochim. et Biophys. Acta* **12**, 23–40 (1953).
504. Tamiya, H. Mass culture of algae. *Ann. Rev. Plant Physiol.* **8**, 309–334 (1957).
505. Tanada, T. The photosynthetic efficiency of carotenoid pigments in *Navicula minima*. *Am. J. Botany* **38**, 276–283 (1951).
506. Theorell, H. Heme-linked groups and modes of action of some hemo-proteins. *Advances in Enzymol.* **7**, 265–301 (1947).
507. Thimann, K. V., and Bonner, W. D. Organic acid metabolism. *Ann. Rev. Plant Physiol.* **1**, 75–108 (1950).
508. Thomas, J. B., and Nijenhuis, L. E. On the relation between phototaxis and photosynthesis in *Rhodospirillum rubrum*. *Biochim. et Biophys. Acta* **6**, 317–324 (1950).
509. Thomas, J. B., and Goedheer, J. C. Relative efficiency of light absorbed by carotenoids in photosynthesis and phototaxis of *Rhodospirillum rubrum*. *Biochim. et Biophys. Acta* **10**, 385–390 (1953).
510. Thomas, J. B. The chloroplast as the photoreceptive mechanism in photosynthesis. *In* "Conference on Solar Energy: The Scientific Basis" (E. F. Carpenter, ed.), Vol. IV. University of Arizona Press, Tucson, Arizona, 1955.
511. Thomas, J. B., and de Rover, W. On phycocyanin participation in the Hill reaction of the blue-green alga *Synechococcus cedrorum*. *Biochim. et Biophys. Acta* **16**, 391–395 (1955).
512. Thomas, J. B. Structure and function of the chloroplast. *Progr. in Biophys. and Biophys. Chem.* **5**, 109–139 (1955).
513. Thomas, J. B., Minnaert, K., and Elbers, P. F. Chlorophyll concentrations in plastids of different groups of plants. *Acta Botan. Neerl.* **5**, 315–321 (1956).
514. Thomas, J. B., Goedheer, J. C., and Komen, J. G. pH-Dependence of bacteriochlorophyll fluorescence in aqueous extracts of purple bacteria. *Biochim. et Biophys. Acta* **22**, 342–348 (1956).
515. Thomas, J. B., Minnaert, K., and Elbers, P. F. Submicroscopic structure of some chloroplasts. *Acta Botan. Neerl.* **6**, 345–350 (1957).
516. Thomas, J. B., van der Leun, A. A. J., and Koning, J. Photosynthetic activity of fragments of *Spirogyra* chloroplasts. II. Measurements with the mass spectrometer. *Biochim. et Biophys. Acta* **23**, 443–444 (1957).
517. Thomas, J. B., Haans, A. J. M., van der Leun, A. A. J., and Koning, J. Photosynthetic activity of isolated chloroplast fragments of *Spirogyra*. *Biochim. et Biophys. Acta* **25**, 453–462 (1957).

517a. Thomas, J. B., and Nuboer, J. F. W. Fluorescence induction phenomena in granular and lamellate chloroplasts. *J. Phys. Chem.* **63**, 39–44 (1959).

518. Tolbert, N. E., and Zill, L. P. Photosynthesis by protoplasm extruded from *Chara* and *Nitella*. *J. Gen. Physiol.* **37**, 575–588 (1954).
519. Tolbert, N. E., and Zill, L. P. Excretion of glycolic acid by *Chlorella* during photosynthesis. *In* "Research in Photosynthesis," pp. 228–231. Interscience, New York, 1957; *J. Biol. Chem.* **222**, 895–906 (1956).
520. Tollin, G., Fujimori, E., and Calvin, M. Delayed light emission in green plant

materials: Temperature-dependence and quantum yield. *Proc. Natl. Acad. Sci. U.S.* **44**, 1035–1046 (1958).

521. Tolmach, L. J., and Gaffron, H. Influence of triphosphopyridine nucleotide upon evolution of oxygen and fixation of carbon dioxide by illuminated chloroplasts. *Federation Proc.* **10** (1951).
522. Tolmach, L. J. The influence of triphosphopyridine nucleotide (TPN) and other physiological substances upon oxygen evolution from illuminated chloroplasts. *Arch. Biochem. Biophys.* **33**, 120–142 (1951).
523. Tolmach, L. J. Effects of triphosphopyridine nucleotide upon oxygen evolution and carbon dioxide fixation by illuminated chloroplasts. *Nature* **167**, 946–949 (1951).
524. Tonnelate, J. Mesure calorimetrique du rendement de la photosynthese. *Compt. rend.* **218**, 430–432 (1944).
525. Towers, G. H. N., and Mortimer, D. C. The role of keto acids in photosynthetic carbon dioxide assimilation. *Can. J. Biochem. and Physiol.* **34**, 511–519 (1956).

525a. Trurnit, H. J., and Colmano, G. Absorption spectra of chlorophyll monolayers at liquid interfaces. *Biochim. et Biophys. Acta* **31**, 434–447 (1959).

526. Tsukamoto, A. On the oxidation of fatty acids by purple bacteria. *Botan. Mag. (Tokyo)* **62**, 159–167 (1949).
527. Umbreit, W. W., Burris, R. H., and Stauffer, J. F. "Manometric Techniques and Tissue Metabolism." Burgess Publ., Minneapolis, Minnesota, 1951.
528. Urey, H. C. "The Planets." Yale Univ. Press, New Haven, Connecticut, 1952.
529. Uri, N. A new approach to photosynthesis *in vitro. J. Chem. Phys.* **20**, 348 (1952).
530. Uri, N. Chlorophyll photosensitized polymerization and free radical intermediates in photosynthesis. *J. Am. Chem. Soc.* **74**, 5808 (1952).
531. Uri, N. Free radical intermediates in photosynthesis. *Biochim. et Biophys. Acta* **18**, 209–215 (1955).
532. Utter, M. F., and Wood, H. G. Mechanisms of fixation of carbon dioxide by heterotrophs and autotrophs. *Advances in Enzymol.* **12**, 41–152 (1951).
533. van Baalen, C., Forrest, H. S., and Myers, J. Incorporation of radioactive carbon into a pteridine of a blue-green alga. *Proc. Natl. Acad. Sci. U.S.* **43**, 701–705 (1957).
534. van de Hulst, H. C. "Light Scattering by Small Particles." Wiley, New York, 1957.
535. van der Veen, R. Induction phenomena in photosynthesis. I. *Physiol. Plantarum* **2**, 217–234 (1949).
536. van der Veen, R. Induction phenomena in photosynthesis. II. *Physiol. Plantarum* **2**, 287–296 (1949).
537. van Niel, C. B. Photosynthesis of bacteria. *In* "Contributions to Marine Biology," pp. 161–169. Stanford Univ. Press, Stanford, California, 1929.
538. van Niel, C. B. On the morphology and physiology of the purple and green sulphur bacteria. *Arch. Mikrobiol.* **3**, 1–112 (1931).

538a. van Niel, C. B. On the metabolism of the Thiorhodaceae. *Arch. Mikrobiol.* **7**, 323–358 (1936).

539. van Niel, C. B. The bacterial photosyntheses and their importance for the general problem of photosynthesis. *Advances in Enzymol.* **1**, 263–328 (1941).
540. van Niel, C. B., Thomas, J. O., Ruben, S., and Kamen, M. D. Radioactive car-

bon as an indicator of carbon dioxide utilization. IX. The assimilation of carbon dioxide by protozoa. *Proc. Natl. Acad. Sci. U.S.* **28,** 157–161 (1942).
541. van Niel, C. B. The culture, general physiology, morphology and classification of the non-sulfur purple and brown bacteria. *Bacteriol. Revs.* **8,** 1–118 (1944)
542. van Niel, C. B. The comparative biochemistry of photosynthesis. *In* "Photosynthesis in Plants" (J. Franck and W. E. Loomis, eds.), pp. 437–496. Iowa State College Press, Ames, Iowa, 1949.
543. van Niel, C. B. Bacterial photosyntheses. *In* "The Enzymes" (J. B. Sumner and K. Myrback, eds.), Vol. 2, Part 2, pp. 1074–1080. Academic Press, New York 1952.
544. Vatter, A. E., and Wolfe, R. S. The structure of photosynthetic bacteria. *J. Bacteriol.* **75,** 480–488 (1958).
545. Vennesland, B., and Felsher, R. Z. Oxalacetic and pyruvic carboxylases in some dicotyledonous plants. *Arch. Biochem.* **2,** 279–306 (1946).
546. Vennesland, B. Carbohydrate metabolism. *Ann. Rev. Biochem.* **17,** 227–25? (1948).
547. Vennesland, B., and Ceithaml, J. The synthesis of tricarboxylic acids by carbon dioxide fixation in parsley root preparations. *J. Biol. Chem.* **178,** 133–14? (1949).
548. Vennesland, B., and Conn, E. E. Carboxylating enzymes in plants. *Ann. Rev. Plant Physiol.* **3,** 307–332 (1952). See also refs. 45 and 396.
549. Vernon, L. P., and Kamen, M. D. Studies on the metabolism of photosynthetic bacteria. XV. Photoautoxidation of ferrocytochrome c in extracts of *Rhodospirillum rubrum. Arch. Biochem. Biophys.* **44,** 298–311 (1953).
550. Vernon, L. P., and Kamen, M. D. Hematin compounds in photosynthetic bacteria. *J. Biol. Chem.* **211,** 643–662 (1954).
551. Vernon, L. P. Photoreduction of pyridine nucleotides by cell-free extracts and chromatophores of *Rhodospirillum rubrum. J. Biol. Chem.* **233,** 212–216 (1958)
552. Vishniac, W., and Ochoa, S. Photochemical reduction of pyridine nucleotides by spinach grana and coupled carbon dioxide fixation. *Nature* **167,** 768 (1951).
553. Vishniac, W., and Ochoa, S. Phosphorylation coupled to photochemical reduction of pyridine nucleotides by isolated chloroplasts. *J. Biol. Chem.* **198,** 501–506 (1952).
554. Vishniac, W., and Ochoa, S. Reduction of pyridine nucleotides in photosynthesis. *In* "Phosphorus Metabolism" (W. D. McElroy and B. Glass, eds.), Vol. 2 p. 467. Johns Hopkins Press, Baltimore, Maryland, 1952.
555. Vishniac, W. Biochemical aspects of photosynthesis. *Ann. Rev. Plant Physiol.* **6,** 115–134 (1955).
556. Vishniac, W., and Reazin, G. H. Photoreduction in *Ochromonas malhamensis. In* "Research in Photosynthesis," pp. 239–242. Interscience, New York, 1957.
557. Vishniac, W., Horecker, B. L., and Ochoa, S. Enzymic aspects of photosynthesis. *Advances in Enzymol.* **19,** 1–78 (1957).
558. Vorobiova, L. M., and Krasnovsky, A. A. Transformation of a photochemical active form of chlorophyll in sugar beet leaves. *Biokhimiya* (Transl.) **21,** 123 (1956).
559. Walker, D. A., and Brown, J. M. S. Effects of carbon dioxide concentration on phosphoenolpyruvate carboxylase activity. *Biochem. J.* **67,** 79–83 (1957).
560. Warburg, O. Über die Geschwindigkeit der photochemischen Kohlensäurezersetzung in lebenden Zellen. *Biochem. Z.* **100,** 230–262 (1919).
561. Warburg, O. Über die Geschwindigkeit der photochemischen Kohlensäurezersetzung in lebenden Zellen. II. *Biochem. Z.* **103,** 188–202 (1920).

62. Warburg, O. and Negelein, E. Über die Reduktion der Salpetersäure in grünen Zellen. *Biochem. Z.* **110**, 66–113 (1920).
63. Warburg, O., and Negelein, E. Über den Energieumsatz bei der Kohlensäureassimilation. *Z. physik. Chem.* (*Leipzig*) **102**, 235–266 (1922).
64. Warburg, O., and Negelein, E. Über den Einfluss der Wellenlänge auf den Energieumsatz bei der Kohlensäureassimilation. *Z. physik. Chem.* (*Leipzig*) **106**, 191–226 (1923).
65. Warburg, O., Tsunao, V., and Uyesugi, T. Über die Blackmansche Reaktion. *Biochem. Z.* **146**, 486–492 (1924).
66. Warburg, O. Versuche über die Assimilation der Kohlensäure. *Biochem. Z.* **166**, 386–406 (1925).
67. Warburg, O., and Lüttgens, W. Photochemische Reduktion des Chinons in grünen Zellen und Granula. *Biokhimiya* **11**, 303 (1946).
68. Warburg, O. Photochemische Reduktion von Chinon in grünen Zellen und Granula. *In* "Schwermetalle als Wirkungsgruppen von Fermenten," p. 170. Springer, Berlin, 1946.
69. Warburg, O. Assimilation quotient and photochemical yield. *Am. J. Botany* **35**, 194–204 (1948).
70. Warburg, O., Burk, D., Schocken, V., and Hendricks, S. B. The quantum efficiency of photosynthesis. *Biochim. et Biophys. Acta* **4**, 335–346 (1950).
71. Warburg, O., and Burk, D. The maximum efficiency of photosynthesis. *Arch. Biochem.* **25**, 410–443 (1950).
72. Warburg, O., and Geleick, H. Über den Gewinn im Kreisprozess der Photosynthese. *Z. Naturforsch.* **6b**, 134–141 (1951).
73. Warburg, O., Geleick, H., and Briese, K. Weitere Steigerung des Energiegewinns im Kreisprozess der Photosynthese. *Z. Naturforsch.* **6b**, 285–292 (1951).
74. Warburg, O., Burk, D., and Schade, A. L. Extensions of photosynthetic experimentation. *Symposia Soc. Exptl. Biol.* **5**, 306–312 (1951).
75. Warburg, O., Geleick, H., and Briese, K. Über die Messung der Photosynthese in Carbonat-Bicarbonat-Gemischen. *Z. Naturforsch.* **7b**, 141–144 (1952).
76. Warburg, O., and Krippahl, G. Über die funktionelle Carboxylgruppe des Chlorophylls. *Z. Naturforsch.* **11b**, 179–180 (1956).
77. Warburg, O., and Krippahl, G. Über die funktionelle Kohlensäure der *Chlorella. Z. Naturforsch.* **11b**, 718–726 (1956).
78. Warburg, O., Schröder, W., Krippahl, G., and Klotzsch, H. Photosynthese. *Angew. Chem.* **69**, 627 (1957); *Science* **128**, 68–73 (1958).
79. Warburg, O., and Schröder, W. Quantenbedarf der Photosynthese. *Z. Naturforsch.* **12b**, 716–722 (1957).
80. Wassink, E. C., Vermeulen, D., Reman, G. H., and Katz, E. On the relation between fluorescence and assimilation in photosynthesizing cells. *Enzymologia* **5**, 100–109 (1938).
81. Wassink, E. C. On the ratio between the uptake of carbon dioxide and of the hydrogen donor in purple sulphur bacteria. *Enzymologia* **10**, 257–268 (1942).
82. Wassink, E. C., Katz, E., and Dorrestein, R. On photosynthesis and fluorescence of bacteriochlorophyll in Thiorhodaceae *Enzymologia* **10**, 285–354 (1942).
83. Wassink, E. C., Tjia, J. E., and Wintermans, J. F. G. M. Phosphate exchanges in purple sulfur bacteria in connection with photosynthesis. *Proc. Koninkl. Ned. Akad. Wetenschap.* **52**, 412–422 (1949); Wassink, E. C., and Kersten, J. A. H. Observations sur le Spectre d'Absorption et sur le Role des Carotenoides dans la Photosynthese des Diatomees. *Enzymologia* **12**, 3–32 (1946).
84. Wassink, E. C., Wintermans, J. F. G. M., and Tjia, J. E. Phosphate exchanges

in *Chlorella* in relation to conditions for photosynthesis. *Proc. Koninkl. Ned Akad. Wetenschap.* **C54,** 41–52 (1951).

585. Wassink, E. C., Wintermans, J. F. G. M., and Tjia, J. E. The influence of glucose on the changes in TCA-soluble phosphates in *Chlorella* suspensions in relation to conditions of photosynthesis. *Proc. Koninkl. Ned. Akad. Wetenschap* **C54,** 496–502 (1951).
586. Wassink, E. C., and Rombach, J. Preliminary report on experiments dealing with phosphate metabolism in the induction phase of photosynthesis in *Chlorella. Proc. Koninkl. Ned. Akad. Wetenschap.* **C57,** 493–497 (1954).
587. Wassink, E. C., and Spruit, C. J. P. The simultaneous observation of oxidation-reduction potentials and chlorophyll fluorescence of *Chlorella* suspensions. *Biochim. et Biophys. Acta* **15,** 357–366 (1954).
588. Wassink, E. C., and Spruit, C. J. P. A comparison of various phenomena connected with photosynthesis (fluorescence, redox potentials, phosphate exchanges gas exchange and others) with special reference to induction effects in *Chlorella. 8th Congr. intern. botan., Paris,* pp. 3–8 (1954).
589. Wassink, E. C. Phosphate in the photosynthetic cycle in *Chlorella. In* "Research in Photosynthesis," pp. 333–339. Interscience, New York, 1957.
590. Waygood, E. R., and Clendenning, K. A. Carbonic anhydrase in green plants *Can. J. Research* **28,** 673–689 (1950).
591. Weinman, E. O., Strisower, E. H., and Chaikoff, J. L. Conversion of fatty acids to carbohydrates. *Physiol. Revs.* **37,** 252–272 (1957).
592. Wessels, J. S. C. A possible function of vitamin K in photosynthesis. *Rec trav. chim.* **73,** 529–536 (1954).
593. Wessels, J. S. C., and Van der Veen, R. The action of some derivatives of phenylurethane and of 3-phenyl-1,1-dimethylurea on the Hill reaction. *Biochim. et Biophys. Acta* **19,** 548–549 (1956).
594. Wessels, J. S. C. Studies on photosynthetic phosphorylation. I. Photosynthetic phosphorylation under anaerobic conditions. *Biochim. et Biophys. Acta* **25,** 97–100 (1957); II. Photosynthetic phosphorylation under aerobic conditions *Biochim. et Biophys. Acta* **29,** 113–122 (1958).
595. Wessels, J. S. C. Relation between photosynthetic phosphorylation and reduction of triphosphopyridin nucleotide by chloroplasts. *Biochim. et Biophys. Acta* **35** 53–64 (1959).
596. Whatley, F. R. Coenzymes in plants. *New Phytologist* **50,** 244–257 (1951).
597. Whatley, F. R., Allen, M. B., and Arnon, D. I. Photosynthetic phosphorylation by isolated spinach chloroplasts. *In* "Research in Photosynthesis," pp. 340–348 Interscience, New York, 1957.
598. Whatley, F. R., Allen, M. B., Trebst, A. V., and Arnon, D. I. Photosynthesis by isolated chloroplasts from different plants. *Plant Physiol.* **33** (Suppl.), p. 2[illegible] (1958).
599. Whittingham, C. P. The chemical mechanism of photosynthesis. *Botan. Rev* **18,** 245–290 (1952); Chloroplast structure and energy conversion. *Progr. in Biophys. and Biophys. Chem.* **7,** 319–340 (1957).
600. Whittingham, C. P. Rate of photosynthesis and concentration of carbon dioxide in "*Chlorella.*" *Nature* **170,** 1017 (1952).
601. Whittingham, C. P. Some features of the chloroplast reaction. *In* "Research in Photosynthesis," pp. 263–273. Interscience, New York, 1957.
602. Whittingham, C. P. Induction phenomena in photosynthetic algae at low partial pressures of oxygen. *In* "Research in Photosynthesis," pp. 409–411. Interscience, New York, 1957.

603. Willstätter, R., and Stoll, A. "Untersuchungen über Chlorophyll. Springer, Berlin, 1913. (American ed., 1928.)
604. Willstätter, R., and Stoll, A. "Untersuchungen über die Assimilation der Kohlensäure." Springer, Berlin, 1918.
605. Wilson, P. W. The comparative biochemistry of nitrogen fixation. *Advances in Enzymol.* **13,** 345 (1952).
606. Winogradsky, S. Über Schwefelbakterien. *Botan. Ztg.* **45,** 489 (1887).
607. Wintermans, J. F. G. M., and Tjia, J. E. Some observations on the properties of phosphate compounds in *Chlorella* in relation to conditions for photosynthesis. *Proc. Koninkl. Ned. Akad. Wetenschap.* **C55,** 34–39 (1952).
608. Wintermans, J. F. G. M. On the formation of polyphosphates in *Chlorella* in relation to conditions for photosynthesis. *Proc. Koninkl. Ned. Akad. Wetenschap.* **C57,** 574–583 (1954).
609. Wintermans, J. F. G. M. Polyphosphate formation in *Chlorella* in relation to photosynthesis. *Mededel. Landbouwhogeschool Wageningen* **55,** 69–126 (1955).
610. Witsch, H. von. Physiologischer Zustand und Wachstumsintensität bei *Chlorella. Arch. Mikrobiol.* **14,** 128–141 (1948).
611. Witt, H. T. Kurzzeitige Absorptionsänderungen beim Primärprozess der Photosynthese. *Naturwissenschaften* **42,** 72–73 (1955).
612. Witt, H. T., Moraw, R., and Müller, A. Zum Primärprozess der Photosynthese an Chlorophyllkörnern auserhalb der pflanzlichen Zelle. *Z. Elektrochem.* **60,** 1148 (1956).
613. Witt, H. T. Reaction patterns in the primary process of photosynthesis. *In* "Research in Photosynthesis," pp. 75–84. Interscience, New York, 1957.
614. Witt, H. T. Moraw, R., and Müller, A. Neue Absorptionsänderungen beim Primärprozess der Photosynthese. *Z. physik. Chem.* (*Frankfurt*) [N. F.] **14** (1/2), 127–129 (1958).
615. Wohl, K. Zur Theorie der Assimilation. *Z. physik. Chem. Abt. B* **37,** 105–147, 169–230 (1937).
616. Wolken, J. J., and Mellon, A. D. Light and heat in the bleaching of chloroplasts in *Euglena. Biochim. et Biophys. Acta* **25,** 267–274 (1957).
617. Wood, H. G., and Werkman, C. H. The utilization of CO_2 by the propionic acid bacteria in the dissimilation of glycerol. *J. Bacteriol.* **30,** 332 (1935).
618. Wood, H. G., and Werkman, C. H. The utilization of CO_2 in the dissimilation of glycerol by the propionic acid bacteria. *Biochem. J.* **30,** 48–53; 618–623 (1936).
619. Wood, H. G., and Werkman, C. H. The fixation of CO_2 by cell suspensions of *Propionibacterium pentosaceum. Biochem. J.* **34,** 7–14; 129–138 (1940).
620. Wood, H. G., Vennesland, B., and Evans, E. A. The mechanism of carbon dioxide fixation by cell-free extracts of pigeon liver: Distribution of labeled carbon dioxide in the products. *J. Biol. Chem.* **159,** 153–158 (1945).
621. Wood, H. G. The fixation of carbon dioxide and the inter-relationships of the tricarboxylic acid cycle. *Physiol. Revs.* **26,** 198 (1946).
622. Woods, D. D. Hydrogenlyases. IV. The synthesis of formic acid by bacteria. *Biochem. J.* **30,** 515 (1936).
623. Yabuseo, M. Über den Temperaturkoeffizienten der Kohlensäureassimilation. *Biochem. J.* **152,** 493–498 (1924).
624. Yocum, C. S., and Blinks, L. R. Light induced efficiency and pigment alterations in red algae. *J. Gen. Physiol.* **41,** 1113–1119 (1958).

CHAPTER FIVE

Chemosynthesis: The Energy Relations of Chemoautotrophic Organisms

MARTIN GIBBS AND JEROME A. SCHIFF

I. Introduction

At the present time, it is hard to conceive of the discussion of any fundamental property of life without reference to microorganisms. This has come about through the work of a distinguished succession which includes such honored names as Louis Pasteur, Th. W. Engelmann, M. W. Beijerinck, S. Winogradsky, and in more recent times A. J. Kluyver and C. B. Van Niel. In fact, much general information along these lines can be found in the summary lectures of Kluyver and Van Niel (35a) which were printed under the title of "The Microbe's Contribution to Biology" (1956). It is, however, in the general context of the ways in which metabolism negotiates energy changes in cells that the diversity in the physiology, nutrition, and metabolism of microorganisms has been particularly helpful. In this chapter, attention will be turned to some examples of this sort.

Nutritional observations extending back to the nineteenth century have revealed the existence of various chemosynthetic bacterial forms which are capable of deriving all of their energy requirements from the oxidation of inorganic compounds. Parallel studies on a wide variety of photosynthetic forms have brought energy relations and metabolism to the stage where it is now possible to speculate on the basic similarities of photosynthesis and chemosynthesis.

Nutritional observations of many animals, plants, and microorganisms have also revealed major differences in the assimilation of inorganic substances into the architecture of cells. The fact that plants and microorganisms utilize highly oxidized forms of nitrogen and sulfur to build structures such as proteins and nucleic acids which contain the reduced forms of these elements has prompted investigations into the metabolic mechanisms of reduction of inorganic compounds. Again, there are metabolic parallels to be drawn between the chemosynthetic oxidation-reduction reactions of inorganic compounds and the corresponding reactions in assimilation.

Although observations on the metabolism of autotrophic organisms are appearing at an encouraging and increasing rate, there are not enough data as yet to make a complete picture for any one process or organism. We are still largely dependent on nutritional observations and on "balance sheets" between what an organism takes up and what it releases into the environment. Since the validity of hypotheses for the metabolic sequences which intervene between import and export may often be judged on thermodynamic grounds, let us begin with a discussion of the application of thermodynamic principles to biological systems.

II. Thermodynamic Considerations

A. GENERAL ASPECTS

In their classical review of 1927 Baas-Becking and Parks (3) noted that with the advent of fairly reliable thermodynamic data for biologically important substances, the need for a "Maxwell's demon" in living systems disappeared. Knowledge which has been accumulated from studies of intermediary metabolism has been thoroughly consistent with the methods of analysis employed by students of thermodynamics. Some fundamental thermodynamic concepts which are of importance for this review will now be considered.

The capacity of a system to do chemical work is measured by the difference (ΔF) between the free energies of the reactants and the products. The value for the change in heat of a reaction (ΔH) contains within it a certain amount of energy ($T\Delta S$) which is unavailable for chemical work. The relationship between ΔH and ΔF is:

$$\Delta F = \Delta H - T\Delta S \tag{1}$$

where ΔS is the entropy change and T is the absolute temperature. The value of ΔF may be used to predict whether a reaction will proceed without an uptake of energy, given the proper conditions for the reaction to take place (see the discussion of energy of activation which follows). Reactions which will proceed spontaneously (given the proper conditions) occur with a net release of free energy and are called exergonic reactions (they are assigned, by convention, a negative sign ($-\Delta F$)). Reactions which require a net increase of free energy in order to proceed are called endergonic reactions and receive a positive sign ($+\Delta F$). The value of ΔF for a reaction only indicates whether the reaction is thermodynamically possible, but it does not determine

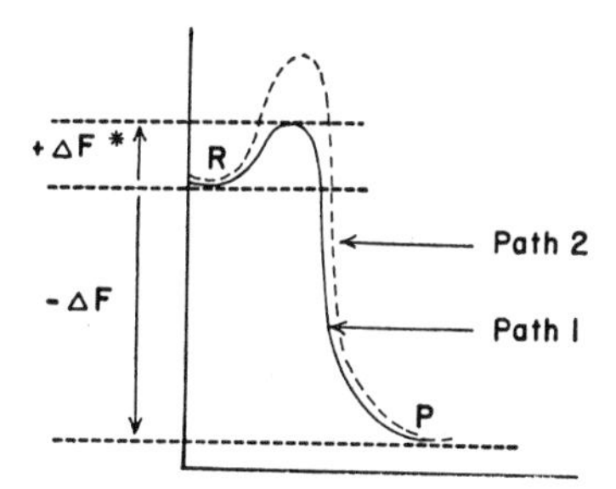

FIG. 1. Hypothetical path for an enzymatic reaction.

whether the reaction will actually proceed under a given set of conditions. The reason for this may be seen from the pictorial representation in Fig. 1.

Although there is a net negative difference in free energy ($-\Delta F$) in passing from reactants (R) to products (P) for this reaction, the reaction will not take place until an amount of energy (ΔF^*) is invested to overcome the barrier of activation energy. This is a fairly common situation. A piece of coal may exist for millions of years without reacting with oxygen to yield the energy which it contains because a certain amount of heat energy must be invested to raise the coal to the kindling temperature before the carbon and oxygen will react with the release of energy as heat. If it were not for the barrier of activation energy, we would have only one stable compound for each combination of elements since as soon as a compound was formed which could react with a release of free energy, it would do so to form the most stable configuration to minimum free energy.

The activation energy depends upon the path which the reaction takes, as may be seen from the diagram in which two paths with different activation energies are indicated. Note, however, that the net difference in free energy between the initial and final states is independent of the path of the reaction. This is the great utility of free energy calculations. Since the net free-energy change is dependent only on initial and final states, one may predict whether a reaction is possible, or not, without knowing the mechanism that intervenes. When we make these calculations for biological systems, we usually know that a reaction has occurred, i.e., we can measure the compounds which disappear as they are utilized and those which appear as products. We may calculate the free-energy change which occurred without knowing the reactions which occur in-between. For example, a cell utilizes a mole of glucose and converts it to carbon dioxide and water. Since we know that the reaction occurred, we know the cell has some means of overcoming the activation energy barrier and we may calculate the free-energy change which occurred from the differences in free energy between glucose and water plus carbon dioxide.

If one reflects on the reactions of living cells, a limitation to the use of the expressions described above presents itself. The free-energy difference between initial and final states is appropriate only for equilibrium reactions. For a single isolated reaction, the system will reach a certain equilibrium concentration of reactants and products and the standard free-energy change, designated as ΔF° and defined more fully in Section II,B will be given by the expression:

$$\Delta F^{\circ} = -RT \ln K \qquad (2)$$

where R is the gas constant (1.987 calories per degree per mole), T is the absolute temperature, and ln denotes the natural logarithm. Since catalysts, such as enzymes, do not affect the position of equilibrium but merely the rate at which equilibrium is reached, the over-all free-energy change of the system will not be changed by enzymatic catalysis. The reactions within the cell, however, are not usually isolated one from the other, but are generally members of chains of reactions in which the products of one reaction become the reactants of the next:

$$\rightarrow A \xrightarrow{1} B \xrightarrow{2} C \xrightarrow{3} D \xrightarrow{4}$$

The pools of compounds A, B, C, D, etc., are members of a system in a "steady state;" their concentrations do not change with time since when a molecule of A is converted into B, a molecule of B is converted into C, etc. The size of these "pools" of compounds in the steady state is determined by the rates of reactions 1, 2, 3, 4, etc., and not by their equilibrium concentrations as isolated reactions. Since the rates of the reactions are dependent on their activation energies rather than on the over-all difference of free energy between each reactant and its product, one cannot predict the pool size from the difference in free energies. One should be wary, therefore, of predicting the concentration of compounds within the cell from their behavior in equilibrium reactions in the test tube. The free-energy calculations between initial and final states are only approximate since the actual concentration of reactants within the cell generally is not known.

B. THE MEASUREMENT OF FREE-ENERGY CHANGES

The standard free energy of formation of a substance ($\Delta F_f°$), often simply called the "free energy," refers to its formation from the elements which compose it. The free energies of all elements and of H^+ are conventionally taken to be zero when they are in the standard state, i.e., the most common stable form of the element at 25°C, 1 molal for solutes and 1 atmosphere (atm) for gases.

The free-energy change of a reaction is a function of the concentration of the reactants. The convention has been established that free-energy values are recalculated with reference to substances under specified conditions, these being 1 molal for solutes and 1 atmosphere for gases at a temperature of 25°C. When the reactants are present at these concentrations, the maximum useful work obtainable from the system is called the standard free-energy change and is designated by $\Delta F°$ in place of the more general term ΔF. The standard free-energy change is related to the concentration of the reactants and products by

$$\Delta F° = -RT \ln K = -RT \ln \frac{\text{(products)}}{\text{(reactants)}} \qquad (3)$$

where R is the gas constant (1.987 calories per degree per mole), T is the absolute temperature, and ln denotes the natural logarithm. K is the equilibrium constant, i.e., the ratio of the concentrations of the products and reactants at equilibrium.

If the reactants are not in the standard state, concentration corrections must be employed. The expression which relates the change in free energy (ΔF) and the equilibrium constant under unspecified conditions is:

$$\Delta F = \Delta F° + RT \ln \frac{\text{(products)}}{\text{(reactants)}} \qquad (4)$$

Some investigators (12) have defined the free-energy change in terms of conditions more likely to prevail in living organisms and have introduced ΔF^s, the specific free-energy change. This is the free-energy change when the solvent is unit activity, CO_2 and O_2 are at partial pressures of 0.05 and 0.2 atm in the gaseous state, the pH is 7.5, and other solutes have concentrations of 0.01 *M*.

Corrections to these conditions from the standard state, however, would not greatly affect the free-energy values of the reactions to be discussed. To make CO_2 0.05 atm would increase the energy required for reduction by $\Delta F° = -4.575\ T\ \log K = 1.365 \times 0.3 = 0.41$ kcal per mole. Using 0.0003 atm, the concentration ordinarily present in air, would increase the value by 4.8 kcal per mole. If the partial pressure of O_2 is 0.2 atm in place of 1 atm, the energy yield from the oxidations would decrease by 0.96 kcal per mole. Taking N_2 at 0.8 atm would decrease the energy yield during its oxidation by 0.1 kcal per mole. It is obvious that the term ΔF^s is still only an approximation of the actual conditions within the cell, and the reader should recognize this as one of the many limitations of the application of thermochemical data to living systems. For a more thorough discussion see Fruton and Simmonds (22).

When the standard free energies of formation ($\Delta F_f°$) are available, the free energy change during a reaction is merely:

$$\Delta F° = \Delta F_f° \text{ (products)} - \Delta F_f° \text{ (reactants)} \qquad (5)$$

For reactions whose equilibrium positions are close enough to unity to permit a precise measurement of the concentrations of reactants and products, the value of the free energy change can be calculated from the equilibrium constant using equation (3). Equation (1) may be used when the entropy change is known from other data.

In reactions involving oxidation and reduction, it is frequently more convenient to calculate the free-energy change from the relationship:

$$\Delta F° = -nF\Delta E_0 \qquad (6)$$

where n is the number of electrons transferred in the reaction, F is the faraday (equal to 23,063 calories per volt equivalent), and ΔE_0 is the potential difference in volts across which the electrons are transferred.

The term ΔE_0 refers to the potential difference between two oxidation-reduction systems at pH 0. Since in the consideration of biological reactions, it has become customary to compare the oxidation-reduction potentials at the more physiological pH of 7, the term ΔE_0 has been replaced by $\Delta E_0'$. The standard free-energy change is given by the term $-nF\Delta E_0'$ and is usually given the symbol $\Delta F'$. The latter term is defined as the free-energy change for a reaction in which all reactants except the hydrogen ion are in their standard states (13).

C. THERMODYNAMIC DATA TO BE USED

The free energies of some of the pertinent reactions of nitrogen and sulfur have been compiled and tabulated in Tables I and II. The spread of the values will be noted. The reasons for the discrepancies in values for the same reaction have several explanations. Many workers in calculating these values have used various sources for thermochemical

TABLE I
FREE ENERGIES OF REACTIONS OF NITROGEN

Reaction	ΔF (kcal per mole of nitrogen)	Methods of calcu-lation	Source
Oxidation of nitrogen by oxygen			
1. $NH_4^+ + 0.5\ O_2 \rightarrow NH_2OH + H^+$	−0.70	E_0'	(38)[a]
2. $NH_2OH + O_2 \rightarrow NO_2^- + H_2O + H^+$	−83.3	3–1	(38)
3. $NH_4^+ + 1.5\ O_2 \rightarrow NO_2^- + H_2O + 2\ H^+$	−84.0	$\Delta F_f°$	(38)
	−75.5	—	(22)
	−66.5	K	(3)
	−73.5	—	(48)
	−65.2	—	(28)
4. $NO_2^- + 0.5\ O_2 \rightarrow NO_3^-$	−17.8	$\Delta F_f°$	(38)
	−17.5	—	(3)
	−18.0	—	(28)
	−20.0	—	(22)
	−24.0	—	(48)
Oxidation of nitrogen by pyridine nucleotides			
5. $NH_4^+ + OH^- + PN^+ \rightarrow NH_2OH + PNH + H^+$	+47.0	E_0'	(45)
6. $NH_2OH + H_2O + 2\ PN^+ \rightarrow NO_2^- + 2\ PNH + 3\ H^+$	+110.0	E_0'	(38)
7. $NH_4^+ + OH^- + 3\ PN^+ \rightarrow NO_2^- + 3\ PNH + 4\ H^+$	+173.0	E_0'	(38)
8. $NO_2^- + H_2O + PN^+ \rightarrow NO_3^- + PNH + H^+$	+38.0	E_0'	(45)
	+38.0	E_0'	(38)

[a] Calculation by Gibbs and Schiff from data in source indicated.

data, generally without quoting the original source. In addition, the free energies have been calculated using different sets of conditions such as concentration of reactants, referring the free energies to different reacting species, and assuming different pH values. Perhaps another cause for the spread of values is the basis of calculation. Since free energies may be calculated from free energies of formation, oxidation-reduction data, or equilibrium data and since each of these methods present their own experimental difficulties and errors, there may be discrepancies in the free energy values for the same reaction.

Unfortunately, most authors have not stated the method by which they have carried out their calculations.

It is evident that investigators applying thermodynamics to biological problems should provide the following information: (a) source of thermochemical figures, (b) concentration of reactants, (c) pH at which the reaction occurs, (d) the method of calculation of the free energy, and (e) an explicit statement of the chemical equation for

TABLE II

FREE ENERGIES OF REACTIONS OF SULFUR

Reaction	ΔF (kcal. per mole of sulfur)	Method of calcu-lation	Source
Oxidation of sulfur by oxygen			
1. $(S^{--} + HS^{+} + H_2S) + 0.5\ O_2 \rightarrow S + H_2O$	−50.2	E_0'	(38)[b]
	−41.5	—	(3)
	−48.7	—	(28)
	−63.0	—	(48)
2. $2\ S + O_2 + H_2O \rightarrow S_2O_3^{--} + 2\ H^+$	−17.0	E_0'	(38)
3. $2\ S_2O_3^{--} + 0.5\ O_2 = 2\ H^+ \rightarrow S_4O_6^{--} + H_2O$	−2.6	E_0'	(38)
4. $S + O_2 + H_2O \rightarrow SO_3^{--} + 2\ H^+$	−59.7	$\Delta F_f°$	(38)
5. $SO_3^{--} + 0.5\ O_2 \rightarrow SO_4^{--}$	−59.7	$\Delta F_f°$	(38)
6. $S + 1.5\ O_2 + H_2O \rightarrow SO_4^{--} + 2\ H^+$	−119.4	$\Delta F_f°$	(38)
	−118.5	—	(3)
	−120.3	—	(28)
	−147.0	—	(48)
Oxidation of sulfur by pyridine nucleotides			
7. $SO_3^{--} + H_2O + PN^+ \rightarrow SO_4^{--} + PNH + H^+$	+33.7	E_0'	(38)
8. $(S^{--} + HS + H_2S) + 3\ H_2O + 3\ PN^+ \rightarrow SO_3^{--} + PNH + 5\ H^+$	+186.0[a]	E_0'	(38)

[a] This value includes hydrolysis of sulfide ion at pH 7:

$$S^{--} + H^+ \rightarrow S^{--} + HS + H_2S;\ \Delta F' = -11.5 \text{ kcal } (47).$$

[b] Calculation by Gibbs and Schiff from data in source indicated.

which the calculations were made. In this review, the thermochemical figures for E_0 and for standard free energies of formation have been taken from Latimer (38). The concentration of the reactants are in the standard state. The pH at which the reaction occurs is 7, and all equations are written in this form. Therefore, all values of E_0 have been corrected to E_0'. The E_0' for TPN and DPN used in this review is —0.32 volt (14). The methods of calculating the free-energy values are listed in the tables.

D. ABBREVIATIONS

The following abbreviations will be used: DPN^+, diphosphopyridine nucleotide; DPNH, reduced diphosphopyridine nucleotide; TPN^+, triphosphopyridine nucleotide; TPNH, reduced triphosphopyridine nucleotide; PN^+, pyridine nucleotide; PNH, reduced pyridine nucleotide; ATP, adenosine triphosphate; kcal, kilocalories; Pi, inorganic phosphate.

III. Chemical Transformation in the Assimilation of Sulfur and Nitrogen

A. COMPARATIVE ASPECTS

1. Sulfur

Sulfur is found in living systems in several states from the highly oxidized form of sulfate as in polysaccharide sulfates to the completely

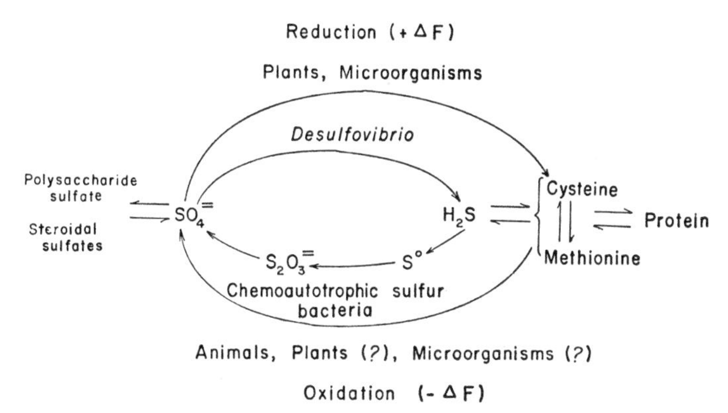

FIG. 2. The sulfur cycle. The principal reactions of sulfur compounds, with emphasis on the chemosynthetic bacteria.

reduced form in the thiol groups of amino acids and proteins (Fig. 2). Although several oxidation states of sulfur are to be found in all cells, there are phylogenetic distinctions which concern the ability of an organism to bring about the oxidation-reduction reactions themselves.

Higher animals, specifically the mammals, are found to be incapable of bringing about the reduction of sulfate to the thiol level and must, therefore, rely on an exogenous source of thiol compounds such as cystine or methionine. Reduction of sulfate with its subsequent incorporation into cystine has been reported in ruminants (11) and in rats (20), but it appears that the microorganisms of the intestinal tract were probably the responsible agents in these cases (1). It has been shown that the chick embryo is capable of bringing about a limited reduction of sulfate to the sulfonic acid level of taurine (42). To the author's knowledge there seems to be no information concerning the sulfur nutrition of the invertebrates with the exception of *Drosophila melanogaster* (31), for which a defined medium has been devised which includes cysteine and methionine.

In descending the evolutionary scale (as far as morphological complexity is concerned) the ability to reduce sulfate to the thiol level, appears to be widely distributed. *Escherichia coli*, for example, utilizes sulfate as the sole sulfur source for growth as well as sulfite, thiosulfate, and cystine (52). This is true of many other bacteria which can be grown on completely inorganic sources of sulfur. Here, as in other groups, species are found which are incapable of sulfate reduction and mutants of sulfate-reducing microorganisms are often encountered which are incapable of carrying out this process (37).

In ascending an evolutionary sequence of plants, the members of the blue-green algae, the diatoms, the green algae, the euglenoids, and dinoflagellates, whose nutrition has been studied, all appear to be able to utilize sulfate as the sole sulfur source for growth. Among the fungi, the ability to utilize sulfate appears to be present in the majority of species studied (49), but here, as in the case of the bacteria, many forms occur, sometimes as variants of forms which can utilize sulfate, which lack this ability. Among the higher plants (85) which have been studied in this respect, the ability to reduce sulfate and to grow on sulfate as the sole sulfur source seems to be universally present.

On the basis of the sampling of the biological world presented above, it would appear that microorganisms in general are capable of sulfate reduction, with occasional forms appearing which are unable to do so, perhaps through secondary loss by mutation. The ability to reduce sulfate completely appears to be absent in higher animals but is universally present in higher plants.

2. *Nitrogen*

Nitrogen is usually found in the reduced or amino form in living systems as a constituent of amino acids, proteins, purines, pyrimidines, nucleic acids, etc. The reduction of nitrate to the amino level appears to be restricted to plants and microorganisms; other groups require a reduced form of nitrogen, such as ammonia or amino acids (Fig. 3). Elemental nitrogen is utilized by certain members of the blue-green algae, bacteria, and the symbiotic relationship between species of *Rhizobium* and legumes.

In the breakdown and excretion of nitrogen compounds, reduced

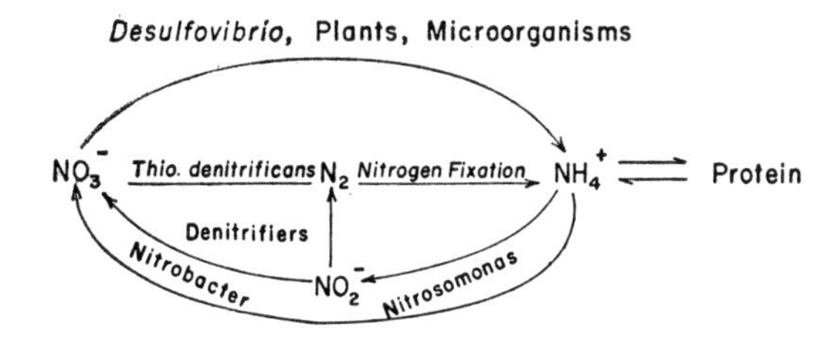

FIG. 3. The nitrogen cycle. The principal reactions of nitrogen compounds, with emphasis on the chemosynthetic bacteria.

forms of the elements are the end products. These include urea, uric acid, and ammonia; nitrate is not encountered.

B. INTERMEDIARY METABOLISM

1. *Sulfur*

a. Oxidation of reduced sulfur compounds. The oxidation of reduced sulfur, specifically the oxidation of the thiol group of cysteine, has been particularly well studied in mammalian systems where most of the intermediary reactions are known. This work has been extensively reviewed by Singer and Kearney (62) and by Greenberg (27). As is often the case, the evidence for plant tissues is regrettably inadequate (83). The evidence for oxidation of thiol-containing amino acids in plants mainly rests upon a correlation of analyses for protein and amino acid sulfur with analyses for sulfate sulfur under various physiological conditions. Wood and Barrien (85), using this approach found that, under starvation conditions, as protein sulfur in the plants decreased, there was an increase in sulfate sulfur. They further showed (84) that cystine added to sand cultures of higher plants resulted in an increase in sulfate in the plants tissues. Since they do not mention any precautions to ensure sterile conditions, the possibility remains that the added nutrient was oxidized by bacteria in the sand to sulfate which was then taken up by the plants. In tomato (*Lycopersicon esculentum*) and tobacco (*Nicotiana tabacum*) plants, DL-methionine added to sand cultures increased the amount of sulfate found in the tissues (44). Methionine also stimulated the growth of sulfur-deficient plants.

Radioactive sulfur dioxide is taken up by leaves of alfalfa (*Medicago sativa*) and sugar beets (*Beta vulgaris*) (69), and is oxidized to sulfate. A small portion is also found in organically bound sulfur. Organic sulfur of leaves is apparently oxidized to sulfate for translocation to other organs and is reconverted to organic form in the roots and grain (68). It is likely that oxidation of reduced sulfur by plants does occur, but the actual enzymatic reactions by which the process proceeds are as yet unknown.

As may be seen from Table II, the oxidation of hydrogen sulfide by oxygen is highly exergonic and releases some 150–200 kcal. If this oxidation could be coupled in some way to endergonic reactions within the cell, the energy released from the catabolism of thiol groups could be utilizable for synthetic reactions. As yet, nothing is known about this in plant systems aside from the chemoautotrophic bacteria which are discussed in Section IV of this review. In animal systems some of the oxidation reactions are intimately connected with other cellular reactions, thereby utilizing the reducing power generated from the oxidation of reduced sulfur compounds (61).

b. General remarks on sulfate reduction. It has been known for some time, from nutritional evidence, that plants and microorganisms are capable of carrying out the process of sulfate reduction, but information concerning the actual stepwise reactions involved has been slow to appear. The reduction of sulfate to the level of hydrogen sulfide (H—S—H) found in the thiol groups of amino acids and proteins (R—S—H, R—S—R′) is a highly endergonic process, the difference in the free energies of formation of sulfate and H_2S being of the order of 170 kcal per mole. This large energy requirement leads one to speculate on possible sources of electrons within the cell at a potential that will allow the reaction to proceed exergonically. The complete reduction of sulfate to H_2S requires eight electrons and, by analogy to other substrate level oxidation-reduction reactions in cells, might be considered to proceed by four separate steps which involve the transfer of two electrons at a time. This would imply that a minimum of four steps would be required in the process and possibly more. There is no reason to believe that energy transfer occurs only from the reductant. It is possible that prior reaction of the inorganic species with other compounds (e.g., ATP) might change the potential of the sulfur sufficiently to permit reduction to proceed with reductants which would not ordinarily reduce the species in question (see also Section IV). As an example of a possible direct reduction of the inorganic species in the cell, the reaction of four molecules of PNH with sulfate to yield H_2S would proceed in a highly exergonic manner as shown in Table II. This calculation for a hypothetical series of reactions indicates that reduction by a compound at the potential of PNH would be extremely wasteful in terms of energy unless the cell had some mechanism to trap the energy released. If the cell employed other reductants closer to the potential of the sulfate-H_2S system, the process would be more efficient. Postgate (47) has shown, for example, that the electrons for the reduction of sulfate to form H_2S in the obligate anaerobe, *Desulfovibrio desulfuricans*, come from cytochrome c_3.

c. Sulfate reduction by heterotrophic organisms. The evidence for the participation of various sulfur compounds as intermediates in reduction is largely indirect from nutritional studies on auxotrophs of various organisms and from competition studies with radioactive precursors. The metabolic schemes presented by various workers are summarized in Fig. 4, A, B, C, and D.

On the basis of earlier work with *Neurospora* auxotrophs which were incapable of utilizing sulfate, Horowitz (33) suggested the presence of two pathways of sulfate reduction, an inorganic pathway and one in which the sulfur was first bound to some carbon skeleton. This scheme, involving cysteic acid and cysteine sulfinic acids as intermediates in reduction, has frequently appeared in discussions of sulfur metabolism. Recently, Horowitz (34) has described some new experiments which have led to a revision of these proposals. Cysteine sulfinic acid, it was found, did not replace thiosulfate, but instead was entirely equivalent to cysteic acid and sulfite. In addition, Horowitz and Fisher have found that all of the mutants which are blocked between thiosulfate and cysteine are able to utilize elemental sulfur. Since *Neurospora* spores rapidly convert sulfur to sulfide, sulfide is probably the active member of the reduction pathway. On the basis of this evidence, Horowitz (34) thinks it likely that the reductive pathway in *Neurospora* involves only inorganic forms of sulfur and that cysteine sulfinic acid is probably oxidized to cysteic acid prior to utilization. A schematic representation of these ideas is shown in Fig. 4, A. Singer and Kearney consider that the oxidation of cysteic sulfinic acid to cysteic acid is unlikely since in systems where it has been studied it is a very slow reaction or is entirely absent (62). They favor a reaction of sulfite and pyruvate to yield β-sulfinylpyruvate as a likely site of incorporation of inorganic sulfur in microorganisms by analogy to similar enzymatic reactions implicated in the oxidation of reduced sulfur compounds.

Roberts *et al.* (52) have investigated the sulfur metabolism of *N. crassa* by the radioactive technique. A radioactive precursor such as $S^{35}O_4^{--}$, cystine-S^{35} or methionine-S^{35} is given to the cells together with an unlabeled sulfur compound which is suspected of being involved in the utilization of the radioactive precursor. The suppression of uptake

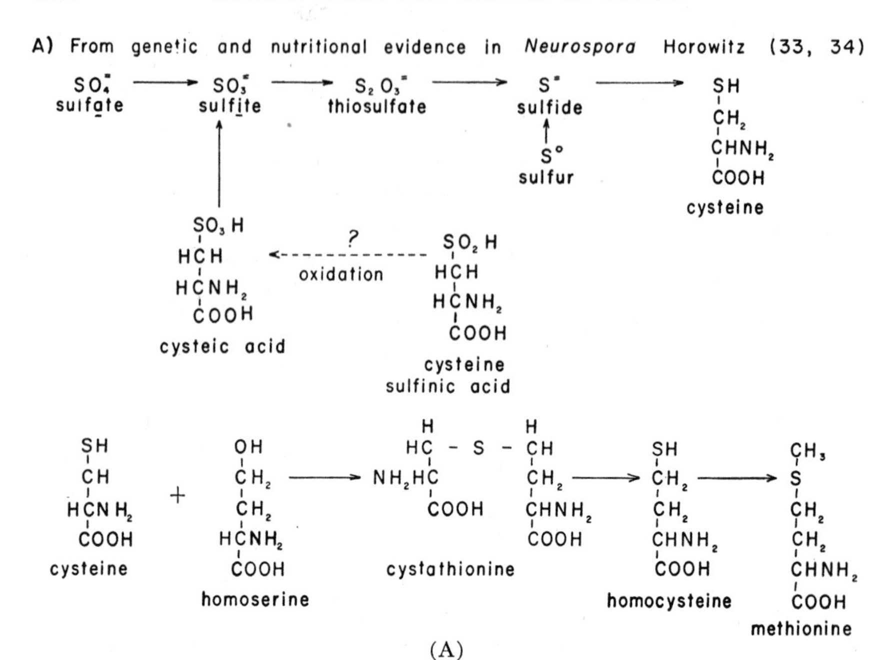

(A)

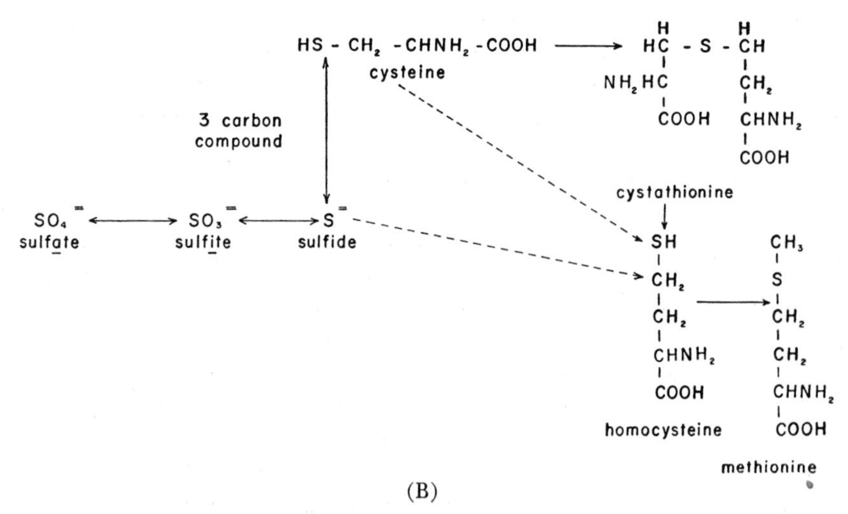

(B)

FIG. 4. A and B. Proposed metabolic sequences in the sulfur metabolism of *Neurospora* and *E. coli*.

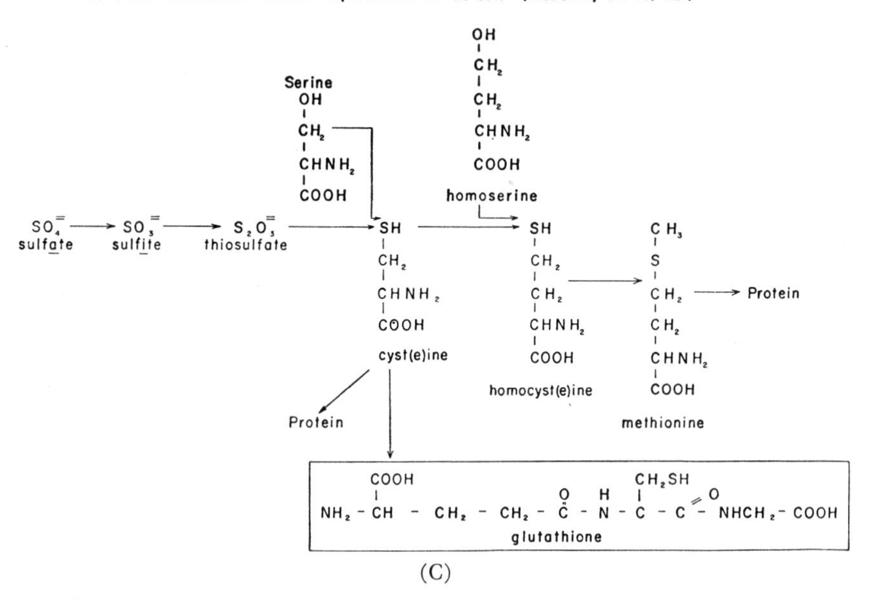

(C)

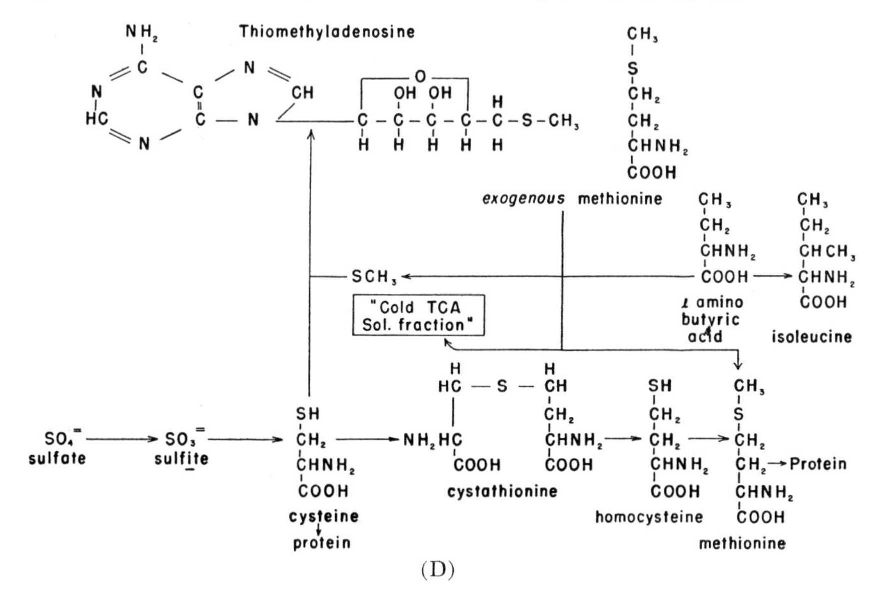

(D)

FIG. 4. C and D. Proposed metabolic sequences in the sulfur metabolism of *E. coli* and *T. utilis*.

of radioactivity relative to controls which have not received the unlabeled sulfur compound is taken as an index of the participation of the unlabeled compound in the metabolic sequence. As limitations to this technique, the failure of a compound to compete may merely represent a permeability barrier of the cells to the compound, while suppression of uptake of radioactivity by a given compound might reflect inhibition of other metabolic processes by the compound other than sulfur metabolism. These objections may be removed by growth studies on the compound in question, and in many cases this has been carried out.

In agreement with the findings of Horowitz, Roberts *et al.* (52) found that sulfite, thiosulfate, cystine, homocystine, and cystathionine suppress the incorporation of radioactive sulfate. Cysteic acid, however, does not compete, this is puzzling in view of the genetic and nutritional evidence. In addition lanthionine, djenkolic acid, and ethionine do suppress radiosulfate uptake and indicate that a place should be found for these compounds in the sulfur metabolism of this organism, if only as competitive inhibitors. The competition of compounds with cystine-S^{35} and methionine-S^{35} is consistent with the Horowitz scheme.

Evidence from genetic studies and from radioactive competition experiments also exists for *Escherichia coli*. Lampen *et al.* (37) have presented the scheme given in Fig. 4, B from their work on auxotrophs of this organism. Sulfate is reduced via sulfite to sulfide; only two reductive steps are indicated. Sulfide is converted to cysteine which is converted via homocysteine to methionine. An alternative path is also shown from sulfide to homocysteine. Cowie *et al.* (19) have employed the radioactive competition technique for *E. coli*. Consistent with Lampen's data, sulfite, sulfide, cystine, homocysteine, and methionine suppress radiosulfate uptake. In addition, lanthionine and thiosulfate also compete with radiosulfate. The inconsistency here is in the data for cystathionine. Cystathionine does not compete with either radiosulfate, cystine-S^{35} or with methionine-S^{35}, indicating its lack of participation in the sulfur metabolism of *E. coli*. Lampen's data, however, indicate that cystathionine is utilizable as a sulfur source although its participation as an intermediate between cysteine and methionine is not clear. One must, however, interpret nutritional data with cystathionine with caution since Binkley has shown (10) that a nonenzymatic cleavage of cystathionine can occur in the presence of chelating agents, cupric ions, and pyridoxal with the formation of homocysteine. With the exception of cystathionine, the competition with cystine-S^{35} and methionine-S^{35} is consistent with the nutritional and genetic data. The scheme of Roberts *et al.* (52) for sulfur metabolism in *E. coli* is presented in Fig. 4, C.

The sulfur metabolism of *Torulopsis utilis*, a yeast, has been subjected to the radioactive competition technique as well. The metabolic sequence proposed by Roberts *et al.* (52) for this organism is presented in Fig. 4, D.

d. Sulfate reduction by plants. The evidence for intermediates of sulfate reduction in green plants is very meager. *Chlorella pyrenoidosa* has been shown to convert radiosulfate to several compounds, one of which appears to be *S*-adenosylmethionine (55). The process of sulfate utilization in this organism is very sensitive to inhibition by iodoacetamide. Radioactive elemental sulfur sprayed on lemon (*Citrus limon*) plants appears in cellular sulfur-containing compounds (72) while sulfur dioxide is also converted to organic form by several plants (68, 70). The incorporation of radioactive sulfate into organically bound sulfur, presumably protein, has been demonstrated in alfalfa (69), and rapid incorporation of radiosulfate into amino acids has been found in Alaska peas (*Pisum sativum* var. 'Alaska') (41). Sulfite has been reported as a product of sulfate reduction in excised tobacco leaves (21). In this case, the reduction seems to be markedly enhanced by light.

The data presented in this review only serve to emphasize how incomplete our knowledge is concerning the reactions involved in sulfate reduction in plants. No mention has been made of the many interesting and esoteric compounds of sulfur which occur in many plant species. The importance of these compounds has been emphasized in the reviews of Bersin (9) and Challenger (18). The possible metabolic roles of these compounds, as well as the nutritional genetic and metabolic work concerned with sulfate reduction reviewed here, suggest several fruitful areas of future research in the metabolism of plants.

e. Other aspects of sulfate reduction. Some workers have proposed the linkage of sulfate or other inorganic ions to carriers prior to reduction (52). In view of this, it is interesting to note that various compounds containing adenosine and sulfur have recently come into prominence. Investigations of the phenol sulfate-forming system of mammalian tissues have revealed the presence of a mixed anhydride between adenylic acid and sulfuric acid. On purification of the phenol sulfate system, Robbins and Lipmann (50) could show that the formation of *p*-nitrophenol sulfate was two-phasic, since sulfate first had to be activated before it could be transferred to *p*-nitrophenol. A second paper by these investigators (51) led to the nature and mechanism of active sulfate. Two yeast enzymes were identified which brought about the formation of active sulfate. They are: (a) adenosine triphosphate sulfurylase, catalyzing the displacement of the pyrophosphoryl group in ATP by sulfate yielding adenosine-5′-phosphosulfate (APS) and pyrophosphate [equation (7)]; and (b) adenosine-5′-phosphosulfate-3′-phosphokinase, producing adenosine-3′-phosphate-5′-phosphosulfate (PAPS) by phosphorylation of APS in the 3′-position [equation (8)].

$$\text{ATP} + SO_4^{=} + H^{+} \longrightarrow {}^{-}O-\underset{\downarrow \atop O}{\overset{O \atop \uparrow}{S}}-O-\underset{\downarrow \atop {}^{-}O}{\overset{O \atop \uparrow}{P}}-O-CH_2-(\text{ribose: 2'-OH, 3'-OH})-\text{adenine} + \text{pyrophosphate} \quad (7)$$

$$\text{ATP} + \text{APS} \longrightarrow {}^{-}O-\underset{\downarrow \atop O}{\overset{O \atop \uparrow}{S}}-O-\underset{\downarrow \atop O^{-}}{\overset{O \atop \uparrow}{P}}-O-CH_2-(\text{ribose: 2'-OH, 3'-O}-\underset{O^{-}}{\overset{}{P}}(\leftarrow O)-O^{-})-\text{adenine} + \text{ADP} + H^{+} \quad (8)$$

The over-all reaction is:

$$2\ \text{ATP} + SO_4^{--} \rightarrow \text{PAPS} + \text{ADP} + \text{pyrophosphate} \quad (9)$$

The apparent equilibrium constant for the ATP-sulfurylase reaction at pH 8 and 37° is about 10^{-8}, which corresponds to a standard free-energy change of approximately +11 kcal per mole. This is a reaction in which APS is formed against a very unfavorable equilibrium. The standard free energy of the second step was estimated to be —6 kcal per mole, since the adenosine-5′-phosphosulfate-3′-phosphokinase was assumed to be analogous to the phosphorylation of glucose. In this manner, the energy of an additional energy-rich phosphate is used to off-set partially the highly endergonic sulfurylation step.

The activating system, equations (7) and (8), has also been found in *Neurospora crassa* (30) and in yeast (6). It is of interest that in mammalian systems which are incapable of reducing sulfate, equation (10), the phenol sulfokinase is present, while in *Neurospora*, which does reduce sulfate, only the activating enzyme system is present (30).

$$p\text{-nitrophenol} + \text{PAPS} \rightarrow p\text{-nitrophenol sulfate} + \text{PAS} \quad (10)$$

Wilson and Bandurski have reported two other reactions in yeast. An enzyme is present which catalyzes the release of pyrophosphate from ATP in the presence of sulfite (79); the mixed anhydride of adenylic acid and sulfite which one would expect has proved to be too unstable to be isolated. Another reaction demonstrated in the same laboratory is the release of pyrophosphate from ATP in the presence of selenate; only trace amounts of adenosine phosphoselenate could be isolated (5).

Compounds of adenosine and sulfur at the thiol level have also been found in living systems. Thiomethyladenosine (see Fig. 4, D) has been isolated from methionine-grown yeast (64) and has been shown to be a transthiolating agent, i.e., a source of methylthiol groups (58). It has been shown recently that at least part of the methylthioadenosine found is produced from hydrolysis of *S*-adenosylmethionine during extraction of the cells (57). Schwartz and Shapiro have shown that thiomethyladenosine can serve as a precursor of the thiomethyl group of methionine in a mutant of *Aerobacter aerogenes* (60). *S*-adenosylmethionine, a compound closely related to thiomethyladenosine, has

S-adenosylmethionine

been shown as the product of a reaction of ATP and methionine which is catalyzed by an enzyme from mammalian tissues (16). A unique aspect of this reaction is the cleavage of all three phosphates of ATP with the formation of a molecule each of orthophosphate and pyrophosphate (17). The ATP-methionine reaction is apparently absent in *Chlorella pyrenoidosa* where exogenous methionine-S^{35} does not enter into sulfur metabolism extensively (55). In this case, *S*-adenosylmethionine is formed from the reduction of sulfate. The occurence of adenosylated compounds of sulfur at various levels of oxidation and reduction indicates that some attention should be paid to their possible roles in sulfate reduction. It is possible that one or more of these adenosylated compounds might play a role as a carrier of the inorganic ions during reduction and subsequent transfer to other acceptors, such as the carbon chains of the amino acids. To date, none of these compounds of adenosine and sulfur have been shown to participate directly in sulfate reduction.

Very suggestive, however, is the very recent work reported in abstract by Wilson and Bandurski (80) and by Hilz (29). Wilson and Bandurski found that cell-free extracts of yeast would reduce inorganic sulfate to sulfite when fortified with ATP, TPN^{+}, Mg^{++}, and glucose-6-phosphate. Hilz reported that cell-free extracts of yeast will reduce

SO_4^{--} to the level of H_2S with the formation of cysteine when fortified with ATP, TPN^+, DPN^+, and α-lipoic acid. Sulfite was shown to be an intermediate in this reduction. The requirement for ATP in these systems strongly suggest that activated species of sulfur compounds participate in reduction. If TPN^+, DPN^+, and α-lipoic acid are all necessary for reduction to the level of H_2S, then different hydrogen donors for various steps in the process are required.

2. *Nitrogen*

Since the literature concerned with the intermediates of nitrate reduction will be dealt with in Volume III, of this treatise, any discussion of this subject will be omitted here.

IV. Chemosynthesis

A. INTRODUCTION

Organisms which are capable of synthesizing their cellular material where the sole source of carbon is carbon dioxide are said to be autotrophic. The reduction of carbon dioxide is a strongly endergonic reaction and therefore requires an investment of energy. Organisms which possess chlorophyll and can obtain this energy from light, are called photoautotrophs. If the energy is obtained from the oxidation of an oxidizable compound or element, the organisms are said to be chemoautotrophic. All of the known organisms which comprise this latter group are bacteria.

Winogradsky's investigations of the filamentous sulfur bacteria in 1887 (81) led him to postulate the concept of chemoautotrophy. He observed that *Beggiatoa* sp. could synthesize its cellular material by utilizing the energy derived from the oxidation of hydrogen sulfide. This oxidation, he noted, was carried out in two steps: first to sulfur and finally to sulfate. Winogradsky's "sulfur bacteria" included both the chemosynthetic and photosynthetic microorganisms (Engelmann's purple bacteria) which oxidized inorganic sulfur compounds. He was led to this classification because he discarded the idea that light may be used as an energy source by organisms which simultaneously oxide hydrogen sulfide. After establishing the concept that organisms exist which derive their energy from the oxidation of sulfur compounds, he began his classical studies on the nitrifiers. Winogradsky (82) was aware of the researches of Schloesing and Müntz (59) and Warington (77) which established that soil contains organisms capable of oxidizing ammonia to nitrate in two stages: first the oxidation of ammonia to nitrate and then the oxidation of nitrite to nitrate. In 1891, using many ingenious techniques, Winogradsky was able to show that the nitrifiers were similar to the sulfur bacteria, since they used carbon dioxide as their source of carbon and coupled its reduction either to the oxidation of ammonia or to the oxidation of nitrite as their source of energy.

Since the observations of Winogradsky with the sulfur bacteria and the nitrifiers, the chemosynthetic mode of existence has been shown to be widespread among bacteria. Bacteria have been reported which can utilize the energy derived from the oxidation of hydrogen, carbon monoxide, methane, and ferrous carbonate (see Table III).

TABLE III
SUMMARY OF CHEMOSYNTHETIC ABILITIES OF VARIOUS SPECIES

Type	Species	Electron donor	Oxidized product	ΔF[a] (kcal)	Reference source for ΔF
Nitrifying bacteria	*Nitrosomonas* sp.	NH_4^+	NO_2^-	Table I	—
	Nitrobacter sp.	NO_2^-	NO_3^-	Table I	—
Sulfur bacteria	*Beggiatoa* sp.	H_2S	S	Table II	—
	Thiothrix sp.	S	SO_4^{--}	Table II	—
	Thiobacillus	S	SO_4^{--}	Table II	—
	thiooxidans	$S_2O_3^{--}$	$2\ SO_4^{--}$	−211	(65)
	Thiobacillus thioparus	$\frac{5}{4}\ S_2O_3^{--}$	$\frac{3}{2}\ SO_4^{--} + S$	−125	(48)
	Thiobacillus denitrificans[b]	5 S	$5\ SO_4^{--}$	−660	(65)
	Thiobacillus thiocyanoxidans	CNS^-	$SO_4^{--} + CO_2 + NH_4^+$	−224	(48)
Hydrogen bacteria	*Hydrogenomonas facilis*	H_2	H_2O	−56.7	(65)
	Desulfovibrio desulfuricans[c]	H_2	H_2O	−56.7	(47)

[a] Free energies expressed in kilocalories per number of moles of electron donor indicated.
[b] Nitrate is reduced to nitrogen.
[c] Sulfate is reduced to hydrogen sulfide.

In general, this section of the chapter will be limited to the manner by which the energy released from the oxidation of inorganic compounds is utilized by the sulfur bacteria and nitrifiers for growth. Some reference will be made to the other types of chemoautotrophic bacteria from the standpoint of comparative biochemistry. No attempt has been made to review the taxonomy, morphology, cultural conditions etc., of these microorganisms. For the bearing of these subjects on chemosynthesis, the reader is referred to Stephenson (65) and the recent symposium sponsored by the Society for General Microbiology (23).

B. THE NITRIFYING BACTERIA

1. General

There are two genera of bacteria which are known to be autotrophic nitrifiers. Species of *Nitrosomonas* oxidize ammonia to nitrite; the further oxidation of nitrite to nitrate is brought about by species of *Nitrobacter*. These are two distinct organisms since neither can oxidize the substrate of the other, but they are usually discussed together because their combined metabolism brings about the process of nitrification.

Chemically speaking, nitrification is the biological process whereby nitrogen is oxidized from its lowest oxidation state (NH_3, -3) to its most oxidized level (HNO_3, $+5$). If it is assumed that the transfer of two electrons occurs in each step, then intermediates of oxidation level, -1, $+1$, and $+3$ should be encountered. The most recent investigations indicate that the chain of reactions in oxidation is:

$$\underset{-3}{NH_3} \rightarrow \underset{-1}{NH_2OH} \rightarrow \underset{+1}{?} \rightarrow \underset{+3}{NO_2} \rightarrow \underset{+5}{NO_3}$$

This series of reactions will be discussed more fully in Volume III, Chapter 5.

2. Energetics

a. Nitrosomonas. The primary oxidation reaction of *Nitrosomonas* is:

$$NH_4^+ + 1.5\ O_2 \rightarrow NO_2^- + H_2O + 2\ H^+;\ \Delta F' = -84\ \text{kcal}$$

This over-all reaction may be considered to occur in two steps:

$$1.\ NH_4^+ + 0.5\ O_2 \rightarrow NH_2OH + H^+;\ \Delta F' = -0.7\ \text{kcal}$$
$$2.\ NH_2OH + O_2 \rightarrow NO_2^- + H_2O + H^+;\ \Delta F' = -83.3\ \text{kcal}$$

The decrease of free energy in the oxidation of ammonia to hydroxylamine is small compared to that of the subsequent reaction.

In many biological oxidations, the electrons are transferred to the two pyridine nucleotides, DPN and TPN, resulting in an oxidation of the electron donor. In the case of *Nitrosomonas*, the pertinent reactions would be:

$$1.\ NH_4^+ + PN^+ + OH^- \rightarrow NH_2OH + PNH + H^+;\ \Delta F' = +47.0\ \text{kcal}$$
$$2.\ NH_2OH + 2\ PN^+ + H_2O \rightarrow NO_2^- + 2\ PNH + 3\ H^+;\ \Delta F' = +110\ \text{kcal}$$

which indicates that the reactions would not occur spontaneously.

The free-energy values when converted to equilibrium constants are approximately 10^{35} for reaction 1 and 10^{80} for reaction 2. When compared to other single-step oxidation-reduction reactions of living systems like glucose-6-phosphate dehydrogenase (10^{6}), these are extremely high. Thus it would appear that the oxidation of ammonia to nitrite by these autotrophic bacteria is not mediated by the pyridine nucleotides.

b. Nitrobacter. The inorganic oxidation reaction of *Nitrobacter*

$$NO_2^- + 0.5\ O_2 \rightarrow NO_3^-;\ \Delta F' = -17.8 \text{ kcal}$$

would appear to be a one-step process. Similar to that of *Nitrosomonas*, the simplest reaction would be the reduction of nitrate by pyridine nucleotides:

$$NO_3^- + PNH + H^+ \rightarrow NO_2^- + PN^+ + H_2O;\ \Delta F' = -39.7 \text{ kcal}$$

However, here again, the equilibrium strongly favors reduction. For all practical purposes, the oxidation of nitrite by pyridine nucleotides would appear to be of little value to *Nitrobacter*.

The system oxidizing ammonia in the *Nitrosomonas* and nitrite in *Nitrobacter* should have a potential of the order of the flavoproteins ($E_0' = 0.0$) or the cytochromes ($E_0' = -0.04, +0.25$). The potential shift would be at least 0.3–0.6 volt more positive, permitting electrons to flow from the primary oxidation steps to a coupling system. A coupling between a cytochrome of *Nitrobacter* with an absorption maximum at 551 mμ in the reduced state and nitrite oxidation has been reported recently by Lees and Simpson (39). A reduced cytochrome produced when nitrite is added to a suspension of *Nitrobacter* is reoxidized by atmospheric oxygen. This link between the cytochromes and the primary energy reactions appear to be a break-through in autotrophic metabolism.

C. THE NONPHOTOSYNTHETIC (COLORLESS) SULFUR BACTERIA

1. General

The sulfur-oxidizing organisms are generally divided into two groups: (a) the filamentous forms which deposit sulfur inside the cell and (b) the unicellular forms that may deposit sulfur outside the cell.

Most of the early investigations on the chemosynthetic bacteria were carried out with the group a forms—*Beggiatoa* (1887) and *Thiothrix* (1912). In more recent years, most attention has been given to unicellular forms. Although a number of species have been reported, Baalsrud and Baalsrud (2) consider them as different strains of three main species: *Thiobacillus thioparus*, *Thiobacillus thiooxidans*, and *Thiobacillus denitrificans.* While *T. thioparus* and *T. thiooxidans* are dependent on molecular oxygen as the hydrogen acceptor, *T. denitrificans* can live anaerobically, requiring nitrate as the ultimate oxidizing agent. Since the carbon dioxide requirement is absolute, the *Thiobacilli* are obligate autotrophs.

2. *Energetics*

a. Beggiatoa and Thiothrix. The primary energy-producing reaction of the two organisms is the oxidation of hydrogen sulfide via elemental sulfur to sulfate. The reactions are:

$$(S^{--} + HS^{-} + H_2S) + 0.5\ O_2 \rightarrow S + H_2O;\ \Delta F' = -50.2 \text{ kcal}$$
$$S + 1.5\ O_2 + H_2O \rightarrow SO_4^{--} + 2\ H^{+};\ \Delta F' = -119.4 \text{ kcal}$$

In contrast to the nitrifiers where two organisms participate in the conversion of nitrogen from its lowest level of oxidation, —3, to its highest, +5, both filamentous sulfur types can bring about a complete oxidation of hydrogen sulfide to sulfate (—2 to +6). In addition, the sulfur bacteria release about twice the amount of free energy during this oxidation, whether calculated on the basis of a mole of nitrogen vs. sulfur or per mole of oxygen.

Very little else is known about the biochemistry of these filamentous forms besides the informaton contained in these two equations. The intermediate steps between elemental sulfur and sulfate are unknown. The organisms can derive energy from both oxidation reactions since they grow on hydrogen sulfide, converting it to sulfur, until the supply is consumed and then proceed to oxidize the sulfur further to sulfate.

b. The Thiobacilli. This group of sulfur oxidizers has received much more attention than the filamentous forms. The types of primary energy-producing reactions found are more varied since hydrogen sulfide, sulfur, thiosulfate, tetrathionate, trithionate, dithionate, and thiocyanate can be utilized as sources of energy. The end product in all oxidations is sulfate which is usually excreted as sulfuric acid.

The oxidations which these organisms can carry out are:

1. $(S^{--} + HS^{-} + H_2S) + 0.5\ O_2 \rightarrow S + H_2O;\ \Delta F' = -50.2 \text{ kcal}$
2. $2\ S + O_2 + H_2O \rightarrow S_2O_3^{--} + 2\ H^{+};\ \Delta F' = -17 \text{ kcal}$
3. $S_2O_3^{--} + 0.5\ O_2 + 4\ H^{+} \rightarrow S_4O_6^{--} + 2\ H^{+} + H_2O;\ \Delta F' = -2.6 \text{ kcal}$
4. $S_2O_3^{--} + 2\ O_2 + H_2O \rightarrow 2\ SO_4^{--} + 2\ H^{+};\ \Delta F' = -100 \text{ kcal}$
5. $CNS^{-} + 2\ O_2 + 2\ H_2O \rightarrow SO_4^{--} + NH_4^{+} + CO_2;\ \Delta F' = -224 \text{ kcal}$

The free-energy values are expressed as *per atom of sulfur oxidized.*

These free-energy data would suggest that during the oxidation of sulfur most of the energy is released after the thiosulfate level. They would further suggest that Trautwein's strain (thionic acid bacteria), whose primary energy-yielding reaction is equation 3, could not derive sufficient energy from this step for growth. This was concluded by Baalsrud and Baalsrud (2) from experimental data.

The intermediate steps between thiosulfate and sulfate are still in doubt. Since these are probably typical biological oxidations involving two electron changes, more than one step must be considered. The experiments of Vishniac (74) with *T. thioparus* showed that tetrathionate and dithionate were both formed during thiosulfate oxidation. On the basis of recent experiments with *T. thiocyanoxidans*, whose primary energy-yielding reaction is equation 5, Youatt (86) has proposed the folowing scheme:

$$HS^- \rightarrow S_2O_2^{--} \rightarrow S_2O_3^{--} \rightarrow S_2O_5^{--} \rightarrow S_2O_7^{--} \rightarrow SO_4^{--}$$

T. thiocyanoxidans which is found in gasworks effluents is of interest since it not only oxidizes the sulfur from thiocyanate for energy but also obtains carbon and nitrogen for growth. According to Youatt, the first step in the metabolism of thiocyanate is a hydrolysis:

$$CNS^- + H_2O \rightarrow HCNO + SH^-$$

followed by another hydrolysis of the cyanate:

$$HCNO + H_2O \rightarrow CO_2 + NH_3$$

The two hydrolyses would run rapidly since each is strongly exergonic. The primary energy-yielding reaction is the subsequent oxidation of the sulfide to sulfate.

D. THE HYDROGEN BACTERIA

1. General

These organisms are discussed briefly in this review since their metabolism is essential to an understanding of the nature of autotrophy. None of the hydrogen bacteria is a strict autotroph. Obligate heterotrophs like *Escherichia coli* can utilize molecular hydrogen but cannot derive energy from its metabolism, but the hydrogen bacteria can oxidize hydrogen to water ($\Delta F = -56.7$ kcal) and are able to utilize this energy for growth.

The hydrogen bacterium of importance to this review is *Desulfovibrio desulfuricans* since it can be grown autotrophically by the reduction of oxidized sulfur compounds to sulfide.

2. *Desulfovibrio desulfuricans*

For most chemoautotrophic bacteria, molecular oxygen is considered to be the ultimate electron acceptor. Butlin *et al.* (15) showed that *D. desulfuricans,* an obligate anaerobe, could live autotrophically on the energy released when hydrogen gas is oxidized to water with sulfate, sulfite, or thiosulfate in place of molecular oxygen as the electron acceptor. An oxidation of this type is internal and is generally regarded as a fermentation. Therefore, energy for autotrophic growth can be derived under anaerobic as well as aerobic conditions.

The over-all reactions for *D. desulfuricans* are:

$$SO_4^{--} + 4\ H_2 \rightarrow S^{--} + 4\ H_2O;\ \Delta F' = -45.6\ \text{kcal}$$
$$SO_3^{--} + 3\ H_2 \rightarrow S^{--} + 3\ H_2O;\ \Delta F' = -43.7\ \text{kcal}$$
$$S_2O_3^{--} + 4\ H_2 \rightarrow S^{--} + H_2S + 3\ H_2O;\ \Delta F' = -46.3\ \text{kcal}$$

The free-energy values in Table II suggest that the reduction of the sulfur compounds could be mediated directly by pyridine nucleotides. As noted in Section IV,B, this would be an extremely wasteful reaction for the cell unless a mechanism for trapping the released energy were present. It would appear to be extremely doubtful that a sulfate reductase of this type will be reported.

Postgate (47) has shown that the reduction process is linked closely to a cytochrome. *D. desulfuricans,* although a strict anaerobe, contains a soluble, autooxidizable, thermostable hemoprotein, designated as cytochrome c_3. The reduced bands show absorption peaks at 553, 525, and 419 mμ. This cytochrome is further characterized by an exceedingly negative potential of $E_0' = -0.205$ volt. The cytochrome c_3 (approximately 94% pure) can act as a carrier in the reduction of sulfite, thiosulfate, tetrathionate, or dithionate by hydrogen by the cetyltrimethylammonium bromide-treated cell. Preparations of this kind do not show a c_3-linked sulfate reduction; the proof of the participation of cytochrome c_3 depends on difference spectra and the inhibition of the spectral changes by analogs of sulfate. Postgate also isolated a green, thermolabile, soluble protein, designated as desulfoviridin, but no metabolic function was described for this material. This preliminary report strongly suggests that the cytochromes play a key role in the coupling of the primary energy-yielding reaction to the reduction of carbon dioxide.

It is interesting to note that Sisler and Zobell (63) reported that strains of *Desulfovibrio* could fix molecular nitrogen during this reduction. This could not be confirmed in the laboratory of R. H. Burris [see Bach (4)].

E. EFFICIENCY OF CHEMOAUTOTROPHIC BACTERIA

The efficiency of the chemosynthetic bacteria has been expressed in two ways: by the ratio between the total heat energy (ΔH_c) consumed in carbon dioxide assimilation and the energy (ΔH_p) liberated by the primary inorganic oxidation, or by the corresponding ratios of the free energies. The sulfur and nitrogen organisms possess total-energy efficiencies ($\Delta H_c/\Delta H_p$) in the order of 5–6% and free-energy efficiencies ($\Delta F_c/\Delta F_p$) in the order of 6–8%. Both of these calculations are based on the false premise that all of the electron donor is oxidized by oxygen and that water is the reductant of carbon dioxide to cellular material.

This may be illustrated by data on *Nitrobacter* which derives its energy from

$$NO_2^- + 0.5\ O_2 \rightarrow NO_3^-;\ \Delta F' = -17.8 \text{ kcal}$$

Concomitant to this energy-releasing reaction is the reduction of 1 mole of carbon dioxide with water into organic matter (CH_2O) which is assumed to have the same energy content as ⅙ glucose. When carbon dioxide and water are in the standard state, the free-energy value is +115 kcal. If oxygen and carbon dioxide at pressures 0.2 and 0.0003 atm, respectively, are used instead of the standard state, the value is +118 kcal. Under conditions favorable for growth ($NO_2^- = 0.03\ M$), the oxidation of approximately 90 moles of nitrite to nitrate will cause the reduction of 1 mole of carbon dioxide to organic matter.

For the efficiency of *Nitrobacter* we obtain:

$$\frac{118}{90 \times 17.8} \times 100 = 7.4\%$$

This calculation suggests that only 7.4% of the energy liberated by nitrite oxidation is used for carbon dioxide reduction. It should be pointed out that this efficiency value is subject to the limitation expressed above and may not be a true interpretation of what is occurring in the cell. Expressing the oxidative and reductive systems as two completely independent processes is an oversimplification of chemosynthesis.

Expressing the efficiency of the chemoautotrophic bacteria in this manner has been criticized on several grounds. For instance, the efficiency of photosynthetic organisms (about 30% derived from the quantum yields) is determined in short-time experiments, while those for the chemosynthetics is an over-all value derived during the growth of the organism. Hofmann and Lees (32) have shown that the efficiency of *Nitrosomonas* varies with the age of the culture and the content of the culture medium. Young cultures gave values approaching 50%; in older cultures the efficiency dropped to 7%.

Although the over-all efficiencies may be low (6–8%), they compare favorably with the oft-quoted values for the utilization of light energy by green plants in the field. Therefore, it does not appear necessary to suggest, as many workers have, that the chemosynthetic bacteria are inefficient and wasteful. Rabinowitch (48) has remarked that "if chemoautotrophic organisms did not succeed in spreading over the whole surface of the earth, as did the green plant, it was not for lack of efficiency, but merely because chemical energy is available only in a few non-equilibrated spots while sun light flows abundantly everywhere."

F. CARBON METABOLISM

1. Energetics Involved in the Reduction of Carbon Dioxide

The over-all process of carbon dioxide reduction by the chemosynthetic bacteria can be roughly approximated by the equation:

$$CO_2 + 4\ (H) \rightarrow (CHOH) + H_2O$$

where (H) represents the "reducing power" or "assimilatory power" and (CHOH) is a convenient but not entirely precise representation of cellular material. This is a strongly endergonic process but since the source and nature of (H) is unknown, it is not possible to calculate how much energy must be invested to drive the reaction. We may, however, speculate on the nature of various chemical steps of this process.

A probable first reaction is the reduction of CO_2 (or its equivalent—COOH) to an aldehyde. The change in free energy in this reaction is larger than in any other step in the conversion of carbon dioxide to the (CHOH) state. The normal potentials (E_0') of systems involving a carboxylic acid and an aldehyde are among the most negative of biological couples. For example, the acetaldehyde-acetate and the 3-phosphoglyceraldehyde-3-phosphoglycerate systems have normal potentials of —0.598 volt and —0.48 volt, respectively. These potentials are sufficiently low so that reduction is negligible even by hydrogen gas under standard conditions in the presence of suitable catalysts. In addition to the free energy invested in the actual reducing step, the energy of ionization of the acid must be considered, since under physiological conditions the acid is dissociated.

If we invoke this primary reduction to the aldehyde, then a major route of carbon dioxide by the chemosynthetic bacteria involves a reduction whose potential is at least 0.05 volt below the hydrogen electrode and 0.15 volt more negative than the pyridine nucleotides. Thus far, no coenzyme or oxidation-reduction catalyst whose potential is negative enough to reduce carbon dioxide to (CHOH) has been found in any living cells. It must be assumed that the main pathway for hydrogen transport in the chemosynthetic bacteria is similar to other living tissues, namely through DPN and TPN. Then a mechanism to bridge the gap of approximately 0.15 volt must be found. By analogy with other known systems, it seems logical to infer that the bridge is ATP. The reduction step in the conversion of carbon dioxide to the aldehyde level, therefore, would involve the formation of the reduced carrier (PNH) and ATP. By this reasoning, the chemosynthetic bacteria must possess mechanisms of using the free energy released by the primary energy-producing reaction for the formation of the reduced carrier and ATP. These processes are unknown.

Two hypotheses for the formation of the reducing agent can be suggested. In one mechanism, the substrate itself could provide the (H) for the hydrogen bacteria, the ammonia-oxidizing bacteria, and the hydrogen sulfide oxidizers. Even when the substrate does not contain hydrogen, a hydrated substrate could be oxidized as in the case of *Nitrobacter:*

$$H_2O.NO_2^- \rightarrow 2\,(H) + NO_3^-$$
$$PN^+ + 2\,(H) \rightarrow PNH + H^+$$
$$\overline{H_2O.NO_2^- + PN^+ \rightarrow NO_3^- + H^+ + PNH}$$

On thermodynamic considerations, this mechanism is probably applicable only to the hydrogen bacteria since the characteristic potentials of the pyridine nucleotides are 0.1 volt more positive than the hydrogen electrode and therefore at least 0.5–1.0 volt more negative than the potentials of the primary energy-producing reactions of the hydrogen sulfide oxidizers and the nitrifiers.

A second hypothesis is the coupling of the oxidation of the substrate to the reduction of a flavin or a cytochrome. Which protein would be the primary acceptor of electrons would depend on the characteristic potential of the reduced substrate (XO) and the oxidized product (XO_2). Electrons could then flow from the reduced system to molecular oxygen coupled with the formation of chemically stored energy in any of the steps.

The pertinent reactions are:

$$XO + H_2O + \text{oxidized flavin} \rightarrow XO_2 + \text{reduced flavin } H_2$$
$$\text{reduced flavin } H_2 + 2 \text{ oxidized cytochrome}^{2+} \rightarrow \text{oxidized flavin} + 2 \text{ reduced cytochrome}^{3+} + 2\,H^+$$
$$2 \text{ reduced cytochrome}^{3+} + 2\,H^+ + \tfrac{1}{2}\,O_2 \rightarrow 2 \text{ oxidized cytochrome}^{2+} + H_2O$$
$$\overline{XO + \tfrac{1}{2}\,O_2 \rightarrow XO_2 + \text{energy}}$$

Finally this accumulated chemical energy could be used to split water with the formation of the reduced hydrogen carrier. In this system the essential reaction brought about by the primary energy producing reaction would be:

$$PN^+ + H_2O + \text{energy} \rightarrow PNH + H^+ + (0)$$

The amount of free energy needed to drive this strongly endergonic reaction can only be approximated, since the final state of the oxygen is not known. An investment of about 50 kcal per mole is probably required. The major drawback to this speculation is the mode of accumulating the energy needed to split water. At present there is no known mechanism of "pooling" the energy from the oxidation of many molecules into a compound capable of producing (H) from water.

The reasons for proposing this second hypothesis are twofold: (a) water is the only large source of hydrogen available and (b) by analogy to photosynthesis. There is no available evidence that the substrates like NH_4^+ and H_2S can donate hydrogen directly to pyridine nucleotide.

In addition to producing reduced pyridine nucleotide, the chemoautotrophic bacteria must derive a sufficient supply of ATP. This is probably synthesized during the reoxidation of a reduced flavin or cytochrome by molecular oxygen. Evidence is not available whether such a coupling occurs.

The energy needed to produce the "reducing power" and permit the reaction to proceed from left to right must derive ultimately from the primary energy-producing reaction. It is evident that the theoretical requirements may vary greatly dependng on the chemical nature of the electron donor. For example, chemosynthesis as carried out by the hydrogen bacteria is an endergonic process proceeding with only a small increase in free energy of approximately 1600 calories per mole of carbon dioxide converted to cell material. This compares with an investment of about 37,600 calories per mole during carbon dioxide reduction by sulfur bacteria in accord with the following reaction:

$$2\ H_2S + CO_2 \rightarrow (CH_2O) + 2\ S + H_2O$$

Bacterial chemosynthesis is not nearly so strong an endergonic process as green plant photosynthesis, since the latter runs with a $\Delta F = +115{,}000$ calories per mole of carbon dioxide reduced to the aldehyde level.

Probably the most important problem confronting the investigator of the chemosynthetic bacteria is the mechanism whereby energy produced by the energy-yielding reacton is captured and then transferred to the systems which convert carbon dioxide to cellular material. This problem will be dealt with more thoroughly in the next section.

2. *Energy Transfer in the Chemoautotrophic Bacteria*

Chlorophyll-containing organisms derive their energy from light, while the chemoautotrophic bacteria derive their energy from the oxidation of inorganic substances. However, a number of heterotrophic organisms are known that can carry out the latter process and presumably produce energy, but are unable to couple this process to their energy-requiring metabolic reactions. It would appear that the major difference between the autotrophic organisms and at least some of the heterotrophic systems is in the coupling mechanism, and not in the system of energy production itself.

The relation between sulfur oxidation and carbon dioxide-assimilating power by *Thiobacillus thiooxidans* was studied by Vogler (75). Young cultures, oxidizing sulfur to sulfate in the absence of carbon dioxide, generated energy which could be stored and later used for carbon dioxide fixation. In a later paper, Vogler and Umbreit (76) proved that this oxidation in the absence of carbon dioxide resulted in a diminution of inorganic phosphate within the cell. The fixation of carbon dioxide, in the absence of concomitant sulfur oxidation, was dependent on the amount of inorganic phosphate converted to organic phosphorus. During this "delayed" carbon dioxide fixation, inorganic phosphate was released in an amount proportional to the carbon dioxide assimilated. Vogler and Umbreit, therefore, concluded that phosphate transfer, coupled with sulfur oxidation and carbon dioxide assimilation by *T. thiooxidans*, was evidence that energy released during the oxidation of sulfur is stored in the cells as phosphate anhydride compounds. They assumed that the phosphorus-containing compound which stored the energy was adenosine triphosphate.

Baalsrud and Baalsrud (2) were not able to confirm these results. Cell suspensions of *T. thioparus*, *T. thiooxidans*, and *T. denitrificans* which had oxidized thiosulfate in the absence of carbon dioxide, did not accumulate carbon dioxide assimilating power ("reducing power"). Carbon dioxide was incorporated only during thiosulfate oxidation. In addition, there was only a small diminution of inorganic phosphate indicating the inability of these cells to accumulate phosphate anhydride compounds.

The data of Baalsrud and Baalsrud induced Umbreit (73) to reinvestigate the "delayed" carbon dioxide fixation in *T. thiooxidans*. The tracers, P^{32} and C^{14}, were used in place of manometric methods. Umbreit concluded again that the amount of carbon dioxide "reducing power" accumulated is proportional to the amount of sulfur oxidized. He further concluded that labile "7-minute phosphate" (presumably ATP) is formed within the cell during sulfur oxidation which is released later when carbon dioxide is supplied. Umbreit explained the disparity between his work and that of Baalsrud and Baalsrud's results in the following way: (a) by use of different strains of the organism, (b) by use of sulfur as the electron donor in his experiments while Baalsrud and Baalsrud had supplied $S_2O_3^{=}$, and (c) by the use of faulty analytical methods for phosphate analysis by Baalsrud and Baalsrud.

Newburgh (46) has reinvestigated this question using the same methods employed by Vogler (75) and Umbreit (73). His findings could only partially confirm Vogler and Umbreit. When washed cells of *T. thiooxidans* oxidized sulfur for 30 minutes in an atmosphere of nitrogen, CO_2-free air, or ordinary air and when $C^{14}O_2$ was admitted for 1 to 5 minutes, those cells which had $C^{14}O_2$ present during the sulfur oxidation, assimilated approximately sixfold more tracer. Newburgh did find that *T. thiooxidans* could accumulate a small amount of "reducing power" but that it was subject to rapid decay and therefore the manometric methods of Baalsrud and Baalsrud were not sensitive enough to detect it. In contrast to Vogler and Umbreit, however, Newburgh showed that P^{32} entered the cell only in the simultaneous presence of sulfur, oxygen, and carbon dioxide; that is, phosphorylation occurred only when carbon dioxide was present.

Schlegel (56) has confirmed Newburgh's observation that there is an absolute need for carbon dioxide if the oxidation of hydrogen by *Hydrogenomonas* is to be coupled to the uptake of inorganic phosphate.

It would appear that if the chemoautotrophic bacteria can store up carbon dioxide-assimilating power for use independently of their energy-yielding reactions, the amount of such storage must be small or it depends on extremely labile compounds. These investigations do suggest, however, that there is a link between the generation of high-energy phosphate compounds and the primary energy-yielding reaction, but they yield little knowledge of the nature of the mechanism by which the energy of the primary reaction is actually coupled.

This confusing situation is somewhat reminiscent of the controversy over the ability of photosynthetic organisms to accumulate "reducing power." Seeking a "delayed" enhanced dark fixation, Benson and Calvin (8) illuminated *Chlorella* sp. and *Scenedesmus* sp. anaerobically (under nitrogen or helium) in the absence of carbon dioxide. On subsequently introducing $C^{14}O_2$ the result was a ten- to one-hundredfold increase in the initial dark-fixation rate, followed by a rapid decline to the normal dark-fixation rate ($t_{1/2} = 2$ minutes). In the *Scene-*

desmus sp. 1 or 2 minutes of preillumination was required for the fixation rate to reach its normal level; in the *Chlorella* sp. this took longer. The possibility that this enhanced dark fixation could have been due to a mass-action reversal of respiratory decarboxylation was considered and rejected. Since preilluminated algae showed the same tracer pattern as under normal photosynthesis, Benson and Calvin interpreted this echancement as the formation of "reducing power," such as a powerful reductant which could later reduce a limited amount of carbon dioxide in the dark.

Gaffron (24) could not reproduce these results. Preillumination in *Scenedesmus* sp. resulted only in tracer entering the carboxyl groups of phosphoglyceric acid and pyruvic acid. He concluded, therefore, that the carbon dioxide-assimilating power cannot be stored in the photosynthetic organism.

It would appear that the whole question whether chemoautotrophic organisms can store "reducing power" produced from their primary energy source is an open one.

3. *Metabolism of Carbon Dioxide*

a. General. Studies on the fixation and subsequent metabolism of CO_2 by the chemoautotrophic bacteria have been few and have been limited to the genus *Thiobacillus.* The available data suggest that the metabolism of the thiobacilli is similar to that of many plant, animal, and microbial cells. Most of the research deals with the cyclic mechanism for CO_2 fixation and the citric acid cycle. No data have appeared which concern their fatty acid and protein metabolism. The scarcity of information is probably due to the difficulties involved in obtaining the large numbers of organisms required for enzyme studies.

b. CO_2 fixation and assimilation. Attempts to demonstrate the carboxylation enzymes previously shown in bacterial and animal cells have been successful. Santer and Vishniac (54) noted that unfractionated extracts of *Thiobacillus thioparus* could convert ribulose diphosphate $C^{14}O_2$ into C^{14}-phosphoglyceric acid. Trudinger (71) confirmed and extended this observation. This investigator also showed that extracts of *T. denitrificans* could apparently substitute ribose-5-phosphate and ATP for ribulose diphosphate. Evidence has been given by Suzuki and Werkman (67) for the presence of an irreversible phosphoenolpyruvate carboxylase and a reversible oxaloacetate carboxylase in a cell-free extract of *T. thiooxidans.*

The Michaelis constant of the phosphoenolpyruvate carboxylase for HCO_3^- is 1.2×10^{-3} *M*. This value indicates that the enzyme requires a low CO_2 tension. Since the value is approximately ten times smaller than that reported by Weissbach *et al.* (78) for the ribulose diphosphate carboxylation enzyme, this may be significant for those autotrophic bacteria which grow at an acid pH where the supply of CO_2 from the air could be limiting. Malic enzyme could not be demonstrated in the extracts of *T. thiooxidans.*

These data suggest that the enzyme(s) which is apparently responsible for carbon dioxide fixation in photosynthesis is also present in the chemoautotrophic bacteria.

c. Enzymes other than those involved in carboxylation. Trudinger (71) has reported that extracts of *T. denitrificans* contain the enzymes common to heterotrophic cells. The presence of glucose-6-phosphate dehydrogenase and 6-phosphogluconate dehydrogenase indicates the presence of a "direct oxidative" pathway. The extracts contain the enzymes capable of synthesizing hexose phosphates from carbon dioxide and pentose phosphates by a cyclic mechanism similar to that suggested for green plants, namely, phosphopentose isomerase, phosphoribulokinase, aldolase, fructose-1,6-diphosphatase, hexose monophosphate isomerase, phosphoglycerokinase, triose phosphate dehydrogenase linked only to DPN, transketolase, and transaldolase. The presence of phosphoglyceromutase and enolase complete the list of Embden-Meyerhof-Parnas enzymes in these extracts. The enzymes of the citric acid cycle present in the extracts are: isocitrate dehydrogenase, aconitase, succinate dehydrogenase, fumarase, and malate dehydrogenase. However, Suzuki and Werkman (67) could not demonstrate either a TPN- or DPN-linked malate dehydrogenase in extracts of *T. thiooxidans.*

These observations suggest a marked similarity between the carbohydrate metabolism of *T. denitrificans* and *T. thiooxidans* and that of many oxygen-consuming cells. It differs in one respect from autotrophic chlorophyll-containing cells since Trudinger could not demonstrate a TPN-linked triose phosphate dehydrogenase. This TPN-linked enzyme has been shown by Gibbs (25) and Rosenberg and Arnon (53) to be present only in those tissues of both lower and higher forms of plants which contain chlorophyll.

d. Studies with the intact cell. Investigations with the strict autotrophic bacteria have been hindered by the inability of carbon-containing compounds other than CO_2 to be metabolized by the intact cell. The availability of $C^{14}O_2$ has permitted an insight into the internal metabolism of these organisms. The tracer technique developed by Bassham *et al.* (7) for photosynthetic systems has been applied with success to the *Thiobacilli.*

Suzuki and Werkman (66) observed that in *T. thiooxidans* practically all the $C^{14}O_2$ fixed in 2 seconds is found in the carboxyl carbon of phosphoglyceric acid. After 10 seconds, they isolated aspartic acid with 84% of the compound's tracer in the β-carboxyl and the remainder in the other carboxyl. After 3 minutes, the glucose phosphate esters had 50% of the tracer.

A similar study has been carried out with *T. denitrificans* by Milhaud and co-workers (43). After a 10-second incubation with $C^{14}O_2$, 75% of the tracer was located in phosphoglyceric acid, sedoheptulose phosphate (11%), ribulose diphosphate (6%), and aspartic acid (8%). About twenty compounds contained tracer after 5 minutes, including uridine diphosphate glucose and uridine diphosphate galactose.

The distribution of the tracer among the various carbon atoms of the compounds isolated from *T. denitrificans* after a 10-second exposure to $C^{14}O_2$ as a percentage of the total incorporated in these compounds was given (see Table IV).

TABLE IV
DISTRIBUTION OF TRACER AMONG CARBON ATOMS OF COMPOUNDS ISOLATED FROM *Thiobacillus denitrificans*[a]

Phosphoglyceric acid		Fructose-6-phosphate		Sedoheptulose-7-phosphate		Ribulose-1,5-diphosphate	
Carbon atom number	%	Carbon atom number	%	Carbon atom number	%	Carbon atom number	%
1	94	1	1	1	0	1	10
2	4	2	1	2	0	2	10
3	2	3	49	3	32	3	80
		4	47	4	29	4	0
		5	1	5	39	5	0
		6	1	6	0		
				7	0		

[a] From Milhaud *et al.* (43).

These tracer data are essentially similar to those published by Bassham *et al.* (7) for the pathway of carbon in photosynthetic organisms. As pointed out by Gibbs and Kandler (26), the scheme proposed by the California group for the conversion of carbon dioxide to hexose in photosynthesis is not consistent with this distribution of tracer in C_6, C_7, and C_5 compounds. While C-1 and C-2 of ribulose diphosphate are heavily labeled, C-1 and C-2 both of hexose and sedoheptulose contain little or no tracer. According to the scheme of Bassham *et al.* (7), C-3 and C-5 of sedoheptulose phosphate should be equally labeled since both are derived from the carboxyl carbon of phosphoglyceric acid.

Gibbs and Kandler (26) have reported an asymmetric distribution of tracer in the hexose isolated from photosynthesizing algae and the leaves of higher plants. It would, therefore, be of interest to degrade the hexose isolated from the chemoautotrophic bacteria other than *T. denitrificans* and determine the distribution of labeled carbon. (For a more complete discussion on this point, see Chapter 4 by Gaffron.)

G. A Hypothesis to Explain Chemoautotrophic Growth

The fundamental problem posed by the chemosynthetic bacteria is the manner whereby the energy set free by the primary energy-yielding reaction is made available for the synthesis of cellular material. Lipmann (40) in 1941 stated the probem simply when he pointed out that the energy released by one reaction could not be transferred to another with which it is coupled unless a common compound linked the two reactions. Since then, compounds have been isolated which possess the function of capturing energy from reactions which release energy (exergonic, $-\Delta F$), holding this energy, and then giving it to reactions which require energy (endergonic, $+\Delta F$). Therefore, at least one chemical compound must be common to the oxidation reaction ($H_2 + O_2$; $NH_4^+ + O_2$) and to the synthesis of cell material ($2\ H_2 + CO_2$).

The hypothesis here set forth for chemoautotrophic growth is as follows:

(1) The electron donor is activated enzymatically. For instance, the hydrogen bacteria possess hydrogenase. The activating enzymes have not been isolated in other chemosynthetic bacteria.

(2) A reduced carrier must be formed. Thus, the hydrogen bacteria may transfer molecular hydrogen to a carrier whose potential is close to that of the hydrogen electrode ($E_0' = -0.42$ volt) and therefore, more negative than that of the pyridine nucleotides ($E_0' = -0.32$ volt). The experiments of Korkes (36) showed that extracts of *Clostridium kluyveri* are capable of reducing pyridine nucleotides by molecular hydrogen. It must be noted that extracts of autotrophically grown *Hydrogenomonas* sp. could not reduce TPN^+ and DPN^+ with gaseous hydrogen (35).

This leads to the following mechanism for the hydrogen bacteria:

$$H_2 + X \xrightarrow{\text{hydrogenase}} X\,H_2$$

This type of formulation may not be applicable to other chemosynthetic bacteria. In the case of the organisms using sulfur and nitrogen compounds, oxidation linked directly to pyridine nucleotides does not appear to be thermodynamically feasible. An alternative mechanism discussed in Section IV,F,1, and suggested by the data of Lees and Simpson (39) and Postgate (47) is a linking of the primary energy-yielding reaction to the cytochromes.

The resultant energy would probably be in the form of unstable phosphorus or sulfur compounds generated by the reoxidation of the reduced cytochrome (Fe^{++}) by molecular oxygen. Each electron which passes from cytochrome c (yeast) to molecular oxygen releases about 19 kcal. This energy could be accumulated and used to split water with X as the electron acceptor. Assuming X to have a potential of the order of the hydrogen electrode, the mechanism would be:

$$X + H_2O \rightarrow X\,H_2 + 0.5\,O_2;\ \Delta F = 56.7 \text{ kcal}$$

It was pointed out in Section IV,F,1, that this reaction is not wholly applicable to the autotrophic bacteria since molecular oxygen is not liberated.

(3) The reduced carrier ($X\,H_2$) has two fates. This process, termed "energy dismutation" by Rabinowitch, is a coupled oxidation of the carrier by oxygen and carbon dioxide.

(4) Simultaneous with the formation of "reducing power" is the conversion of carbon dioxide to a carboxyl group catalyzed by ribulose diphosphate carboxylase. The ΔF of this type of reaction is approximately zero.

(5) The addition product of ribulose diphosphate and carbon dioxide (keto acid) could be cleaved by H_2O to yield two molecules of phosphoglyceric acid accompanied by a loss of approximately 7 kcal per mole. The phosphoglyceric acid would be reduced with PNH and ATP. An alternative to the hydrolytic cleavage (7) has been suggested by Gibbs and Kandler (26). The latter authors have proposed a direct reduction of the six-membered keto acid leading to a hexose phosphate.

(6) Experiments with isolated and partially purified enzyme systems indicate the rearrangements of the hexose phosphate can occur without the need of energy.

V. Conclusion

In this chapter, the relations between the chemosynthetic oxidation-reduction reactions involving certain inorganic nutrients and the growth and metabolism of organisms which derive their energy from these sources have been examined. Despite its long history, this now rapidly expanding area of biology presents many unsolved problems. If the hypotheses that have been presented here are found satisfying, they may serve as an incentive to further research to establish them: otherwise they should stimulate work to disprove them. In either event, a useful purpose will have been served.

REFERENCES

1. Andrews, J. C. Reduction of certain sulfur compounds to hydrogen sulfide by the intestinal microorganisms of the dog. *J. Biol. Chem.* **122,** 687–692 (1937).
2. Baalsrud, K., and Baalsrud, K. S. The role of phosphate in CO_2 assimilation of *Thiobacilli. In* "Phosphorus Metabolism" (W. D. McElroy and H. B. Glass, eds.), pp. 544–576. Johns Hopkins Press, Baltimore, Maryland, 1952.
3. Baas-Becking, L. G. M., and Parks, G. S. Energy relations in the metabolism of autotrophic bacteria. *Physiol. Revs.* **7,** 85–106 (1927).
4. Bach, M. *In* "Inorganic Nitrogen Metabolism" (W. D. McElroy and H. B. Glass, eds.), p. 370. Johns Hopkins Press, Baltimore, Maryland, 1956.
5. Bandurski, R. S., and Wilson, L. G. A comparison of sulfate and selenate as substrates for adenosine triphosphate sulfurylase. *Plant Physiol.* **32,** XLI (1957).
6. Bandurski, R. S., Wilson, L. G., and Squires, C. L. The mechanism of active sulfate formation. *J. Am. Chem. Soc.* **78,** 6408–6409 (1956).
7. Bassham, J. A., Benson, A. A., Kay, L. D., Harris, A. Z., Wilson, A. T., and Calvin, M. The path of carbon in photosynthesis. XXI. The cyclic regeneration of carbon dioxide acceptor. *J. Am. Chem. Soc.* **76,** 1760–1770 (1954).
8. Benson, A. A., and Calvin, M. Carbon dioxide fixation by green plants. *Ann. Rev. Plant Physiol.* **1,** 25–42 (1950).
9. Bersin, T. Die Phytochemie des Schwefels. *Advances in Enzymol.* **10,** 223–324 (1950).
10. Binkley, F. Catalytic cleavage of thioethers. *J. Am. Chem. Soc.* **77,** 501 (1955).
11. Block, R. J., Stekol, J. A., and Loosli, J. K. Synthesis of sulfur amino acids from inorganic sulfate by ruminants. II. Synthesis of cystine and methionine from sodium sulfate by the goat and by the microorganisms of the rumen of the ewe. *Arch. Biochem. Biophys.* **33,** 353–363 (1951).
12. Bray, H. G., and White, K. "Kinetics and Thermodynamics in Biochemistry." Academic Press, New York, 1957.
13. Burton, K., and Krebs, H. A. The free energy changes associated with the individual steps of the tricarboxylic acid cycle, glycolysis and alcoholic fermentation and with the hydrolysis of the pyrophosphate groups of adenosine triphosphate. *Biochem. J.* **54,** 94–107 (1954).
14. Burton, K., and Wilson, J. H. The free-energy changes for the reduction of diphosphopyridine nucleotide and the dehydrogenation of L-malate and L-glycerol-1-phosphate. *Biochem. J.* **54,** 86–94 (1954).
15. Butlin, K. R., Adams, M. E., and Thomas, M. The isolation and cultivation of sulfate reducing bacteria. *J. Gen. Microbiol.* **3,** 46–59 (1949).
16. Cantoni, G. L. *S*-Adenosyl methionine, a new intermediate formed enzymatically from L-methionine and adenosine triphosphate. *J. Biol. Chem.* **204,** 403–416 (1953).
17. Cantoni, G. L., and Durell, J. Methionine activating enzyme. *Federation Proc.* **15,** 229 (1956).
18. Challenger, F. The biological importance of organic compounds of sulfur. *Endeavour* **12,** 173–183 (1953).
19. Cowie, D. B., Bolton, E. T., and Sands, M. K. Sulfur metabolism in *Escherichia coli.* II. Competitive utilization of labeled and non-labeled sulfur compounds. *J. Bacteriol.* **62,** 63–74 (1951).
20. Dziewiatkowski, D. D. Utilization of sulfate sulfur in the rat for the synthesis of cystine. *J. Biol. Chem.* **207,** 181–186 (1954).

21. Fromageot, P., and Perez-Milan, H. La réduction du sulfite par la feuille détachée de tabac. *Compt. rend.* **243**, 1061–1062 (1956).
22. Fruton, J. S., and Simmonds, S. "General Biochemistry." Wiley, New York, 1958.
23. Fry, B. A., and Peel, J. L. "Autotrophic Microorganisms." Cambridge Univ. Press, London and New York, 1954.
24. Gaffron, H. Mechanism of photosynthesis. *In* "Autotrophic Microorganisms" (B. A. Fry and J. L. Peel, eds.), pp. 152–185. Cambridge Univ. Press, London and New York, 1954.
25. Gibbs, M. Triosephosphate dehydrogenase and glucose-6-phosphate dehydrogenase in the pea plant. *Nature* **170**, 164 (1952).
26. Gibbs, M., and Kandler, O. Asymmetric distribution of C^{14} in sugars formed during photosynthesis. *Proc. Natl. Acad. Sci. U.S.* **43**, 446–451 (1957).
27. Greenberg, D. M. Metabolism of sulfur-containing compounds. *In* "Chemical Pathways of Metabolism" (D. M. Greenberg, ed.), Vol. II, pp. 149–171. Academic Press, New York, 1954.
28. Hill, R., and Wittingham, C. P. "Photosynthesis." Wiley, New York, 1955.
29. Hilz, H. Sulfat-Reduktion durch Hefeextrakte. *IV. Intern. Congr. Biochem., Abstr. Sect.* 5, **23** (1958).
30. Hilz, H., and Lipmann, F. The enzymatic activation of sulfate. *Proc. Natl. Acad. Sci. U.S.* **41**, 880–890 (1955).
31. Hinton, T. The genetic basis of a nutritional requirement in *Drosophila. Genetics* **40**, 224–234 (1955).
32. Hofmann, T., and Lees, H. The biochemistry of the nitrifying bacteria. 3. The free-energy efficiency of *Nitrosomonas. Biochem. J.* **52**, 140–142 (1952).
33. Horowitz, N. H. Biochemical genetics of *Neurospora. Advances in Genet.* **3**, 33–71 (1950).
34. Horowitz, N. H. *In* "A Symposium on Amino Acid Metabolism" (W. D. McElroy and H. B. Glass, eds.), pp. 631–632. The Johns Hopkins Press, Baltimore, 1955.
35. Judis, J., Koffler, H., and Powelson, D. M. The incorporation of $C^{14}O_2$ into organic compounds by cell-free extracts of *Hydrogenomonas. Bacteriol. Proc.* p. 117 (1954).
35a. Kluyver, A. J., and Van Niel, C. B. "The Microbe's Contribution to Biology." Harvard Univ. Press, Cambridge, Massachusetts, 1956.
36. Korkes, S. Enzymatic reduction of pyridine nucleotides by molecular hydrogen. *J. Biol. Chem.* **216**, 737–748 (1955).
37. Lampen, J. O., Roepke, R. R., and Jones, M. J. Studies on the sulfur metabolism of *Escherichia coli.* III. Mutant strains of *Escherichia coli* unable to utilize sulfate for their complete sulfur requirements. *Arch. Biochem. Biophys.* **13**, 55–66 (1947).
38. Latimer, W. M. "The Oxidation States of the Elements and their Potentials in Aqueous Solutions." Prentice-Hall, New York, 1938.
39. Lees, H., and Simpson, J. R. The biochemistry of the nitrifying organisms. 5. Nitrite oxidation by *Nitrobacter. Biochem. J.* **65**, 297–305 (1957).
40. Lipmann, F. Metabolic generation and utilization of phosphate bond energy. *Advances in Enzymol.* **1**, 99–162 (1941).
41. Liverman, J. L., and Ragland, J. B. Metabolism of sulfur-35 in the Alaska pea. *Plant Physiol.* **31**, VII (1956).
42. Lowe, I. P., and Roberts, E. Incorporation of sulfate sulfur into taurine and other substances in the chick embryo. *J. Biol. Chem.* **212**, 477–483 (1955).

43. Milhaud, G., Aubert, J. P., and Millet, J. Métabolisme du carbone dans la chimioautotrophie. Cycle d'assimilation de l'anhydride carbonique. *Compt. rend.* **243,** 102–105 (1956).
44. Miller, L. P. Utilization of DL-methionine as a source of sulfur by growing plants. *Contribs. Boyce Thompson Inst.* **14,** 443–456 (1947).
45. Nason, A. Enzymatic steps in the assimilation of nitrate and nitrite in fungi and green plants. *In* "Inorganic Nitrogen Metabolism" (W. D. McElroy and H. B. Glass, eds.), pp. 109–136. Johns Hopkins Press, Baltimore, Maryland, 1956.
46. Newburgh, R. W. Phosphorylation and chemosynthesis by *Thiobacillus thiooxidans. J. Bacteriol.* **68,** 93–97 (1954).
47. Postgate, J. R. Cytochrome c_3 and desulfoviridin; pigments of the anaerobe *Desulfovibrio desulfuricans. J. Gen. Microbiol.* **14,** 545–572 (1956).
48. Rabinowitch, E. I. "Photosynthesis," Vol. I. Interscience, New York, 1945.
49. Raistrick, H., and Vincent, J. M. Studies in the biochemistry of microorganisms. 77. A survey of fungal metabolism of inorganic sulfates. *Biochem. J.* **43,** 90–99 (1948).
50. Robbins, P. W., and Lipmann, F. Separation of the two enzymatic phases in active sulfate synthesis. *J. Biol. Chem.* **233,** 681–685 (1958).
51. Robbins, P. W., and Lipmann, F. Enzymatic synthesis of adenosine-5′-phosphosulfate. *J. Biol. Chem.* **233,** 686–690 (1958).
52. Roberts, R. B., Abelson, P. H., Cowie, D. B., Bolton, E. T., and Britten, R. J. Studies of biosynthesis in *Escherichia coli. Carnegie Inst. Wash. Publ.* **607,** 318–405 (1955).
53. Rosenberg, L. L., and Arnon, D. I. The preparation and properties of a new glyceraldehyde-3-phosphate dehydrogenase from photosynthetic tissues. *J. Biol. Chem.* **217,** 361–371 (1955).
54. Santer, M., and Vishniac, W. CO_2 incorporation by extracts of *Thiobacillus thioparus. Biochim. et Biophys. Acta* **18,** 157–158 (1955).
55. Schiff, J. A. Preliminary studies on the sulfur metabolism of *Chlorella pyrenoidosa* with sulfur-35. *Plant Physiol.* **31,** VII (1956).
56. Schlegel, H. G. Die Beeinflussung des Phosphathaushaltes von Mikroorganismen durch Kohlendioxyd. *Arch. Mikrobiol.* **23,** 195–206 (1955).
57. Schlenk, F., and DePalma, R. E. The formation of *S*-adenosylmethionine in yeast. *J. Biol. Chem.* **229,** 1037–1050 (1957).
58. Schlenk, F., and Smith, R. L. The mechanism of adenine thiomethylriboside formation. *J. Biol. Chem.* **204,** 27–34 (1953).
59. Schloesing, T., and Müntz, A. Sur la nitrification par les ferments organisés. *Compt. rend.* **84,** 301–303 (1877).
60. Schwartz, M., Shapiro, S. K. The mechanism of utilization of thiomethyladenosine in the biosynthesis of methionine. *J. Bacteriol.* **67,** 98–102 (1954).
61. Singer, T. P., and Kearney, E. B. Chemistry, metabolism, and scope of action of the pyridine nucleotide coenzymes. *Advances in Enzymol.* **15,** 79–140 (1954).
62. Singer, T. P., and Kearney, E. B. Enzymatic pathways in the degradation of sulfur containing amino acids. *In* "A Symposium on Amino Acid Metabolism" (W. D. McElroy and H. B. Glass, eds.), pp. 558–590. The Johns Hopkins Press, Baltimore, 1955.
63. Sisler, F. D., and Zobell, C. E. Hydrogen utilization by some marine sulfate-reducing bacteria. *J. Bacteriol.* **62,** 117–127 (1951).
64. Smith, R. L., Anderson, Jr., E. E., Overland, R. N., and Schlenk, F. The occurrence, formation, and isolation of thiomethyladenosine. *Arch. Biochem. Biophys.* **42,** 72–82 (1953).

65. Stephenson, M. "Bacterial Metabolism." Longmans, Green, London, 1949.
66. Suzuki, I., and Werkman, C. H. Chemoautotrophic fixation of CO_2. *Bacteriol. Proc.* **120,** 1957.
67. Suzuki, I., and Werkman, C. H. Chemoautotrophic carbon dioxide fixation by extracts of *Thiobacillus thiooxidans.* I. Formation of oxalacetic acid. *Arch. Biochem. Biophys.* **76,** 103–111 (1958).
68. Thomas, M. D., Hendricks, R. H., Bryner, L. C., and Hill, G. R. A study of the sulfur metabolism of wheat, barley and corn using radioactive sulfur. *Plant Physiol.* **19,** 227–244 (1944).
69. Thomas, M. D., Hendricks, R. H., and Hill, G. R. Some chemical reactions of sulfur dioxide after absorption by alfalfa and sugar beets. *Plant Physiol.* 19, 212–226 (1944).
70. Thomas, M. D., Hendricks, R. H., and Hill, G. R. Sulfur metabolism in alfalfa. *Soil Sci.* **70,** 19–26 (1950).
71. Trudinger, P. A. Fixation of CO_2 by extracts of the strict autotroph *Thiobacillus denitrificans. Biochem. J.* **64,** 274–286 (1956).
72. Turrel, F. M., and Chervenak, M. B. Metabolism of radioactive elemental sulfur applied to lemons as an insecticide. *Botan. Gaz.* **111,** 109–122 (1949).
73. Umbreit, W. W. Phosphorylation and CO_2 fixation in the autotrophic bacterium, *Thiobacillus thiooxidans. J. Bacteriol.* **67,** 387–393 (1954).
74. Vishniac, W. On the metabolism of the chemolitho-autotrophic bacterium *Thiobacillus thioparus* Beijerinck. Ph.D. Thesis, Stanford University, California, 1949.
75. Vogler, K. G. Studies on the metabolism of the autotrophic bacteria. II. The nature of the chemosynthetic mechanism. *J. Gen. Physiol.* **26,** 103–117 (1942).
76. Vogler, K. G., and Umbreit, W. W. Studies on the metabolism of the autotrophic bacteria. III. The nature of the energy storage material active in the chemosynthetic process. *J. Gen. Physiol.* **26,** 157–167 (1942).
77. Warington, R. On nitrification. *J. Chem. Soc.* **59,** 484–529 (1891).
78. Weissbach, A., Horecker, B. L., and Hurwitz, J. The enzymatic formation of phosphoglyceric acid from ribulose diphosphate and carbon dioxide. *J. Biol. Chem.* **218,** 795–810 (1956).
79. Wilson, L. G., and Bandurski, R. S. An adenosine triphosphate sufite reaction. *Plant Physiol.* **31,** viii (1956).
80. Wilson, L. G., and Bandurski, R. S. *In vitro* reduction of inorganic sulfate. *Plant Physiol.* **33,** xxiv (1958).
81. Winogradsky, S. Über Schwefelbakterien. *Botan. Ztg.* **45,** 489–526 (1887).
82. Winogradsky, S. Recherches sur les organismes de la nitrification. *Ann. inst. Pasteur* **4,** 257–265 (1890).
83. Wood, J. G. Metabolism of sulfur in plants. *Chronica Botan.* **7,** 1–32 (1942).
84. Wood, J. G., and Barrien, B. S. Studies on the sulfur metabolism of plants I. Preliminary investigations on the effects of different external concentrations of sulfate, ammonia and cystine on the amounts of sulfur-containing compounds in leaves. *New Phytologist* **38,** 125–149 (1939).
85. Wood, J. G., and Barrien, B. S. Studies on the sulfur metabolism of plants. III. On changes in amounts of protein sulfur and sulfate sulfur during starvation. *New Phytologist* **38,** 265–272 (1939).
86. Youatt, J. B. Studies on the metabolism of *Thiobacillus thiocyanoxidans. J. Gen. Microbiol.* **11,** 139–149 (1954).

AUTHOR INDEX

Numbers in boldface refer to pages on which the complete reference is listed at the end of a chapter. Numbers in lightface indicate the pages in the text on which the references are cited. Numbers in parentheses are reference numbers and are included to assist in locating the reference in cases where the author's names are not mentioned in the text.

C

F

G

L

INDEX TO PLANT NAMES

T

U

V

W

Y

SUBJECT INDEX

A

D

I

K

L

Q